SLOW CHILDREN PLAYING

On the way to Band Camp

A Memoir

Shelby L. Syckes

Dedication

For Karen

Table of Contents

"Oh, Auntie Em, There's no place like home"
Dorothy

"You Can't Go Home Again"
Thomas Wolfe

"You can go home again, just don't expect anyone to care."
Shelby

Foreword

Shelby Syckes and I are old friends, I have known him for many years. More than I care to count or remember. I have always enjoyed knowing him. We went to high school together, Allegany High School in our old hometown, Cumberland, Maryland. To be honest, Shelby and I never really had much in common. He was a great musician and I couldn't play the cymbals if I had a hundred lessons. Shelby was always better looking than me and more confident too. But even with all that going against him, I still liked the guy.

I have had the pleasure of reading Shelby's new memoir. It is filled with very interesting stories. Some funny, some sad, some exciting, some touching. I really enjoyed reading this book, much more than I thought. After reading it, I remembered another thing about Shelby. He tells it like it is. Whether you like him or not, whether you agree with him or not, Shelby is and always was a straight shooter. These marvelous stories are, above all, candid and truthful. My old friend Shelby has lived himself a very interesting life. I highly recommend this book. I hope you enjoy it as much as I did.

I think you will. Well done, Shelby.

Eddie Deezen

Actor, comedian, and entertainment commentator

Prologue

Music is magic. I truly believe that. When you least expect it, a song can reach out and transport you somewhere far away. It doesn't matter where you are, at home or in a car, a song can catch your ear and zap—it takes you back to where you were when you first heard it, and for a moment, relive that time and place. That happens to me all the time, and I love it. I spend hours organizing my collection of songs, creating playlists with silly names that only make sense to me, like "Barracuda Sounds." Listening to them melts away the years and takes me to an earlier time; not necessarily a better one, just a time when I was younger and facing life anew, and there's no time in life when things seem newer than high school.

This book is about my high school years and my adventures from that time. High school is formative and leaves lasting memories and sometimes scars, but I was lucky. Although I had some scuffs and scrapes, all in all, it was a happy time. Music was a big part of it, and as I tell my story, I'll reference the music from then. Don't worry; it was damn good music from artist like Neil Young, Al Green, Elton John, and Led Zeppelin. I've named each chapter after an appropriate song title. Please stop and listen to some of them while reading.

But what's that got to do with band camp?

Not much. Although I don't get to band camp until chapter 18, this book covers much more as I stumble through my teenage years on the way to Band Camp. The "SLOW Children Playing" part of the story is both true and a metaphor. Think of me as the child—*playing at life*—"slowly" learning as I go.

I'll share family facts and my thoughts and feelings about growing up in Western Maryland. Although the narrative is mostly linear—*be warned*—I often divert from it to a different character, place or time, but I always return to the main subject within a paragraph or two so, hang in there.

I don't pretend to be an author, so let me apologize in advance for my limited literary skills (Forgive me, Mrs. Long and all of my other English teachers). There are composite characters, blended situations, embellishments, and the dialog is only representative of what was said. I also change names and take liberties with the sequence of events. But, I think I stay within the conventional lines of artistic license.

My memories are my source material, and I'm sure my ego has warped them in one way or another over the past half-century, but I think I have captured the essence of what happened. Please step back and view this as a Monet, not an Ansel Adams.

Allegany High School Cumberland, Maryland (Allegwee, 1972)

Chapter 1 - I Can See Clearly Now

— ALCO —

By the time I found out I would go to band camp, I was finishing up a good year. It was June 1972, and I was at the end of my junior year of high school and facing a jam-packed summer.

June wasn't anything special, just the start of another all-American summer with The Doobie Brothers' *Toulouse Street* album about to be released, *Time Magazine* running photos of napalmed Vietnamese children, the movie *Deep Throat* making its debut, and five men getting arrested for burglarizing the Democratic National Committee in the Watergate office building. How *Deep Throat* and Watergate intertwined a couple of years later still amazes me.

It was my third year at ALCO, the nickname for Allegany High School of Cumberland Maryland and the high school every one of the Syckes family has attended beginning with my grandmother Beatrice. The school was called Allegany County School then, and that's how the nickname ALCO came to be. They combined the AL from Allegany and the CO from County.

Beatrice was followed by her eldest son Lu (my dad), her second son, Wilton, his wife Eleanor, cousin Nini, sister Barbara, and sister Betsy. I ended the string with my graduation in 1973. ALCO was one of three high schools in Cumberland, but only two of them counted. They were Allegany and Fort Hill. The third was Bishop Walsh, the Catholic High School, and it was so small it was not on anyone's radar, except that it hosted a great dance every Friday night.

Why were ALCO and Fort Hill so important? Because they were the dominant high schools in Cumberland, accounting for 90 percent of all high-school-age students. They were located on opposite sides of town, and the rivalry between them was fierce. The two schools' colors defined everything in Cumberland. Things were either blue for ALCO or red for Fort Hill with no exceptions. Elementary schools, junior high schools, playgrounds, restaurants, roller rinks, even city events were either places for ALCO students or Fort Hill students but not both.

Even dating was confined by the color barrier. The rule was blue dated blue and red dated red—period.

I mean, if a Fort Hill boy dated an ALCO girl, what color mum corsage would he give her to wear to the football game, red or blue? And if it was red, how could she possibly sit on the Allegany side of the stadium with that gawdawful thing pinned to her?

It sounds silly, but these were the facts in my hometown. To this day, when I meet someone who grew up in Cumberland, the first thing I ask is, "Blue or red?"

Given this level of rivalry, any sporting event that pitted the two schools against each other rose in significance far beyond the norm. The annual football game was the biggest of these events of the year. It was called the Turkey Day game, and as the name suggests, it was played on Thanksgiving. That was the day Cumberland staged its most fierce and contentious high school football game.

Since 1936, these two schools have met in mortal combat in the last game of each team's season to determine who can claim the title of City Champions. It doesn't matter if you lose every other game of the season: if you win Turkey Day, you are declared the reigning sports gods of the year. In retrospect, it was crazy, but at the time, it seemed perfectly sane. And remember, it was the adults who set this up, not the kids. I can hear them at the 1936 football season planning meeting:

"Hey, I've got an idea. Why don't we have the homecoming football game on Thanksgiving?"

"Wait, you want to schedule an event that draws 8,000 people, and consumes most of a day on the holiday we set aside each year to give thanks for our friends and family?"

"Yes."

So, Turkey Day became "*the*" sporting event of the year. I'll share much more about a special Turkey Day later. However, it was not on my mind that June in 1972 because I was thinking about band camp and how great things were going for me. In order for you to understand why I felt this way, I need to back up the story fourteen months and tell you how I got there.

In March of 1971, I was just another face in the crowd of 330 other sophomores, but I wanted to change that. There was a tradition in my family of ALCO band leadership. My dad started it in 1935 when he was elected president of the band. His brother continued it by becoming the drum major and both my sisters were drum majors, too. They had the job for both their junior and senior years, and I was thinking of trying to match their achievement.

I wanted to be the next drum major but wasn't sure I had what it took to compete for and win the job as my sisters did. But I still wanted it, and not only because of my family's tradition. I knew if I became the drum major it would put me on the right track in school. I'm not talking about good grades or anything as mundane as that. No, I'm talking about more important stuff like becoming one of the cool kids. You know what I mean; the elite clique of kids who everyone else in the school looks up to.

That was what defined success in my high school, and I wanted it.

— Cool Kids —

High school is the cruelest of social delineators, and it's the cool kids that decided if you are one of them or not. There is little you can do to control how they determine your social standing, but if you can't change it before you graduate, you're branded as "uncool," and you are "uncool" forever.

Anyone who went to high school in the United States understands this caste system, and it is defined very simply. You are either one of the cool kids, or you're not.

The cool kids are jocks, babes, and winners.

The uncool kids are everyone else.

Most of the male cool kids came from the ranks of the football, baseball, basketball and track teams. The female cool kids were cheerleaders, prom queens, drill team members and any other gorgeous girls whose figures developed early.

Band, orchestra, and choir members, tennis team, chess club or any other well-intentioned organizational members need not apply.

There was only one way to become a cool kid that didn't require you to be a jock or a babe, and that was to be a winner. Winners were anyone who, through some accomplishment, received school-wide recognition such as getting elected president of their class or saving a puppy from getting squished by a bus. They became proto-cool kids because the cool kids wanted to be seen with them, especially if there was a chance they could get their picture taken. But cool kid membership as a winner was tenuous and could be withdrawn quickly. They were watched carefully for any infractions of the cool kid by-laws and often, as their fame receded, they found themselves on the outside again looking in.

It would be wrong to leave you with the impression that cool and uncool were the only two categories of students. That was not the case. There were harmless sub-categories like freaks (those who smoked dope), straights (those who didn't), nerds (those who read books not assigned by teachers and who knew how to use slide rules), Jesus freaks (the born-again Christians), and others. These kids didn't care about the cool kids and embraced their category.

Notice I did not mention gays in any of the subcategories above. That's because that term was not in wide use yet to identify homosexuals. I'm not sure kids my age believed homosexuality was real. It was like saying you were from Mars. I suppose I thought it was possible but not very likely in Cumberland. I know now that many of my classmates were gay (much more on that later), but I did not have a true understanding of it, and I don't think they did, either. We were all in the dark on this subject. That didn't stop us from using colorful terms to describe more girl-like than man-like characteristics. Catchy names like queer, fag, fruit, sissy or fairy were applied. We could be very creative, and it was more a cruel way to make fun of someone than believing they were gay. From my adolescent brain's perspective, the thought of a man desiring a sexual relationship with another man was unthinkable.

How in the world did that work anyway?

I was confused enough about heterosexual relationships, so why on earth would I bother to think about homosexual attraction? Band camp would provide me an education on this.

Except for the kids in these final categories, you could change your caste designation by becoming a winner. Winners knew they were being considered for cool kid status if they were invited to take part in an event with other cool kids, like a party. But you couldn't be sure because cool kids were cruel. They might be selecting and readying you for something special like a ritualistic social sacrifice. Instead of inviting you to be cool with them, they may plan to stuff you into a locker or use you as an example of how not to dress.

— Drum Major —

Now that you know my motivation for becoming drum major, let me tell you about the process I was facing to accomplish it. Remember, we are in March 1971; the spring of my sophomore year, fourteen months before band camp. Being a cool kid was the main reason, but I had a related personal reason I didn't mention above. If drum major meant becoming a cool kid, then maybe I'd be exempt from the harassment I endured while walking through the halls at school. This was a big deal because it meant I could walk from Biology to Latin and not be called "band fag" or "Syckes, you woman." I wanted that, but to get there was a long process that involved a lot of hard work and a little bit of good luck.

When I started high school, I was a 5-foot-no-inch 125-pound *C* student with the habit of being labeled the class clown. My sisters before me were either very popular, superior students, or both. I'd grown five inches and added ten pounds since my freshman year, but there was another obstacle—a darker thought buried in my mind—I might not be up to the job of drum major. Despite this, everyone figured I was a shoo-in, given my dad was the band director. What they didn't know was that Dad was under pressure to make the competition for drum major fair and unbiased.

Could he make it too fair? I liked being a shoo-in.

In late March of 1971, the tryout competition started with Dale Bowman, the current drum major, holding weekly classes on the basics of conducting and leading a band. One thing you need to know is the ALCO band was a big thing. It had 120 members, the *de facto* largest student organization in the school, representing about 10% of the student body, so to lead it, the drum major needed to be seen, heard, and understood. To do this, Dale taught us how to conduct using our arms and signal the band with whistle blasts and voice commands.

There were two other students taking the drum major course along with me. One guy, whose name I don't remember dropped out after the first week, and Katie Kline. Already a cool kid, Katie was a smart, pretty, talented, and determined junior who got good grades and was a drummer in the band. I knew right away I was facing stiff competition.

Dale's focus was teaching us how to direct the band using our arms and hands. He stressed maintaining correct hand position, body position, and command presence. You've got to be taken seriously as drum major for the rest of the band to follow you.

Directing is essentially bouncing your arms in a pattern emphasizing the beats of the music. The downbeat is the most important, and your hands have to look as if they are bouncing off a brick wall so band members can use you as a means to stay together.

Dale also taught us whistle and marching commands. The drum major uses these commands to start the band then functions as a metronome, beating out the time with his or her arms until the next hard part comes: the ending. Good bands have a symbiotic relationship in that the individual members sense the rhythm and flow of the music and work together to stay together. The goal is for everyone to reach the same endpoint at the same time, but that doesn't always happen. I don't think there is anything more embarrassing than a drum major continuing to conduct after the band stops playing.

That reminds me of one of my dad's favorite stories. Back in 1963, the ALCO drum major was Eunice Brando. She was a beautiful, tall, blonde girl who got the job because she was competent and looked striking while standing in front of the band. Although she could get the band members started, she was never sure when they (or she) were supposed to stop. To her embarrassment, Eunice would often find herself flapping away as the band stood waiting for the next command. To assist her, my father enlisted the help of my sister Betsy, who was a freshman flute player and an excellent musician who always knew where she and the band were in the music. He would position Betsy right in front of the drum major so that at the appropriate time, she could give her a signal to let her know the song was coming to an end soon. Eunice was very pleased with this arrangement and rarely did the problem occur again, but if you looked real close, you'd see the drum major watching a particular flute player in the front row during every performance.

Katie and I didn't have Eunice Brando's problem, and since there were only two of us in his class, it wasn't long before Dale had taught us everything he could. Now it was up to us to perfect our skills and prepare for our performance before the tryout judges.

Ever since he'd gotten the job as band director, Dad had selected who became drum major. He would hold a competition and be the sole judge. But, when my sister Barbara tried out for drum major, he had to make changes. The conflict of interest and perception of bias were so obvious and indefensible Dad enlisted the help of others to do the job for him. For both my sister's competitions, he recruited three respected members of the community to be the judges. When I tried out, Dad did the same thing, asking three local school band directors to substitute for him and be the drum major tryout judges. He asked Bill AuMiller, Emerson Miller, and Lynn Zeller.

I knew all of these men, and they knew me, and that was not necessarily a good thing. In the case of Bill AuMiller, he had been in the band at ALCO in the early 1960's and had taken trumpet lessons from my dad. Like most high school band directors, Dad earned extra money on the side by giving private lessons to promising musicians, and I remember him having no fewer than five students per week come to the house for a half an hour of scales and fingering exercises.

Bill was one of them, and while he was trying to learn, I would make a nuisance of myself (I was very good at that and still am). Bill also knew me from band trips. I was often with Dad for football games, and this meant I'd travel on the bus with the band. I was a little kid hanging around a bunch of high school students, which never works out well. My nickname was Little Lu, and I felt right at home given my dad was the director, but I'm sure the big kids felt otherwise. I got stuffed into the overhead storage bin of the bus many times when they had had enough of me.

The second judge, Emerson Miller, was the band director at a high school in a neighboring town and was an accomplished musician. I knew him from playing in the Potomac Concert Band, which was a county amateur group. Emerson was a drummer, and I sat right in front of the drum section. I'm sure my poor musicianship and smartass demeanor did not impress him, but the judge who scared me the most, and I was certain he would vote against me no matter what, was Lynn Zeller.

Lynn had been my first band director at Braddock Junior High School from 1967 to 1969, and to put it mildly; I was a poor student. I started out as a trumpet player (because it was the instrument Dad played), but my poor skills placed me in the third section. Trumpet players in bands are divided into sections according to their abilities. The best players are in the first section and the lesser skilled ones in the second and third. I was near the bottom of the third section, and this meant I played very boring music. Not long after school started, Lynn asked me to change instruments. He needed French horn players, but I'm sure his real reasons for wanting to move me were to end my troublemaking in the trumpet section. I was always making wisecracks or bothering others because I was bored playing crappy third-part charts. I'd be joking around when I realized it was quiet, and then I'd feel the cold stare of Mr. Zeller boring down on me. I guess he hoped playing the French horn would keep me better occupied, and it did.

In retrospect, he did me a big favor by moving me off the trumpet; it was not the instrument for me, but once on the French horn, I enjoyed band a lot more. French horns, unlike third-trumpets, often have the melody or interesting harmony parts, so I took band much more seriously. There were only five French horn players in the junior high school band, and by the time I was in the eighth grade, I was battling for first chair. This turned out to be very important because at the end of each school year, Lynn would make recommendations to my dad which eighth-grade students should go into Allegany's Senior Band vs. Junior Band.

Junior Band was nothing like Senior Band, and as far as I can remember, they didn't do much. No parades or football game performances, nothing. All Junior Band members did was mark time until they graduated to Senior Band, and not all of them did. Many of them realized their skills were lacking and shifted to a different elective class.

Anyway, if I had stayed a third trumpeter and never advanced up the seating chart, I would have ended up in Junior Band because only the first trumpet section made it onto Lynn Zeller's list. But two, yes two, French horn players out of five made the cut for Senior Band, and I was one of them. I owed Lynn a lot, but I never got over the impression he thought I was a smartass-slacker. I didn't stay on the French horn for long. Soon after joining the Senior Band, Dad moved me to the baritone horn, and I've been playing it ever since. You'll hear a lot more about my baritone when I get to band camp.

With the judges selected, the competition was set for Friday, May 21st, and it would take place in the Allegany High School gymnasium. I spent many hours standing in front of my bedroom mirror practicing what Dale taught me. I'd direct to any song playing on the radio, so picture, if you will, a fifteen-year-old kid waving his arms around while Led Zeppelin's "Immigrant Song" plays in the background.

As the tryout date neared, my practice intensified, and so did my anxiety. The competition's structure was released, and it was challenging. Contestants would have to show their competency in three areas:

1. Conducting - Contestants will conduct a march and "The Star-Spangled Banner."

2. Band Leadership - Contestants will march a squad in the gymnasium using as many commands as necessary.

3. Solo March Performance - Contestants will perform a solo march around the gymnasium to music, demonstrating their marching and directing skills.

I felt confident in my ability to conduct the band and control the marching squad, but the Solo Marching Performance section scared me and would pit my creativity against Katie's.

Should I go big and bold or competent and conservative?

When the day of the tryout came, I remember planning what I would wear carefully. I wanted to stand out and be unique but not garish. The standard dress of the day was blue jeans and T-shirts, but I felt that was a little too dull, so I went with a pair of white jeans along with a collarless blue and white shirt with an attractive diamond pattern. I added a blue belt and grounded my outfit with gold suede tennis shoes.

Yes, gold suede tennis shoes!

These wild mod fashions were thanks to my mom, who shopped for all my clothes. My outfit was blue, white, and gold, the three colors found on ALCO's drum major uniform.

I went to school that day as usual by riding with my dad in our 1968 Barracuda fastback. I was two months away from turning sixteen, so I was dependent on others for transportation but being chauffeured to school was neat.

It was a perfect spring day, starting off in the low fifties with a promise of mid-70-degree temperatures by late afternoon. Dad took the route he'd been taking since he got the job as ALCO's band director twenty-three years earlier. It was always my impression that Dad was happy in his work, although I'm sure at times his work was just that—*work*. I sometimes wondered how different his life would have been if he had made alternative career choices. Let me tell you a little bit about Dad.

— Lu Syckes —

Dad was smart, studious, and determined. He was also confident of success. It was as if he knew what he wanted and what he had to do to get it, and if an obstacle appeared along the way, he'd figure out how to go around it. I don't remember him worrying about anything, at least from a career point of view; he worried about me often and openly.

After he graduated from Allegany, he decided to go to Potomac State Teachers College for a year. He did well there and pledged a local fraternity. I don't remember the name of it, but what I do remember is for his initiation into the frat, he was required to report to the house at midnight one Friday. There the brothers gave each pledge a name and a birth date. It was their job to go to the local cemetery and find the gravestone with that name and birth date on it and return with the correct death date before dawn, or they were out. After several hours of searching, Dad returned accomplishing his mission, only to find out the initiation wasn't over.

Phase two required him to stand naked before the Brotherhood while they ceremoniously painted him the frat's color green from head to toe. This sounds horrible, but it was much worse when you realize that in 1936, there were no latex-based paints, only oil, so when Dad got home, he had to sit outside and remove the paint with kerosene. *Ouch!* However, he survived and finished his year at the state college, and then it was off to a big school—Oberlin College in Ohio.

He studied mathematics, and I don't know a whole lot about his college days except that he participated in the marching and concert bands while maintaining a high grade point average. *I told you he was smart.*

One story that Mom shared but Dad denied was the bicycle incident. In his yearbook from Oberlin, there is a picture of the school's flagpole with a bicycle attached to the top. Mom said Dad put it up there; Dad said nothing. Graduating from Oberlin in 1940, he returned to Cumberland and got a job teaching mathematics at the then-new Beall High School in Frostburg, Maryland, ten miles from Cumberland. There he met the most important person in his life.

In Dad's first homeroom class as a teacher, there was a pretty young freshman girl named Stella Chidester, who six years later, would become his wife. Now, before your mind wanders to the dark side of student-teacher relationships, let me clarify that Dad paid no outward attention to Stella; although knowing my father was a full-blooded American male, and my mom was a natural beauty, he had to of notice her from a discrete distance.

Dad's time at Beall was brief, given world affairs conspired to change his life's course completely. The month he started his teaching career; Congress passed the first peacetime draft in the history of the United States.

Dad's number was among the first selected, making him a member of the Armed Forces whether he liked it or not. He was assigned to the Army and ordered to report to Fort Meade, Maryland, but requested a delay until the end of the school year so he could fulfill his teaching obligations. The Army agreed.

When school was over, Dad was off to Fort Meade, transforming from a teacher making $100 per month to a Private in the Army making $25. The good news was that his enlistment was for only one year, so he'd be out by July 1942. Unfortunately, a little thing called Pearl Harbor happened in December of 1941, and one of the first acts of the now-at-war government was to extend the enlistment of all draftees to the duration of the war.

When this happened, Dad knew he had to get out of his current situation. He'd been lucky enough to be assigned to the Army Band at Fort Meade and spent his time before December 7th playing concerts around the East Coast. After Pearl Harbor all concerts were canceled, and he found himself guarding bridges over the Potomac River with a rifle in his hands. Dad was not a gun guy, so he looked for a way to change things. Surprisingly, as a one-year draftee, the Army hadn't noted his college education. When Dad pointed it out, his commanding officer immediately transferred him to Officer Candidate School. Selman Field, Louisiana, was next for navigator training.

In the summer of 1943, Dad was commissioned a second lieutenant in the Army Air Corps, and because he finished at the top of his navigator training class, he was assigned to stay on at Selman Field and teach future classes. Staying at Selman Field may have saved his life because the rest of his navigator classmates were assigned to the bloody European theater and over 50 percent of them died before that Christmas.

By the summer of 1944, Dad had had enough of teaching navigation and requested reassignment to a combat theater. Near year's end, his commanding officer informed him his navigator skills qualified him for a special assignment, and it was on the front lines like he wanted. The location was top secret, and he would not know where it was until he got there. Dad volunteered, and on the day ordered, he boarded a transport plane for Miami, Florida, along with ten other navigators. The bet was they were going to the European theater to support the mopping up of Nazi Germany after the failure of Hitler's winter offensive, and when the plane took off and headed east over the Atlantic, they were sure of it, but they were wrong. After refueling at the Azores instead of turning northeast for France, they went southeast to Africa. Several days later after traveling more than halfway around the world, they found themselves in far eastern India on the border with China in the foothills of the Himalayan Mountains. Dad would be flying The Hump.

According to the China-Burma-India Hump Pilots Association's webpage (1): The Hump was a high-altitude military aerial supply route between the Assam Valley in Northeastern India to Yunnan province in Southwestern China. This operation was the first sustained, long-range, 24 hours around-the-clock, all-weather, military aerial supply line in history. There was no precedent for it.

Dad spent six months and 600 combat mission hours navigating the wilds of China in a C-47 delivering supplies to the National Chinese Army and earning two Air Medals and the Distinguished Flying Cross.

Soon after he returned from China, the war came to its quick end, and Dad found himself at a turning point. Should he remain in the service or resign his commission? The Board of Education had promised him a job, but the Army wanted him to stay and teach as well. He chose to resign from active duty but stay in the reserves and take advantage of his GI Bill of Rights college scholarship. With that decision made, he packed up and headed for Columbia University in New York City. There Dad earned his Master's degree in Music and was on course to be an Allegany County educator until an unexpected opportunity arose.

1st Lt Lu Syckes 1945 (Syckes Family Photos)

The Columbia music department's head trumpet instructor recognized Dad's performance talents and asked him to take his place playing with pit orchestras in downtown New York City while he was recovering from dental surgery. Dad did so well the instructor encouraged him to stay in New York and make trumpet performance his career. Of course, Dad didn't make that choice, but who knows what kind of life that would have been.

Mom and Dad's romance kindled at the Beall High School Christmas dance of 1943. Mom was now a senior and looking better than ever, and Dad was home on leave from Air Force duty. Here's where the facts as told seem to be a bit questionable but understandable.

Stella Chidester 1945 (Syckes Family Photos)

According to Dad, he just happened to decide to go to the Christmas dance at Beall as a former teacher there, and of course, he had to wear his uniform, so he was looking pretty darn good. The dance was going strong with Bing Crosby crooning "White Christmas," and Mom was talking with friends when she saw a silhouette of a lean-mean-fighting-machine Air Force guy standing in the doorway.

Her friend said, "That's Mr. Syckes, the math teacher," and the next thing she knew, he was standing beside her.

Mom's side of the story always emphasized she was not interested at first although she thought her homeroom teacher was cute, but he was too much of a disciplinarian for her. Her most vivid memory of her days in his homeroom was him rapping his oversized Oberlin class ring on the desk to quiet the students. Stella and Lu talked and danced and then he drove her to her house. I'm not sure the evening ended in a kiss, but it was the start of something special. The squirrelly part of this story is believing Dad never dreamed of bumping into that beautiful young girl he'd spied in his homeroom class three years earlier, but we shall never know. What we do know is that as soon as he finished his Master's degree, he was on a train back to Cumberland to marry Stella.

Dad got a job teaching math at Fort Hill High School in the fall of 1946 but only stayed a year when he accepted the position of Director of Music at Allegany.

I never got the sense that Dad felt he made a mistake by staying in Cumberland, but I know he wondered what might have been from time to time. I'm pretty sure he wasn't thinking about this as he drove me to school on drum major tryout day, but he might have been. I know I was only thinking about one thing. Will I win?

— Tryouts —

We pulled into ALCO's parking lot and walked to the band room. Dad looked at me and asked, "Are you ready?"

Crap, how do you answer that?

"I think so," popped out of my mouth.

Then he asked a more pointed question, "Have you thought about your solo routine? You know, the part where you have to march around the gym by yourself?"

Crap, squared!

I'd thought about it, but I really didn't have a concrete plan, and I had done no real practicing. Dad could tell from my face I was less than confident and told me to come to the gymnasium at lunchtime, and he'd meet me there. This was the first time he had said anything of substance about the tryout, and I knew he was leaning in as far as he could to help me without crossing any lines.

When I arrived, the gymnasium was set up for the tryout with the massive collapsible door that divided the gym into two sections closed so only half of the basketball court was available. This worried me because I had envisioned having the entire gym in which to maneuver the marching squad. With two of the extendable bleacher sections pulled out, the area for marching was even smaller. One of the bleachers was for the band members to sit on, and the other was for spectators. In front of the band's bleacher was a six-foot-long table with three chairs and an amplified record player.

I remember looking around and thinking, *What am I going to do?*

My stomach felt like molten lead.

I paced around following the basketball court's out-of-bounds line, trying to imagine what I could do to stand out from Katie in my marching. I didn't get far when Dad came in and closed the door behind him. He had a record in his hand as he called me over. Sensing it was a good time to listen and not talk, I walked over and stood quietly. He put the record on the player and turned it on but didn't start it playing. It was the "National Emblem March" the song for the solo marching portion of the competition.

Dad then said, "I can't stay here, and you should return this record to my desk when the lunch hour is up. Only the first two strains of the march will be played during the competition. Don't overthink it, and don't get fancy. Competence is more important, and fancy can get you in trouble."

He also told me not to over march the band member squad stating, "Only go as far as it takes to show that you can control them, and make sure they are formed up properly before you start." And finally, he said, "Remember to give the turning commands long before they reach the end of the basketball court. The last thing you want to do is run them into a wall."

With that, he was gone, and I was alone again in the half gym to come up with my winning strategy.

The Allegany High School gymnasium was the pride of the Allegany County sports world. Built in 1959, it was a gleaming box of pink brick. Just the architectural design you would expect from the late 1950's, functional but flat. Unfortunately, the big pink brick gym did not in any way match the design of the other school buildings. The rest of Allegany, built between 1926 and 1936, was a mixture of toned-down Art Deco design, and it was made entirely of red brick, not pink.

After Dad left the gym, I stared at my feet for a while, hoping something brilliant would pop into my head. It didn't. I listened to the march and counted how many measures I had to do my performance. I knew the march well because it was the standard pre-game opener the band played at all home games. "National Emblem" was a simple march and the section that would be played was less than two minutes long. That doesn't sound like much, but I could march around that half-a-gym quite a few times if that's all I planned to do. I started walking along the out of bounds line again thinking of ways to fill the time.

I didn't want to only march in a square, so I looked for ways I could be creative. Wherever it was possible, I'd add an oblique instead of a left or right flank. I also decided to stop in the middle of the court and direct the march for a few measures.

In the end, the path of my routine looked like a big "M" that ended right in front of the judges' table.

Sigh. A Big "M," is that all? Oh well, it would have to be enough.

All I had time left to do was practice my Big "M" and then plan the marching commands I'd use in the squad drill part of the competition. For that, I planned to keep it very simple, just a box maneuver around the gym floor. I also planned to make sure the band members were in a perfect rectangle before starting the march. With that, the lunch hour was up. I took the record to Dad's office and left it on his desk. Now all I had to do was sit through three more hours of classes before the tryout started.

Conveniently, my last class of the day was band, and since we'd already had our spring concert, there was nothing left for us to do. I slipped out for one more practice run in the gym, but that was not to be. As I opened the door to the gym, I heard the "National Emblem" march playing and saw Katie marching around the floor. That sinking feeling returned to my stomach as I realized Dad had not done me any exclusive favor by letting me practice at lunchtime. Katie got an equal shot of trying out her routine with the music, just at a different time. Everything was still fair-and-square.

I backed out of the door but kept watching through the window in it. Katie looked good, damn good. Not only was she marching like a pro, but she was gorgeous, and I wasn't the only one trying to dress like a drum major. She wore white, tight short-shorts that highlighted her well-formed rear, a light blue double-breasted blouse with shiny buttons, high-top patent leather go-go boots and on her shoulders were epaulets.

Epaulets! Holy crap, it's over.

Suddenly, the all-male panel of judges seemed impossible for me to sway. How in the world was I going to get any attention from a bunch of middle-aged men when my competition is a seventeen-year-old hottie in short-shorts and epaulets? I thought of Eunice Brando, the beautiful, tall, blonde drum major from 1963 who didn't know when the songs ended.

Hell, if she got the job, Katie was a shoo-in because she could count.

I looked around the empty hallway that connected the band room with the gymnasium. The minutes were ticking away, and this was the only place I had to do whatever practicing I could before the competition started. I went through my routine marking time instead of marching the full distances I'd need to on the basketball court. I also reviewed the steps I planned to take in preparing the squad for marching, and finally, I directed "The Star-Spangled Banner," humming the tune in my head. My concentration was interrupted when the band room doors burst open, and the students came flooding out. My time was up. I went to the gym and took a seat in the upper left corner of the bleacher section set aside for supporters and waited.

It wasn't long before band members with their instruments filed in and mingled near their bleacher seats, and other kids passed through on their way home from school. To my surprise, I saw my sister Betsy walking towards me from the door in the collapsible wall. I had forgotten she was home from Bucknell University and planned on attending. This was not a good thing. Although I appreciated her showing up to support me, at that moment, I was sure I would lose, and I did not want to do so in front of her. As she climbed up the bleachers, I said, "Hello" and walked down to the gym floor.

There weren't many spectators and the band members numbered fewer than twenty-five. They were all seniors, with a few juniors sprinkled in to fill out the instrumentation. Fifteen of them would make up the drill squad. I knew them all, but I don't recall if any of them were rooting for me. Katie was a junior and popular in the band while I was still a sophomore trying for something that could be perceived as a year ahead of my time. This was Katie's one chance. I had another chance next year.

Oh well, there's no backing out now.

As I was thinking this, the doors of the gym opened, and in came four familiar faces—the judges, and Dad. I saw Katie standing to the left of the judges' table, and I decided to go over and stand with her.

As I approached, she smiled and said, "Good luck."

The judges came up to us, introduced themselves, and took their seats behind the table. Dad fiddled with the record player and made sure it was ready to go, and then in his typical fashion, he rapped his ring on the table to call the proceedings to order.

After introducing the judges, Dad reached into his pocket and took out a quarter. He asked Katie to call heads or tails, she called heads, and he flipped the coin.

It came up heads. Katie would be contestant number one, and I'd be number two.

He then turned to Katie and me and reviewed the three phases of the competition. The conducting portion was first and we each had to conduct two songs. "Hey, Look Me Over," was the theme song of the Allegany drill team and Katie handled it well and so did I. It broke the ice on the competition and my nervousness dissipated. No matter what happened from this point forward, it would all be over soon.

Next came "The Star-Spangled Banner," and this song was much more complex. You can't direct it straight through. There are parts where it slows and then pauses, twice. We both did it well, and so the first part of the competition ended with what felt like a tie.

Next was the band leadership test. Fifteen of the most senior members of the band left the bleachers and formed up on the gym floor in front of the judges. I watched from the sidelines while Katie used her whistle to get the squad's attention, organize them into three rows of five each, and prepare them for the drill. She ordered a Dress-Right-Dress command and then quickly brought them back to attention. The group looked good.

What followed was an excellent example of how to maneuver a small squad within a limited space.

Quickly it was my turn, and I took to the floor with a plan to distinguish myself from Katie. Blowing my whistle twice to get the group's attention, I yelled in a commanding voice, "Form up," which was followed by, "Squad, atten-hut."

With their full attention garnered, I ordered, "Dress-Right-Dress."

The members of the squad raised their left arms and shifted their eyes to the right. While in this position, they made small adjustments in their location so that their left hands were just touching the shoulder of the member to their left. My next command, "Ready Front," brought them back to facing forward and at attention. Then I executed my plan.

I strode around the squad, looking down the lines and making adjustments where needed. Once I was back in front, I commanded "Right Face." Next, I ordered another "Dress-Right-Dress."

I did this because I wanted to be sure that the squad's alignment was correct both from the front and the side perspectives. The reality was, they looked great before I gave any orders, but that was not the point. I was trying to impress the judges with my thoroughness.

With the alignment finished and having the squad already facing to my left, I yelled, "Forward March."

This was nearly a catastrophic mistake. Although Katie had done only one Dress-Right-Dress command, she had wisely ordered an "About Face" before starting the squad marching.

With her squad facing away from the Judges and towards the aluminum wall, she had more room and time to maneuver them before hitting it. I, on the other hand, started my squad marching when they were already halfway across the narrowest part of the court, and the gymnasium wall was approaching fast.

All marching commands must be given in rhythm with the speed that the squad is marching. But giving the command itself uses up time which equates to steps forward. In my case, that was a few steps closer to the wall. Realizing my mistake, I immediately shouted, "Right Flank March."

It took four beats or four steps for me to give the order. Then it took another two beats or steps for the squad to execute it. Add this to the time it took for me to realize my mistake, and my margin for error was gone. I thought for sure we were headed for a smash-up. Luckily, the squad made a sharp flanking maneuver in time and narrowly missed piling up on the wall like a rugby scrum.

To avoid the judges thinking I'd made the mistake I had, I ordered another "Right Flank," and then four counts later in rhythmic sequence a "Left Flank," and then four counts later another "Right Flank."

This gave the appearance that the squad was stair-stepping up and across the court. With a few more commands I had the squad back on the line where they began, and I ordered "Squad Halt" in front of the judges.

Before I left the court, I quietly said thank you to the squad members, and I meant it, because without their keen marching skills and attention to command, my drill would have been a disaster, a total disaster.

Two down and one to go, but it was the big one, the solo marching performance.

Again, Katie was up first, and she began her routine in front of the judges. After coming to attention, she signaled to Dad she was ready, and he put the needle on the already spinning record. The gymnasium filled with the sound of Edwin Eugene Bagley's "National Emblem March."

Katie saluted smartly and then made an immediate Right Face and marched in time with the music. She hit the corner of the basketball court and executed a sharp Right Flank then marched all the way down the line. With her arms crisply swinging and thrusting up and about, she got to the end of the line and, to my surprise, she did a 45-degree oblique and made a beeline for the center of the court.

Oh my God, she's going to steal my Big "M" routine!

But that was just the beginning. When she got to the center of the court, she stopped, and as my mouth dropped open, she began to conduct the march in front of the judges as I had planned to.

Oh, sweet holy Moses! Had she been watching me at lunchtime?

Thankfully, after she stopped directing, she did not complete the Big "M" but instead continued to the opposite end of the court nearest the band room and then turned 45 degrees to the left. She turned again at the wall and marched catty-corner across the court. She ended where she began, right in front of the judges, as the march came to an end. With another perfect salute and a big beautiful smile, she was finished, and so was I.

I didn't notice Dad signaling me. It was my turn. It took one of the band members nudging me to get my attention. Startled, I jumped up and moved onto the court. My mind was spinning.

What can I do to change up my routine to distinguish it from Katie's?

I had nothing. All I could do was buck up and march the best damn Big "M" the world had ever seen. I saluted and cued Dad to start the music. With the downbeat, I was off in the same direction Katie took and did a good job at the turn. I was concentrating on my arm maneuvers, keeping them crisp and clean so not to look like a baby bird trying to fly and all the time trying to come up with something new to add a spark of difference to my routine. I made the oblique at the top of the line and started toward the center of the court. I could see the judges watching me, and I figured this was it, I either did something now, or it was over.

As I came to a halt and began to direct the march, I remembered our teacher, Dale Bowman, telling Katie and me, "Sometimes a drum major has to march backward while conducting the band."

I could hear him saying, "It's not something you want to do all the time. It's tough to direct and march backward, especially since you can't see where you're going. You should only do it when there is a need to keep the band moving but also make sure they are staying together musically."

The second the thought entered my mind I impulsively stepped backward with my left foot and then followed it with my right, all the time continuing to conduct the march. I was marching backward towards a big aluminum wall with no good way to tell when I'd get there. I couldn't turn my head and peek. That would be cheating and look unprofessional, so I had to guess. I figured there were about eighteen steps before I would hit the wall—nine measures of the music, so I waited for eight measures to pass, then I swung around sharply to my left and marched towards the observers' bleachers. The wall was less than a foot to my left, but I pretended it was a mile away and that this was what I had practiced a hundred times before.

So much for the Big "M." I was winging it again; as I did during the drill competition. Knowing I had used up precious time with my backward marching, I figured I needed to take the most direct route I could to the judges' table, so at the corner, I turned inward and marched to the center of the court again. When I reached it, there were only about two measures left in the song, so I high-kick marched for three counts, covering about twice the normal territory in the same amount of time. This took me right up to the judge's table, and I sharply pulled my left foot forward and even with my right—clicked my heels.

By the way, gold suede sneakers make little noise when clicked together.

In one final unplanned act, I shot off a smart salute in the British fashion with my palm facing forward and a bit of a bounce as it reached my eye. It was over.

I walked off the court and made my way up the bleacher steps to where my sister was sitting to wait for the judges' decision. They gathered up their notes and retired to Dad's office to deliberate. I blended into the bleachers. Betsy was very supportive and said I had done a great job, but her praise fell on deaf ears. I was spent and had no idea what the judges thought of my spontaneously improvised performance. My wait was short, and before I could catch my breath, the judges filed back into the gym.

Bill AuMiller spoke for the group and asked for the crowd's attention. "The other judges and I want to thank the members of the band who took part today, and we also want everyone to know this was a very close call. But, we decided the next drum major of the Allegany High School Band is contestant number two."

No name, just contestant number two!

I'd been so focused on winning; I'd forgotten my number. Bill wasn't using a microphone, so I looked at Betsy quizzically. She smiled and gave me a big hug. "You are contestant number two, silly. You won!"

By the time the reality of the situation sank in, I looked up and saw that almost everyone in the gymnasium was looking at me and smiling or applauding, although it didn't last long.

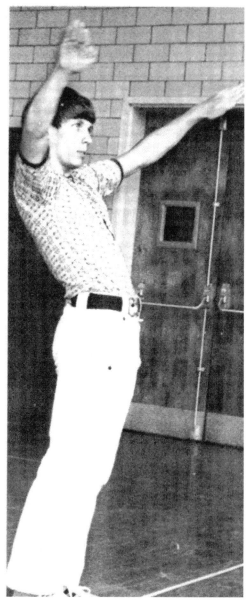

Drum Major Tryout Day (Allegwee, 1972)

I didn't talk to Katie, but I knew she must be disappointed, and although I was glad to have won, I empathized with her because I truly thought I would be the loser. The judges disappeared back into the band room, and Dad stayed clear of me, avoiding any public display of affection given his position.

I remember how happy I was. For the first time in my life, I tried for something big on my own and succeeded. I also knew I got lucky. Whatever convinced the judges to pick me, I knew I had come close to falling on my face. I tried to be as humble as I could.

When I got home, I didn't want to go into the house. It was a beautiful day, and I was experiencing a special moment. I sat on the big porch swing and glided back and forth for a while. I felt proud, and I remember savoring it. The next thing I felt was dread.

Oh my God! I'm the ALCO drum major, and I have to lead the largest organization in the school next fall, and I don't have a clue how I'm going to do that!

I found out quickly all the work I had to do to prepare both myself and the band for the coming season. Dad let me enjoy my triumph for a few days, but then he sat me down and gave it to me straight, "You're in charge now and the band's success or failure is in your hands."

Not only did we participate in all ten football games, but we also competed in parades. The first step for me was to attend a one-week drum major training camp where I'd learn the finer points of band management. Also, I needed to work with the other band officers to schedule, organize and execute a two-week Summer Band program in August. In between, I had to come up with at least an outline of what music and drills we would perform. It was a daunting list of chores, and after Dad finished telling me all about it, I felt like running away. So, I did, to the swimming pool, that is.

— Hey Shelby —

We were members of the Cumberland Country Club, and I had enjoyed swimming in the pool there for years. It was a nice pool with lush green lawns surrounding three sides. The fourth side was all concrete and the location of the diving board. The pool was home to one of the most elite cliques of high school students on the planet. On the left half of the far side of the pool was a secluded lawn area. It was unofficially but very clearly known to all as the ALCO cool kids zone, and absolutely no other losers could trespass without risk of serious consequences. The area was fronted by the deep end of the pool near the diving board and boxed in by high shrubs.

For all the years I had been swimming at the pool, that area was off limits. I could walk on the narrow concrete walkway in front of the zone, but that was it. I was to stay off the grass. It was for cool kids only. On this sunny day, when I arrived at the pool, I spread out my towel in my usual area on the opposite side of the pool from the cool kids. There was no anger, no feeling of banishment or segregation. It was just the way things were, and I accepted it. As the number of swimmers increased and more and more cool kids arrived and gathered on their hallowed ground, I noticed the Queen of the Cumberland Country Club ALCO cool kids, Joyce Carman, standing up and waving her hand in my direction.

Joyce was the epitome of what a cool kid was at ALCO. She was beautiful, well developed, gregarious, popular, and involved in all the right stuff. She was a member of the drill team and co-captain her senior year, member of the drama club, and sports editor of both the yearbook and the school newspaper. She also dated only the coolest of the cool starting lineup football players, but the coolest of cool jobs she had at ALCO, and she had it for four years, was track team manager. Now you ask, "What's so big a deal about managing the girls' track team?" The answer is nothing. She wasn't the manager of the girls' track team; she was the manager of the boys' track team.

As I noticed her waving in my direction, I thought I heard her shout my name.

But that couldn't be so. What on earth would she be calling me for?

There it was again: "Hey, Shelby, yeah you, Shelby! Come on over!"

There was nothing but stunned silence among my friends, and I was not sure at all what I was supposed to do next. I stood and walked towards the pool, intending to get close enough to ask, politely, what she needed.

"Hey, Shelby, go back and get your towel and come on over!" Joyce yelled.

"It's okay now, you're the drum major."

I know you think I'm exaggerating this, that there could not have possibly been that strict a divide between members of the same school but, as God is my witness, these things happened as I'm describing them. It was in June of 1971 that my invitation arrived. Life was good. I was a cool kid.

Chapter 2 - You've got a Friend

— Tim & Mike —

It didn't last long. I enjoyed crossing over to the cool side of the pool, but I realized quickly that my friends were still on the other side. I'm talking about my two best friends at the time; Mike and Tim. Mike as the star kicker on the football team was eligible for the cool kids clique, but wasn't interested. He had recently moved to Cumberland when his dad became the minister at the Lutheran church, and they lived in a neat old stone home nearby. Well, I thought it was neat because it backed up to the Western Maryland railroad tracks, and there isn't anything neater to a fifteen-year-old kid than a train, and that pretty much sums up my problem. I was still a fifteen-year-old kid and wasn't ready to be a young adult, which is what all the cool kids were pretending to be. On top of that, my other good friend, Tim, was a freshman and in the Junior Band, so he had no chance at cool kid status. After a few days of sunbathing on the cool side of the pool, I returned to throwing Frisbees with my friends on the other side.

I'd known Tim much longer than Mike. He lived four houses down the street from me. We met soon after Tim's family moved into my neighborhood, and we clicked right away. We didn't spend much time apart from then on. We were either on bikes or building a fort or camping out in our backyards all the time and all great fun.

By 1971, Tim and I had moved away from bikes and building forts, and our camping out had turned into late-night shenanigans. The scenario went like this: either Tim would stay overnight at my place, and we'd sneak out, or I'd stay over at Tim's, and we'd sneak out, but the ultimate scheme was for each of us to tell our parents we were staying over at the other one's house and then walk around all night. While we were out, we'd explore our local surroundings, look in people's windows, throw rocks at the garbage men, stand by the side of the highway yelling, "Slow down—radar!" or look for something to purloin.

One of our favorite targets was road signs.

When Mike came along, he joined in the fun. He was beginning his senior year of high school and was tall, sculpted, and good looking. Tim was smart but quiet and always knew what was going on but stayed in the background. He was tall but not as tall as Mike and had not yet developed into the well-built man he would be a decade later.

I was the shortest of them all having somehow missed the class on growth spurts. I came in at five-foot-five—that's 65 inches, and inches for boys are like boobs for girls; you either have them, or you don't. There's no faking them.

Soon after I won the drum major tryout, Tim, Mike, and I decided we needed a shenanigans night. The first thing we did was choose Mike's house as our base camp because it was close to a particularly desirable road sign we'd been eyeing for awhile. The sign was classic: a burnt orange, black lettered, embossed heavy metal wonder that had bold 1930's artwork of a running boy. Above the boys head was the word "SLOW" in all capital letters, and underneath was spelled out "Children Playing." SLOW Children Playing—I love this phraseology. The message was clear: Young lives are at risk, slow down your car; be careful. But, as an aberrant-thinking teenager, I read into it a different and more deviant meaning. I'll illuminate with a joke:

"Hey, Mac, you know that 'SLOW Children Playing' sign we saw yesterday?"

"Yes. Why, Fred?"

"Well don't worry about those poor little tykes because I saw a 'SLOW Men at Work' sign today, so apparently, they get jobs when they grow up."

I wanted that sign, and I intended to get it. We needed to pick a good day, and as Lady Luck would have it, all of our parents were going out to the same event at the Country Club the next Saturday night. That was perfect; parents after an active night at the Country Club were very unlikely to be alert to the goings-on of the three kids in the basement.

On that Saturday, we gathered early at Mike's house and spent most of the day doing things that, in retrospect, seem insanely dangerous. One of our favorites was playing with trains. Now, I'm not talking about model trains; I mean the 100-ton behemoths that power the primary cargo transportation system in our country. They rumbled down the tracks in Mike's backyard every hour, and we had all kinds of fun with them. They had to go slow while passing through the city and when we'd hear one coming, we'd run to the tracks and put a coin on the rails. Then, we raced back into the yard to watch. The weight of the train would flatten the coins into wafer-thin blades, perfect for throwing at each other, kind of like mini-Frisbees.

Smart, huh? And yes, they would cut if they hit flesh.

When that got old, we'd use the train as a free mode of transportation. We'd wait for the engine to pass, then run alongside a boxcar and grab the bottom rung of the ladder on its side. We wouldn't climb up. No, that was too easy. Instead, we'd hang there, dragging our feet on the gravel. We'd only go a few blocks, then drop off, sometimes rolling down the hill next to the track. I'm sure there are hundreds of examples of idiots like us stumbling at the wrong time and finding themselves sliced to bits by the razor-sharp train wheels, but we never thought that would happen to us. We knew it was a bit dangerous but also a lot of fun. Our take on it was, "What the hell!"

A decade later, I read an article about a kid who was killed putting a penny on a train track.

The train didn't hit him; the penny did.

It turns out a locomotive wheel imparts enough force to accelerate a penny to the speed of a 45-caliber bullet.

Christ, were we lucky!

— The Bridge & Frisbees —

After any train adventure, we'd get down to the business of throwing the Frisbee around, and one of our favorite places to do this was under "The Bridge." The Bridge, as Cumberlanders called it, was an intrusive elevated interstate highway system that bisected the heart of the city. If I were giving someone directions how to get from my house to the Country Club, I wouldn't say, "Take the interstate west." No, instead I'd say, "Take The Bridge west."

When proposed in the late 1950's, city administrators were ecstatic with the prospect of having thousands of travelers passing through Cumberland. When executed, the potential for massive increases in business carried with it heavy, if not overwhelming negatives. There is a good reason why most interstate highways bypass the center of cities: interstate construction is disruptive or destructive on the immediate and surrounding properties.

The Bridge also changed the character of the city from a sleepy little town nestled in a hollow of the Appalachian Mountains to a wannabe bustling intercity metropolis with gleaming on-and off-ramps shooting here, there, and everywhere. Unfortunately, Cumberland wasn't a bustling intercity metropolis; it was a medium-size rural town with a maze of narrow, twisting interconnected streets. Worse, as The Bridge went up, beautiful landmarks and notable old buildings were razed or hopelessly compromised by the nearness of the 100-yard wide steel and concrete python slithering through the city's center. The Bridge did not come to Cumberland; it consumed Cumberland.

In the spring of 1971, I spent a lot of time under The Bridge. The elevated structure created vast covered areas where Tim, Mike and I could throw Frisbees for hours, but on the night of our "SLOW Children Playing" sign operation; we used our alternative Frisbee area, the Cafe-Gym-torium at the Lutheran church.

Mike's father had given us a key, so we had access to it 24 hours a day. Another edifice in 1950's architecture, the church was built entirely of pink brick and would have been right at home next to the Allegany Gym. Clean and classic, with a single-spire steeple and a cross-shaped layout, the church was the focal point of the Lutheran community. Well, the Allegany Lutherans, that is. However, the churchy part of the building did not interest us; it was the large multi-use facility behind it we called home. Housing a full-size basketball court, a stage, a fully-equipped professional kitchen, and seating for several hundred people, the Cafe-Gym-torium was the perfect place for teenage boys to hang out and have fun. It was here that we perfected our masterpiece of Frisbeeology, the game of "Midnight Frisbee Tag" (patent pending—*I wish*).

At the start of the game, each player has two items; a Frisbee and a flashlight. We cleared the Cafe-Gym-torium of all furniture and made sure it was totally dark: no lights. I'm talking not-sure-if-your-eyes-are-open dark. Frisbees lay in a pile in the center of the court. The second the flashlights were turned off all hell would break loose. Frisbees flew here there and everywhere with only one goal in mind: hit the other guy.

Sound fun? It was, but you had to withstand a Frisbee hitting you at full speed. It felt like the principal smacking you with his paddling stick. *THWACK!* But that wasn't the death blow. There is one place a teenage boy hates to get hit, and you know where that is. Now and then, one of us would catch a plastic disc in the crotch, and we'd have to suspend the game until the writhing on the floor ended. The game was adrenaline-filled with elements of today's laser tag or paintball without all the batteries or mess. We loved it and would play for hours.

— Get That Sign —

Back at Mike's, we waited until his parents came home from the country club and went to bed. We then left for the church with a collection of Frisbees and flashlights for another round of battle. Tonight though, we had some specialized equipment. I had a pair of pliers in my back pocket, and Tim had a monkey wrench down the front of his jeans. The mission was on. The objective lay only a block away and up the hill from Mike's house. The street he lived on had huge trees that provided additional cover from the summer moon, so darkness was on our side. We stashed our Frisbees in the shadows and made a bee-line for our objective, the big beautiful orange rectangle.

Road signs today have rivetes attaching them to their poles, so if you want to remove them, you have to drill out the rivets. They also have serial numbers stamped into their metal to identify them with their location, so if found somewhere else, questions will be asked.

I'd like to think I contributed to the implementation of these improvements.

But when I was a kid, things were much simpler. There were no markings, and all you needed to remove a sign was a couple of wrenches and a way to reach the bolts. Our plan was simple. As Tim stood watch for cars, Mike would get down on all fours, and I'd stand on his back. After a couple of twists with the wrenches, we'd be on our way.

What could possibly go wrong?

Ready for our mission, Tim handed me the monkey wrench and then as our signalman, he ran up the road and crouched behind a tree. Mike and I hid in the bushes next to the house closest to the sign until Tim gave the all-clear signal, one blink of his flashlight. Then, Mike shot out and got down on all fours beside the signpost. I followed and stepped up onto his back.

"Easy does it," Mike groaned.

"Sorry," I whispered.

I started turning the bottom bolt. I figured the smart thing to do was to loosen it but not remove it completely, then work on the top bolt and remove it first. If I did it the other way, the sign might fall uncontrollably when the top bolt came out. It was at the limit of my reach, and I was worried I'd drop it.

The bottom bolt was loose, and I reached up to start on the top one. It was stickier, and I was leaning around as far as I could for extra leverage on the rear nut when my foot slipped off Mike's back, and down I came like a bucket of rocks.

Mike raised his head like a dog pausing between drinks of water, "Nice work, Doofus. Do you want me to try?"

"No, I'll get it."

Before remounting Mike, I looked at Tim for a security update. He blinked his light. No cars in sight. Planting my sneaker a little more firmly on Mike's back, I was up and twisting the top bolt again in a flash. I could tell I was far enough along that I didn't need the tools anymore, so I carefully returned them to my back pocket and reached up for the final finger twirl that would release the bolt.

As I gave it a spin, Tim cried out, "Car!"

Mike moved from under me and the wrench fell out of my back pocket, catching him in the shoulder.

"Ouch!" he groaned.

Without my human stepladder, I fell and as I did I pulled the top bolt through the sign's hole as headlights appeared at the crest of the hill.

Tim yelled, "Car!" again and ran behind a bush.

The car was coming straight for me. Mike was gone, and I found myself on the ground. I felt for the wrench but couldn't find it, so I looked for a good place to hide but was distracted by the sign moving. Its metal back was scraping the pole and producing an ungodly screeching noise. As the sign moved to the right, it picked up momentum. It was free from its top bolt but still attached to the bottom one, so it swung in a clockwise pendulum motion down and down and grew louder as it swung.

Everything had an underwater slowness as the car neared and the road sign arched down, reaching its maximum velocity and volume as it passed through the bottom of its geometric curve. I laid there frozen as the car passed and the sign cut through the night air like Death's scythe slices through a victim's dying breath. The sound was deafening. As the sign began its futile climb back to the top, I saw the outline of the car gliding past me. It didn't look special.

Is it two-tone? Wait, what the hell is that on its top? Oh God, it's a bubble gum machine! It's the cops.

But the car didn't stop. The black-n-white of the Cumberland police department just kept gliding down the street without squealing its brakes or flashing its lights. All I heard was the gawdawful *swoosh* of the swinging sign as it ground to a halt at the center of the pole.

I breathed again and looked around for Mike and Tim. They melted out of the dark and came over to me. Our primal instincts took over, and we ran for Mike's house. We got there fast and quietly opened the kitchen door and snuck down to the basement. There we waited, expecting the doorbell to ring or a stun grenade to explode through the window followed by a SWAT team. Something! But again, nothing happened.

After an hour, we knew we had to finish our mission and get that sign. We couldn't leave it hanging there, upside down, with my fingerprints all over it and Mike's dad's wrench lying beneath it. They'd get us for sure, and we'd have gone through all this trouble with nothing to show for it. We went back out to finish the job.

Approaching the sign Tim and I watched for cars while Mike (the tallest of us) walked up and finished spinning the bottom bolt off. It was all done in about thirty-seconds, and Mike was back with the sign and the wrench, so we hurried off to his house to stash away our loot.

The sign was more beautiful than we had hoped. It had sculpted round corners and embossed borders, print, and a beautifully detailed silhouette of a running child complete with collar, belt buckle, and shorts. It was a true roadway work of art from the 1930's. Sliding it under the fold-out couch, we gathered up our disks from the shadows and went to the Cafe-Gym-torium to celebrate, but after one game of Frisbee tag, we wanted to do something different, but what? I came up with the answer, and it would lead to one of the most memorable experiences of my life. We'd go for a walk downtown.

The street in front of Mike's church led to an intersection at the confluence of Wills Creek and the Potomac River. There is what I think is the most photographed building in all of Western Maryland, the Emmanuel Episcopal Church, the church I grew up attending every Sunday. Emmanuel sits fifty feet above the intersection looking out on downtown Cumberland. It is always well illuminated at night with large spotlights shining on its steeple and a lush evergreen tree decorated every year for Christmas.

As we left the Lutheran church, Tim asked, "What about the cops?"

"What about them?" I asked.

"Well, they might be looking for us!" Tim shot back.

We all laughed and kept walking, but as a precaution, we stayed in the shadows and ducked for cover whenever we saw a car. Looming forebodingly on our right like a great shadow was the dark stone structure of Emmanuel Parish. The church appeared to grow larger as we continued down the street. Adding to this tunneling effect was the church's retaining wall, made of the same gray stone that begins at street level and rises to over eight feet. Shining in front of us was the huge neon sign of the Algonquin Hotel, one of Cumberland's downtown skyscrapers coming in at six stories and topped by a water tower, adding another soggy story.

While the eerie, orange, neon hotel sign demanded our attention, it was the harsh fluorescent lighting of the main entrance that had us worried.

How were we going to pass by there unseen?

Beyond the hotel was a bridge across Wills Creek. There were other bridges, but the nearest one would take us a mile out of our way, so we decided to press on and do our best imitations of normal folk out for a stroll. Why we thought this would work, I do not know. It just seemed the thing to do at the time. We strode on walking in front of the floor-to-ceiling framed glass doors of the Algonquin Hotel. I remember looking in as we passed and saw an older woman behind the front desk busy counting money, probably the night auditor. She glanced up, and I smiled and nodded politely but picked up my pace.

We were only steps from safety. A side street was close, and we could stop there and decide what to do next. That's when the shit hit the fan.

There is nothing quite as distinctive as police car sirens, especially in the middle of the night, and that's what we heard, but we couldn't tell what direction they were coming from. That's when we saw the flashing red lights—plural—they were all around us. In front of us about two blocks away, lights were reflecting off the sides of buildings.

Damn! That's near the police station.

But, there were lights behind us, too.

I spun around and saw them rising over Washington Street and crossing a bridge farther down the river. I panicked.

"Head to the church!" I yelled and ran.

What the hell was I thinking? The church? What were we going to do, plead for sanctuary?

Tim and Mike followed me. It was about twenty yards across the intersection to the base of the hill leading up to Emmanuel, but there was one little problem waiting for us there—the eight-foot retaining wall. There was no way we were going to scale that and scramble up the hill before the cops arrived.

Emmanuel Episcopal Church & Algonquin Hotel, Cumberland
(William Bird Postcard Collection 2014)

The sirens were getting louder, and we could see the headlights coming down all four streets of the intersection as we crossed. We also saw the night auditor standing at the door of the Algonquin with a big smile on her face. We spun right and started back up the street along the retaining wall, hoping we'd reach a surmountable level before the cops arrived. Mike was first to jump up and pull himself onto the grassy hill. Tim followed, and he turned and helped me up. As we ran up the remaining hill towards the steeple, we found ourselves face to face with the great evergreen tree in front of the church, bathed in the warm glow of the spotlights. We stopped for a second, looked at each other, and as the cop cars converged in front of the Algonquin, we dove under the tree.

Was this really happening? Do they really take road sign theft this seriously? How many police cars does Cumberland have?

My mind was spinning as I crawled through leaves and dirt, moving as close to the center of the tree as I could. Mike was the farthest and almost to the other side of the tree. Tim was right beside me as we heard the slamming of doors and the crackle of two-way radio traffic.

Then the sirens turned off, and for a moment we thought they'd given up.

Right. That's it. They couldn't possibly have seen three teenage boys run across an open intersection, climb a wall, and run up a flood-lit hill.

We heard the rustling of footsteps as lights blinded us. It was super bright, like the light the dentist shines into your face before he jabs that big needle into your gums. It took a second for our eyes to adjust, then there was an electronic crackle, and we heard a deep voice over-amplified by a bullhorn say, "Come out with your hands up. Slowly. Don't do anything stupid."

Even though I knew we were trapped, I took a second to decide what to do. Mike was already moving and when he said, "They've got guns." I made up my mind to follow him.

Tim and I crawled to the other side of the tree as Mike emerged from the base. As his shoulders broke through the cover of the branches, and he stood, he was tackled by two officers and pinned to the ground. Tim and I paused and watched in amazement as they handcuffed Mike behind his back. *Was it our turn next?*

The bullhorn scratched to life again, this time with a shorter message, "Come out. Now!"

We obeyed.

As I peeked out from under the tree, I saw that Mike was right; they had guns. Two of the cops stood ready to grab us, while two more stood back with their .38 revolvers ready. I don't know if it was that they realized we were kids, or they didn't want to jump on the ground again, but instead of tackling us, they grabbed each of us by the arm. I felt the cold steel of a handcuff lock around my wrist—*click*. I couldn't see how many policemen were hauling us out due to the blinding lights, but there were a lot of them. I heard one of them boast to another, "We got 'em. The State guys are going to be happy."

State guys? What in the world does the State Police have to do with the capture of three kids for vandalism?

The one with the bullhorn said, "Take them down to the station, I'll call it in,"

They led us towards the cars, not back down the hill but along the side of the church to a walkway out to the street.

When we turned right towards the intersection, we saw the entire city glowing with blinking police lights. I know I'd never seen that many cop cars in the city before. There was a car at the mouth of each street, all facing each other, with others behind them. Christ, they even had the K-9 car with an angry German shepherd barking from his cage in the back seat, and an ambulance was there ready to carry our bullet-ridden bodies to the morgue.

What have we done to deserve this kind of attention and how did they mobilize all this manpower so quickly?

As we approached the first police car, officers opened both back doors and shoved us in. It was in the moment we had alone before they got in up front I whispered, "Say nothing. Nothing about the sign. Nothing."

There was no answer because the front doors opened, and two officers dropped into the seats. The siren blared, and we were off to the police station. We were quiet, very quiet, not wanting to add to our troubles. Handcuffed together, Tim and I had no problem settling into the seats, but Mike was struggling having to sit on his steel-clad wrists. We were all glad the ride was short. Although I'm sure there is a rear entrance to the station, the black-and-white pulled up right in front. The cops popped out, and our doors swung open. We did the "perp walk" up the stairs to the front door. Once inside, the guy behind the front desk nodded his head to the right, and the cops pushed us over to a holding cell.

The holding cell was just a small room closed by a steel door with a barred window. Inside, there were benches attached to the walls all the way around the room. We sat. Now, I was scared, but I wasn't crying, although I had something in my eyes that was causing me to tear up. I'm sure it was something from under the evergreen tree.

Well, that's my story, and I'm sticking to it.

The rest of the officers who participated in our arrest came through the front door, and they all walked by our cell and took a look at us. They were not impressed. After about fifteen minutes, an older looking cop came in and sat down. He had a name tag on that said Bullard. He asked us our names and where we lived. When we told him, he stopped writing, and with a quizzical look on his face, got up and walked out.

What? No waterboarding to wrench the truth out of us about the "SLOW Children Playing" sign caper?

A few minutes later, Officer Bullard returned and took off our handcuffs and asked Mike to follow him out.

I said to Tim, "Oh, shit. We are so grounded for the whole summer." I was also worried about whether our misadventure would endanger my newly won drum major's job.

Would Dad give the job to Katie?

Mike came back in, rubbing the red marks on his wrists and told us, "They're calling my dad to come pick us up, but they asked what we were doing in front of the Algonquin at three o'clock in the morning. I told them the truth."

A shiver ran up and down my spine.

Oh no, they'll arrest us for stealing or vandalism or something.

But then Mike winked, and I knew our crime was still off the books. "He didn't ask me anything about the sign," Mike said. "I guess that cop didn't see us."

"What were we arrested for?" I asked.

"I don't know. I told them we were at my place and that after we played Frisbee at the church, we walked downtown. That's it," Mike said.

Officer Bullard came back in and as he removed the handcuffs asked Tim and me to tell him what we were doing downtown at 3 a.m. We told him the truth, well, at least all the truth that occurred after the road sign rustling. He nodded and left. We had to wait another thirty minutes before Reverend Manning showed up in a very dour mood. After a Saturday night of fun at the Cumberland Country Club and the prospect of an eight o'clock church service only a few hours away, the last place he wanted to be was in the police station bailing out his son and friends. As he passed by the door to our cell, he looked through our window and grimaced, then went to the front desk.

A few minutes later, Officer Bullard opened the door and came in with Reverend Manning.

As the door closed, Bullard said, "Now, boys, I don't know what you were doing out there tonight, but it was very dangerous, and although it doesn't appear you've done anything wrong, you never know what can happen at that time of night. So, I don't want to see you in here again, or things will be very different."

"Yes, sir," we all answered in unison.

He shook Reverend Manning's hand then turned for the door. As he touched the knob, he paused and looked back at us, "Tell me, boys, if you did nothing wrong, why did you run when you saw the police?"

Shit! How do we answer that one?

There was a long silence broken by Tim. "Well, sir, Reverend and Mrs. Manning didn't know we were out, and we figured if we could hide we wouldn't get in trouble with them."

I doubt he believed it, but there it was, a bit weak but reasonable. Officer Bullard left, and we were face to face with a very disappointed Lutheran minister. Both Tim and I expected calls to our fathers were next, and they'd have to come down and get us out, but no. The Reverend Manning had convinced the officer that since we were all staying over at his house, it was only right we be released to him.

We all trudged out of the police station and down to Reverend Manning's car. No one said a word until the car doors closed.

As soon as they did, Reverend Manning said, "What in the hell were you boys thinking?"

We stayed silent.

"I should take each of you home to your parents and wake them up and tell them I got you out of jail."

Silence. There was nothing but a long, deep, dreadful silence.

"But, I'm not going to do that," Reverend Manning continued. "I respect your parents too much to ruin their night's sleep. Tim and Shelby, you need to tell your parents yourselves all about tonight sometime within the next two weeks. If I haven't heard from you by then, I'll tell them myself. Is that understood?"

"Yes, sir," Tim and I mumbled.

"Dad, did the cops say why they arrested us? Unless there is a curfew in Cumberland I'm not aware of, we were not breaking any laws," Mike asked.

"Yes, they did, Son. You guys picked the wrong night to go for a walk. Earlier today, three juvenile delinquents roughed up two guards and escaped from the Green Ridge State facility about thirty miles from here. The *State Police* issued an all-points bulletin that went out to police departments, train and bus stations, and hotels. They thought they might be armed and dangerous, so the city police had doubled up the officers on duty. It was the desk clerk at the Algonquin who called the police when she saw three suspicious young males walk by the front doors. You guys fit the bill. Well, at least you were the right number of guys."

He laughed before forcing his face back into a grimace.

So that was it. The police weren't after us for stealing the road sign at all; they didn't even know we'd taken one. They were looking for escaped delinquents on the lam and capable of harming others. Boy, they must have been disappointed when they got us into the station and found out we were the minister's kid, a doctor's son and that band director's brat—all that effort for nothing. Ha! We win.

When we got to Mike's house, his dad said nothing and went straight to bed. We went downstairs and dug out the road sign. We looked at it for a long time until, Mike said, "I don't want it."

"Neither do I," said Tim.

I waited a moment and then said, "I'll take it."

All these years later, I'm looking at it on the wall of my Man Cave.

— Confess —

Two weeks—that's only fourteen days, and it's all the time I had to figure out how to tell my parents I was arrested at gunpoint on the front lawn of our church and spent two hours in the city jail. How were they going to react? There had to be a punishment, but what would it be? Ground me for the summer, stop me from getting my driver's license or the thing I feared the most—turn the drum major's job over to Katie?

My parents were so enjoying their own lives, they could never enforce a summer grounding. Denying me my driver's license was more punishment for them than me for the same reason. Without it, they had to drive me everywhere. That meant killing the drum major's job was what would hit me the hardest and the thought of losing it scared me the most.

I had to figure out a way to mitigate the damage. Tell them but in such a way as to make it sound ordinary.

You know, Dad, this kind of thing happens all the time. It's part of growing up. Aren't I lucky to have gotten my police experience out of the way so early and so smartly?

I was thinking this while sitting at Dad's desk and staring at his desktop calendar. Today was Monday, so 2, 3, 4, 5,—I counted the days off before Reverend Manning would call—6, 7, 8, 9.

Hey, what's this next Wednesday?

Written on Dad's calendar was Shelby's camp.

That's it; I'm due to attend drum major camp two days before my time is up. Okay then, I'll wait and tell Mom and Dad on the way to drum major camp when it will be too late for them to swap me out for Katie. If I'm the one who goes to drum major camp, then I will be the drum major.

Drum major camp, I thought this story was about band camp?

It is, but I went to a lot of camps. There was Camp Cliffside where I learned how to bathe in a river and use an outhouse. Then another riverside camp, but this one had running water and tennis lessons. Then an Episcopal Church camp where I learned to smoke and tell dirty jokes. This summer my camp would be drum major camp but not just any drum major camp. I was going to the great A.R. Casavant's drum major camp.

My dad was a devotee of Albert Richard Casavant (2), a marching band educator and clinician who, in the 1950s, was the driving force behind the development of Precision Drill, a style of marching where the band creates intricate formations using small groups executing marching techniques all while playing music. This style became the standard for marching bands at football game halftime shows across the nation and was also the immediate precursor to the drum and bugle corps competitions of today. A.R. (as he liked to be called) wrote over 150 instruction books showing band directors how to train, motivate, dress, and perform as a proper marching band.

Now you know who to blame.

Well, one of the ways A.R. made money was to provide drum major training camps every summer, where eager young drum majors could learn the intricate science of precision drill and direction. These opportunities required each participant to purchase their very own copies of A.R.'s instruction manuals and accompanying recordings of appropriate marching drill music for practice before camp and use afterward. All for the discount price of $15 (this was above and beyond the $100 the weeklong camp cost.) Luckily, the ALCO band's booster organization, the Camper Club, was covering my cost. That's about $800 in 2017, so think of it as a Jenny Craig and Dale Carnegie course for band geeks. I had the great honor of attending A.R. Casavant's premier drum major camp at Indiana University of Pennsylvania.

How painful it must be to attend a university with a name that always has to be followed by an explanation.

"No, I don't go to Indiana University in Bloomington, Indiana, I go to Indiana University in Pennsylvania."

"You mean it's an expansion campus of IU?"

"No Indiana University of Pennsylvania is named after Indiana County, which is in Pennsylvania."

I'm sure this is always followed by an exasperating sigh.

I called Tim and Mike and told them my plan then asked them to keep a lid on the info until I left for camp. Meanwhile, I reviewed the exercises in my drum major camp book. It was full of diagrams and drawings of chevrons and diamond shapes moving across a football field gridiron pattern with accompanying arrows and numbers indicating direction and velocity. I understood none of it, so I opened the accompanying 45 rpm record to listen to the music I'd be expected to memorize and direct in a test that would occur on the last day of camp. I was expecting a march or maybe one of those neat popular music transcriptions used to keep the kids interested in band.

We had played great ones at ALCO last year, songs like Herb Alpert's "Mexican Shuffle" which we did the Teaberry Shuffle to during the halftime show. But no, to my surprise, the music selected by Mr. Casavant was the "Merry Widow Waltz."

What? The "Merry Widow Waltz" is from an operetta written in 1861 by an Austro-Hungarian composer named Franz Lehár. That country doesn't even exist anymore, and what has a waltz got to do with Precision Drill? I guess the music's copyright has expired, leaving A.R. free to sell it without paying royalties.

I listened to it and practiced directing.

The week passed, and I avoided my parents as much as I could. The night before camp, Mom and Dad took me to Warner's German Restaurant for dinner. Warner's is one of those classic small-town attempts at an exotic restaurant that turned an ordinary dark room on the ground floor of a family home into a Bavarian wine cellar with copious amounts of plastic grapes and vines dangling from the ceiling. They sold tons of Wienerschnitzel served with Blue Nun Liebfraumilch wine. It was for the adventurous only. I ordered pizza. I was quietly about to finish my German interpretation of a pepperoni pizza when I felt a man's hand on my shoulder.

Dad said, "Hello, Dick." I looked up to see the smiling face of Reverend Manning.

He was holding a folded copy of the *Cumberland Evening Times*, and as he and Dad talked, he opened it and laid it on the table in front of me. Glancing down, I read the headline right below the fold: "State Police nab escaped juveniles from Green Ridge facility."

I felt faint and tried to melt into the Naugahyde bench. The Right Reverend shot me a cold glance as he pressed on my clavicle. Retrieving his paper, Reverend Manning turned to move away from our table but stopped and said, "Shelby, what have you been up to? You haven't been to the house since you spent the night last week."

Gulp. "Ahh, I've been pretty busy getting ready for drum major camp," I said.

"Oh, drum major camp, when is that?" the smiling man of the cloth asked.

"We leave tomorrow, and, ahh, I'm looking forward to the ride with Mom and Dad. I've got a lot to tell them," I stammered.

"Right," said Reverend Manning. "I'll see you when you get back."

He looked at his watch as if to check exactly how much time I had left to tell my parents. I'm sure I was sweating, and I couldn't eat another bite of my oil-soaked pizza. All I wanted to do was get out of there before more newspapers showed up.

In the morning, we left for the two-hour drive to camp. I stayed quiet for most of the trip and rehearsed my incarceration explanation.

"Gosh, Mom and Dad, did I tell you about the funny thing that happened to me walking downtown the other day?"

No, I can't be that nonchalant.

"Dad, remember how you told me about your friend who got arrested for tax evasion?"

No, that won't work either; I don't want to paint myself in that light. Remember, as far as anyone is concerned; it was all a big mistake—there was no crime committed—well, at least there was no crime discovered. It was all a big misunderstanding. Right, a misunderstanding that almost got me shot under a pine tree.

I glanced out the window and saw a sign that read University of Indiana, twenty-five miles.

Argh, I'm out of time. This is it. Here we go.

"Hey, seeing Reverend Manning last night reminded me I needed to tell you something."

With that, I told the story straight, no humor and no dodging the truth, starting from the time we left the church until we got back to Mike's. I did not go into a great deal of detail and left out the handcuffs and guns, but I conveyed the critical information about how I was at the wrong place at the wrong time and ended up in the city jail for a few hours and how if it weren't for the kind Reverend Manning, I'd still be there. I tried not to turn it into a funny story, but it was tough because it is a funny story, and so while telling it I choked back a laugh or two.

I finished, and there was absolute silence. I looked out the window praying the university would pop into view when I heard Dad say, "We were wondering when you'd get around to telling us. Dick Manning called us the day after it happened and told us all about it. Your mom and I talked it over, and your punishment is you have to cut the grass every week this summer for nothing. Oh, and did you learn anything?"

Well, I learned never to trust a Lutheran minister.

I didn't say that, but I sure as hell thought it. He must have really enjoyed watching me squirm last night at Warner's. I guess the Lord and Reverend Manning move in mysterious ways. I told Mom and Dad I learned not to run from police and that I wouldn't sneak around downtown Cumberland at night again. None of that was true. I ran from the police, again (That story will have to wait for volume two of my memoir), and I went back to Mike's neighborhood (at night) and got another road sign. It's from the same era as the "SLOW Children Playing" one but says "Speed Limit 20".

Sweet!

Chapter 3 - Do You Know What I Mean

— Drum Major Camp —

Mom and Dad dropped me off at camp registration, and after passing me $5 in spending money, they took off for a golf outing. After checking in, I got my first look at a college dorm room when I walked into Delaney Hall. Waiting for me was my fellow ALCO bandmate, Bob Hartman. He had already chosen his side of the room, unpacked his suitcase, stored it under his twin bed and had all his clothes folded in the matching oak dresser. I put my suitcase down by the foot of my bed, which is where it stayed the entire week along with all my clothes, clean and dirty.

Bob and I were very different, but we got along well, and that was important since he was captain of the band, and we'd be working together for the next ten months.

Dad set up the band's leader structure with three ranks: drum major, band captain, and lieutenants. As drum major, I was the senior ranking member and responsible for all band activities. Bob, as captain, was elected by the band members and was the administrative authority for student attendance, demerit tracking, and fundraising. Each band section had a lieutenant in charge.

The next day was muggy, and as the sun rose, we knew it was going to get hot. We went to the practice field and found kids, not much older than we were, telling us to form up in a straight line. They were college students working at the camp that summer as counselors. By my guess, along with Bob and me, there were another hundred eager band geeks, and at least half of them were girls. I liked this, and assessed each one as I took my place in line. Daydreaming about how nice it would be to kiss that cute blonde about two kids down from me, I was jolted back to reality when I heard a shrill whistle blow—*TWEET!* At the same time, a bullhorn crackled on, and my initial thought was, *Oh my God, it's the cops again!* But it wasn't. It was something completely different.

"Attention ya'll!" screamed the voice from the bullhorn in a deep, commanding, southern baritone. "Attention, and welcome to drum major camp,"

The man behind the horn was Mr. A.R. Casavant himself, and a most imposing character he was. He looked to be nearing sixty-years-old, stood about six feet tall, and had a strong resemblance to General Douglas McArthur. But instead of a general's hat with all its gold-braided "farts and darts," A.R. was wearing a Safari pith helmet with a musical lyre at its center. I half expected him to ask, "Doctor Livingston, I presume?"

The rest of his outfit matched his hat. He wore tan shorts much too long for the style of the day, a loose-fitting khaki shirt with buttoned pockets, and an open collar exposing a loose blue ascot tie. Around his neck was a silver whistle swinging from a gold and white plastic gimp lariat. He had on white knee-high socks and crocodile Arnold Palmer golf shoes with the spikes still in place.

As he walked down the line of attentive campers, he spouted his orders through the bullhorn: "Count off by tens, form up with your fellow numbers in two rows, Dress-Right-Dress, and stand at Parade Rest until further orders."

I say he walked, but he really strutted down the line like a drill sergeant.

"Now pay attention. We are here to do serious work. This is not a fun-in-the-sun summer camp. No, sir, you are here to learn my techniques of Precision Drill and tools you'll need to command a large marching band in the field. We have little time and a great deal to teach you, so pay attention if you want to get your mommy's and daddy's money's worth. Is that understood?" he boomed.

"Yes, sir," we all bellowed.

The whistle sounded again, only this time it was not A.R. who was blowing it. Walking behind him was a shorter and younger man, say about twenty-one, who could not have been more different than A.R. It was Junior. Junior was what we came to call him, but his real name was Charles Casavant. He was A.R.'s son and absolutely nothing like him.

Where A.R. had the dress and swagger of General McArthur, Junior looked more like a mixture of Elton John in his early days (before he went all glittery) and Dean Stockwell in the 1962 film *Long Day's Journey into Night*. He had on a skintight faded red T-shirt, tight-fitting bell-bottom blue jeans, and red Converse All-Star high tops.

I'm not saying he looked effeminate, but he sure as hell didn't look macho.

Along with his whistle, Junior had a clipboard in his hands and was checking things off as he followed his Daddy.

After we finished counting off, the camp counselors pushed us in different directions and formed us into our drill squads. I was a number six and Bob a seven, so we weren't in the same squad. The rest of the day was a blur of instructions: demonstrations by Junior, and practice both as squads and individually. First A.R. would announce the subject of the technique to be learned; then Junior would move out in front of him and demonstrate it. After that, the camp counselors would repeat it in front of the individual squads, and we'd then practice the maneuver. All the while, A.R. strode from squad to squad observing, commenting and sometimes getting downright personal. If he saw someone doing something wrong he'd charge right up to them, pointing his finger in their face, and stuttering, "G-g-g-g-George stop, you're doin' it all wrong, boy. You gotta try harder, George."

The great A.R. Casavant could not be bothered learning names, so everyone was called George, even the girls.

Oh, and that finger he'd point at you was as unique as he was. Somewhere along the line, A.R. lost half of the index finger on his right hand. When he stuck it in your face, you could not help but stare at the stub. In the lexicon of the day, it was a trip. I remember I was out in front of my squad struggling to duplicate a directing style Junior had shown us when I felt A.R.'s nubby digit tugging at my shirt and pulling me to the side.

"G-g-g-g-George, what are you doin', Son? Straighten up, boy; you look like a swayback mule trying to dance."

Although unconventional, A.R.'s teaching technique was effective. I never got the picture of a swayback mule dancing out of my mind, and whenever I was directing, I'd think of it and straighten up as best I could. We did this for six days straight from 8 a.m. to 5 p.m., covering every aspect of marching band Precision Drill.

The weather was hot and sticky, and the only break was for lunch, so I focused on drinking as much lemonade as I could during the brief time off the field. At the end of each day, we'd run straight for the dorm's showers and spend a leisurely half hour letting the cool, cool water flow over our heads, then go to dinner. At night, we would gather in the student union building and socialize, but I don't remember making any lasting friends. Everyone was focused on the task at hand and readying themselves for the final marching and directing test on the last day of camp. I didn't feel the same pressure as I did before my drum major tryout, but I was determined to do well.

The test was to be in two parts. We'd be required to march our little squads around for a few minutes and then direct the "Merry Widow Waltz." At night in the dorms, all you could hear was an endless loop of that damned song as each room's occupants practiced their directing skills. To this day, I hate it. Finally, the lights would go out, and the cycle would repeat.

There was a social at the student union on the evening before the last day. It was the only formal event, and A.R., Junior and all the camp counselors attended. It wasn't anything special, but it was fun to listen to A.R. tell his stories of band performances gone wrong. He held court in grand style as all his tittering teenage supplicants basked in his glory. I was sipping Pepsi and listening till I saw an opportunity to talk to Junior. During camp, he had stayed in the background with his clipboard and whistle, hustling from squad to squad to demonstrate something or running here and there in response to an order from A.R. When he talked, it was in a soft clear voice backed up by a wealth of confidence. I found him sitting on a couch on the side of the room with his legs tucked up and under him lotus-style. He appeared happy away from the center of attention.

I said, "Hi," then followed with something lame, "I guess you get tired of this marching band stuff, huh?"

He paused and looked at me as if he was deciding whether he had to acknowledge my existence (*You get a lot of this when you're fifteen*), then said, "No, I love the marching band stuff."

Okay, good. He's talking. Let's see if I can find something we have in common.

"You know my dad's a marching band director like yours. He teaches at my high school."

"Your dad's a band director. What does he play?" Junior asked.

"Trumpet," I said, "And he's excellent. He got his Masters in Music from Columbia."

"My dad doesn't even play an instrument anymore." Junior sighed.

"Oh, he played the trumpet back in high school, but he majored in business administration at the Tennessee Military Institute. It was there he got pulled into leading the fledgling TMI marching band, and he fell in love. He found the combination of martial music, commands, and all that drilling fascinating, and he was damned good at it too, but it's all about the Precision Drill, not the music. I love the music."

I think I said something profound like, "Cool," and with that loose connection established, I spent the next ten minutes finding out a lot about Junior and how he takes music seriously.

He'd just graduated with a music performance degree from Indiana University (the one in Pennsylvania, not Indiana) and was planning on going for his doctorate in Music Education. Sucked into the whirlwind that was A.R. Casavant as a child, he had learned quickly that it was easier to embrace Precision Drill than resist it. As such, he became a master at it. He also became his high school and university band's drum major. His instrument was the French horn, but he could play about every instrument in the book, at least well enough to teach it to others. I asked how hard it was to be a music major, and he gave me an earful.

"Listen, you've got to love it because if you don't, you'll be miserable. Music majors spend more hours devoted to their studies than any other major. You are either in class, at a rehearsal, practicing alone or performing all the time, and I mean all the time. Before you even think about majoring in music, know what you are getting yourself into."

He finished with an example. "You think you have worked hard this week here at drum major camp? Well, drum major camp is finger painting compared to being a music major. I never worked so hard in my life."

Okay, thank you very much. There goes my back-of-the-mind planning for majoring in music. I don't do hard work that well. I can fake it for a week or two, but that's it. And I know I don't have the patience or determination to master an instrument, let alone learn how to play twenty of them. Maybe animal husbandry is for me. I like dogs.

I'd struck a nerve with Junior, and I figured I better bow out before he asked me what I wanted to major in, so I took a sip of my Pepsi and changed the subject. "Hey, how did your dad lose his finger? Was it in the war?"

"No, it was in the drawer. He had his hand in a file cabinet when a stumbling student fell against it and pinched it right off." Junior laughed.

I snorted Pepsi through my nose.

Deftly wiping myself on my shoulder, I said, "You know, I might be back here next year. I'm only a junior, and if I'm drum major again, I will repeat the camp."

A thin smile grew on Junior's face. "Well, things may be different next year. I think A.R. is slowing down and may give the whole thing up."

Wow, that was news! I gotta tell Bob.

Just then, Bob appeared and looked at me like I had three heads. "Hey, let's get out of here," he said. "I want you to help me direct that damned waltz one more time."

Bob was not as confident with his directing skills as I was, and he was worried about tomorrow's test. The syllabus wasn't clear, but anything labeled a test carried with it the possibility of failure, which might require repeating something, and Bob did not want to repeat anything he had experienced in the last six days. I said good night to Junior and followed Bob out the door.

"Hey, what were you doing talking to that fruit Junior?" Bob asked.

"Cut it out, Junior is okay," I answered.

Remember, Bob and I were different. He was straight-laced, but he had no choice. Like Mike's dad, his father was a minister, a Baptist minister, and Baptists recognize nothing outside of the straight and narrow. There is only one way to live, and that's the Baptist way. That reminds me of a joke. There are three religious truths in the world: Jews don't recognize Jesus as the Messiah. Protestants don't recognize the Pope as the leader of the Christian faith, and Baptists don't recognize each other in the liquor store.

"Listen, Bob, Junior may be different, but I learned a lot from him this week. Oh, and you are not gonna believe how A.R. lost his finger," I said as we walked to our dorm.

Since everyone was preparing for tomorrow's test, we endured another night of endless waltzes.

The next day, as we gathered at the field, all the campers were busy with last-minute practice before the big test. I was wondering how they would do it. There were a lot of kids there.

Please don't tell me we have to listen to that damned waltz 100 more times.

We didn't. In fact, we found out pretty quickly that the whole test thing was a big nothing—a bluff. There was a squad marching drill, but instead of having each of us do it, the camp counselors randomly picked one representative from each squad, and that person led the group. If deemed successful, the entire squad passed. Everyone did. Before we could worry about the directing part, they told us to all form up in one long line, like we did on the first day. With that, Junior stepped out from behind A.R. with a cassette player. A.R. squeezed the trigger on the bullhorn and bellowed, "Now boys and girls, y'all start to direct when you hear the whistle. Arms up!"

He held the bullhorn over the two-inch dynamic speaker of the cassette player. The loud distorted sound of *tweet-tweet-tweet* filled the air, followed by the syrupy sound of "The Merry Widow," one more time. We flapped our arms to that wicked waltz as A.R. marched up and down the line observing our form. No one failed.

"Camp dismissed," sang out A.R. It was over.

Stunned, Bob and I stood there looking at each other for a few seconds. It was only ten o'clock in the morning, and my parents weren't to pick me up till three. We bolted for the dorm. Bob had driven his family's station wagon, so I called my mom and told her I'd hitch a ride home with him.

I needed a little downtime. I had a lot of work in front of me and had only half the summer left to do it all. I had to cut the grass (for no money), outline a plan for the upcoming band season, and oh yeah, there was my job at Uncle Lu's Tastee Freez.

— Uncle Lu's —

To understand how Uncle Lu got a Tastee Freez and how I got a job there, we need to pop into our time machine and set the controls for early 1957. Dad told me he was eating lunch in the teacher's section of the Allegany cafeteria when his friend Mr. Kreider said, "Hey, Lu, you really like my ice cream, don't you?"

Looking up from his mystery meat and succotash, Dad said, "Yeah, Bob, I do. No one makes soft serve ice cream like you do at the Tastee Freez. What do you do to make it so special?"

"Vanilla extract, Lu. That's the secret," Kreider boasted. "I put three tablespoons of vanilla extract in every gallon of the dairy's ice cream mix; it smoothes out the product and differentiates me from the competition."

Dad went back to his mystery meat as Kreider took a sip from the paper straw in his half-pint glass milk bottle.

Then he asked, "You want to buy it?"

"Buy what?" Dad asked.

"The Tastee Freez Lu, do you want to buy my Tastee Freez?"

Without a second thought, Dad said "Yes."

Mr. Kreider's Tastee Freez had been doing business in LaVale since 1953. Fast food franchises were the hot new business opportunity of post-war America, and they popped up on street corners everywhere in the 1950's.

Mr. Kreider was one of those brave men who jumped in early when he built a concrete block single-story building on National Highway—one of the busiest thoroughfares through the Appalachian Mountains. It was red, white, and blue and crowned by a seven-foot high, fifteen-foot long sign that trumpeted Tastee Snacks—Tastee Freez. Tilting out from the front of the sign, precariously dangling over the sidewalk was a six-foot-tall ice cream cone. Spotlights illuminated the letters of the sign, and yellow neon lights outlined the cone.

The store was built with the on-the-go customer in mind. There was no indoor seating. It was not a fine restaurant where you went for a leisurely dinner. Everything was sold to-go through three sliding windows spaced to allow lines to form outside. No china plates or cups, no glasses or silverware. You got your food in a paper bag, wax paper cup, plastic dish, or edible cake-cone—that's it. Only plastic spoons were provided. All of this kept costs down and preparation easy.

By early 1957, Mr. Kreider was eligible to retire from teaching, and his wife wanted to move, so he was looking for a buyer. Dad loved ice cream and was one of Kreider's best customers. No less often than three times a week, Dad would show up at one of the store's sliding windows asking for his favorite, a dip-top cone, and Kreider took notice. When he went looking for buyers, he started with one of his favorite customers: Lu Syckes.

Uncle Lu's Tastee Freez LaVale, MD (Syckes Family Photos)

Dad's snap decision was not like him at all. He was not the kind of guy who winged it, especially when it came to major financial decisions. He was a mathematician. He had to run the numbers before he could make any purchase that could drastically change the family finances. But in this case, he threw all that out the window and just went for it. All he had to do was figure out how to tell his wife and come up with the $15,000 Kreider wanted for the Tastee Freez, and I'm not sure he knew which of those two would be harder.

High School teachers in Allegany County did not make a lot of money when Dad joined the faculty at ALCO. He earned about $120 per month, and although he was lucky to have inherited his beautiful English Tudor family home in the upscale Cumberland neighborhood of the Dingle, he had to maintain and heat the place. Let me tell you a bit about Dad's parents because their house is key to the Tastee Freez story.

— Doctor & Mrs. Syckes —

Doctor Silas Lua Syckes, was the only orthodontist in Allegany County during the first three decades of the twentieth century and did well financially. So well that, by the age of fifty, when he got around to marrying, he could afford to build a home he designed himself in a neighborhood that would suit his rising status.

The house, which he named "The Gables," stood prominently on a hill overlooking tree-lined Windsor Road. It was only two miles from his dental office, and there was trolley service to get him there. He had two children, a musically talented wife, and enjoyed his ever-increasing wealth as the Roaring Twenties kept on roaring. He was just short of his sixty-third birthday when the 1929 stock market crashed, and the decade-long Great Depression began. Like the rest of his peers, Doctor Syckes had most of his money in the stock market because the national zeitgeist was "Buy, buy, buy." So, when the crash came, he lost it all.

What he could sell went for pennies on the dollar, but most of his stock certificates became worthless paper. The experience so soured him; he divested himself completely from the stock market, and from that day forward the matter was not to be discussed in his house.

The Depression hit everyone hard. People lost their jobs, their savings, and worst of all, they stopped going to the dentist. So, Doctor Syckes was going to the office every day to sit and read a book or practice his violin. No money was coming in. If he got a customer, he or she would pay him in barter. Doctor Syckes might get a bag of apples or a few hours of yard work or even tennis lessons for his kids, but he saw no money. That's when things went from bad to worse. He had a heart attack, and because it was 1932, all the doctors could do was order him to bed until he either regained his strength or died. He spent the next two years there. Never fully recovering, he went back to work, and as the Depression eased, his business picked up, but nothing like it was before.

Syckes Family Home (Syckes Family Photos)

He died in March 1942, and I often wonder if he was depressed. He had lost most of what he had worked all his life for, and in his last year, he watched as the world imploded with the start of the Second World War. In the spring of 1942, America was losing that war. Still reeling from Pearl Harbor, by March, America's military was in full retreat (3). There was no good news in the headlines. Even the daring and uplifting raid on Tokyo by Jimmy Doolittle's B-24 bombers was still a month away (4). On top of that, the two Syckes boys were the right age for war. It is sad to think Doctor Syckes did not live to see any of the good that came from all that darkness.

Both the boys were pulled into the war and saw combat operations, but made it home safe. Their mother, Beatrice Syckes, kept up appearances as best she could and lived on her dwindling savings. She also took in boarders. This was a very different life from the one she had lived before 1929 when her successful husband's standing in the community placed her in the top tier of Cumberland society. She was a gifted pianist who had studied at the Institute of Musical Art, Julliard's predecessor in New York City, and had two concert grand pianos in her home. She hosted musical events, taught piano, and performed with the local chamber music group. Sadly, just as she was slowly robbed of her financial status, she also lost her ability to make music due to rheumatoid arthritis. The result was an aging, angry and lonely woman facing an uncertain and unhappy future. Dad's decision to marry my mom (Stella) and move her in with his mother did not improve things.

Mrs. Syckes (which is what Stella had to call her) grudgingly accepted this because she had no other options. She needed the help, and it worked out about as well as you would expect. Like every other mother-in-law, Mrs. Syckes was sure Stella was not the right girl for her son. She had selected the right girl long ago. Unfortunately, Dad was not interested in marrying that girl, even if her daddy did own a brewery. As you know, he had his eye on a beautiful young Frostburg girl from his homeroom at Beall High School. No matter what his mother said, he wasn't listening. Even on their wedding day, she was still fuming.

According to a relative, on the drive to the church, she stated with no hesitation, "I don't know why Lu had to go to Frostburg to find a suitable wife when there are plenty of good Cumberland girls available."

By the time the newlyweds moved in, the house was dirty, drab, and the furnishings were old. Nothing new had come into it since the crash. Stella could not stand it and started cleaning. Mrs. Syckes was "not amused" and let it be known her property must be cleaned by professionals. Stella's simmering pot of discontent began to boil.

Dad found himself caught in the middle, looked for a compromise, and found it in separating the combatants. He decided to reconfigure three rooms and a bath on the second floor into an apartment with a kitchenette where he and Stella could live. This would allow them to have their privacy and Mrs. Syckes to have everything else. It made things better, but it was not a long-term solution because Stella was also expected to provide for Mrs. Syckes's needs. This included cooking, grocery shopping, and transportation, as Mrs. Syckes did not drive. Even though Stella had her little apartment to hide out in, she still had to kowtow to her mother-in-law every day. The marriage suffered. Luckily, or should I say sadly, Beatrice Syckes died twenty-eight months after the wedding, leaving them the house in her will, but no money.

I'm sure for most of her life Mrs. Syckes was a wonderful person, but near the end, she was tough to live with. Mom often told me that if Mrs. Syckes hadn't passed away when she did, there might have been a divorce or a murder. Her death and Dad's inheritance of the house created an opportunity no one foresaw.

— Br'er Rabbit Kindergarten —

Free from her mother-in-law, Mom wanted to fix up the rest of the Dingle house in her style, but that took money, and money was tight, especially since my sister Barbara had been born in July 1948. So Mom looked for ways to bring in some extra money and settled on renting out the little apartment she and Dad had been living in. Their first, and only, renters were a young couple named Deb and Ted Beatty. Ted was a young, inexperienced lawyer trying to get a practice started in Cumberland, and Deb was a young but highly experienced alcoholic. They also liked dogs, big dogs—we're talking Great Danes—and they had two of them.

Every day, while Ted was out practicing his profession, Deb was upstairs practicing hers, often forgetting that the Great Danes needed to go out. The dogs also felt it was their responsibility to alert the entire Dingle to any suspicious sound they heard by loudly barking. Tensions eased somewhat in the evening as Ted and Lu came home, and the two young couples enjoyed a friendly cocktail hour together; that is as long as the dog alarm didn't go off and Deb stayed upright. The Beattys' lease was not renewed. Mom and Dad remained distant friends with them, and I remember seeing them from time to time at parties. By then, Deb's drinking had taken its toll, and she was losing weight fast.

I'll never forget a good friend of Mom's, who had a wicked sense of humor, pointed to Deb from across the room and said, "Look at Deb Beatty she could model coffins at Scarpelli's Funeral Home."

A new way of making money was needed, and Mom looked to apply her skills using what assets were available. It was late 1949, and I think she realized, *Hey, I've got this huge house I only use about 20 percent of, and I spent 18 months studying Early Childhood Education at Frostburg State Teachers College, so why don't I start a kindergarten?*

Kindergartens were not part of the public school curriculum in Allegany County then, so Mom saw an opportunity. She knew raising a kid was hard work, and young mothers could always use a few hours off now and then. Maybe they'd be willing to pay for it, especially if it provided a structured educational surrounding for their little darlings. Mom had a child, and all her friends had children. Children were popping up everywhere like dandelions. There were families with four, five, even ten kids, so the demand was there. All she had to do was supply the right solution, and the money would make itself. With that in mind, Mom created the Br'er Rabbit Kindergarten at 820 Windsor Road, the Dingle.

Mom went back to school and took enough courses to receive a Maryland State Certificate for Pre-School Teaching. This allowed her to sell her kindergarten as meeting state educational requirements, elevating it above what was already available. Her competition was mostly women who watched over neighbors' children a few hours a day but provided no teaching. Mom wanted to have a fully equipped modern facility with a progressive educational process that led to a completion certificate, but she needed seed money, so she turned to Dad for help. He ran the numbers and found that if they had enough students for the right price, the business could break even within two years and turn a decent profit. He agreed to get a mortgage on the house to start the business.

By the time 1957 rolled around and Dad wanted to buy the Tastee Freez, Br'er Rabbit Kindergarten was the kindergarten of choice for Cumberland's middle-class kids. The lower two floors of the stately home on Windsor Road became a fully functioning modern state-certified educational facility. The living room, dining room, sun porch and entire basement were paneled with cork and lined with cubby holes where students stored their coats and crafts. It had a library filled with children's books (a lot of Dr. Seuss), two upright pianos for musical instruction and entertainment (no room for grand pianos anymore), and building blocks for creative play in sizes ranging from small hand-held ones to big suitcase-sized ones big enough to build pretend forts and castles. There were areas for painting and clay sculpting and two six-foot-long sinks for cleanup time. Outdoors, there were three professional-grade swing sets with twelve swings, two six-foot-tall sliding boards, monkey bars, teeter-totters, a push/pull self-propelled merry-go-round, and an electric powered rideable train on a circular track. It was something to behold.

Mom and her paid assistants taught two classes of up to twenty kids per day: one in the morning and one in the afternoon. She even provided door-to-door bus service for the kids who didn't live within walking distance, all for the price of $25 per child per month. Her classes were sold out every semester months in advance. Things were going well. Dad had tenure at Allegany, Mom's business was booming, and the loan needed to start Br'er Rabbit was paid off, but expenses were up. The family had grown (three kids total), mom had a car of her own, and most importantly, there was the cost of social acceptance as a member of the Cumberland Country Club. Mom and Dad loved the Country Club.

This was the stable family financial situation that Dad was thinking of putting at risk by buying a business he had zero experience in running, and restaurants like the Tastee Freez are prone to failure (5).

— Back to the Tastee Freez Story —

Dad knew what failing at a business looked like. His brother's music store had closed its doors only a month before, which forced him into bankruptcy. On top of that, the U.S. economy was sliding into its fourth recession since the end of the war (6). Oh, and Dad had, at best, $500 in the bank.

Was he crazy? Maybe, but something told him a Tastee Freez was a good investment. He loved ice cream; his kids loved ice cream. Hell, everyone loves ice cream, so it should work. All he had to do was convince Mom and get a banker to lend him $15,000. That represented about six times the family's gross annual income, so he'd need to mortgage the house again. The last time he did that, an appraisal of the house came in at $25,000. That meant the house would cover the new loan, but he'd lose it if the business failed.

How did Dad convince Mom? Here's the story I was told. On the day he talked to Mr. Kreider, Dad went home to find Mom out chauffeuring the kids home from afternoon class. Her assistant was cleaning up, and my sisters and I were where all kids of the late fifties were at 5 o'clock on a weekday afternoon, in front of the TV watching *The Mickey Mouse Club*. He went straight to his study and ran the numbers. When Mom got home, Dad met her at the door with a stiff scotch and water, her nightly favorite.

"Honey, I want to buy the Tastee Freez in LaVale," he said.

Tilting her head and staring at him suspiciously, she asked, "Why?"

"Because I love their ice cream, and Kreider wants to sell. He's planning to retire, and if we don't buy it, someone else will and—" Dad stopped talking as Mom's hand came up in front of his face, palm out flat.

"Give me that drink, and let's go to the breakfast nook and talk."

Dad did as he was told and grabbed his drink from the counter, following her into the kitchen. Mom had had a long day that ended as it always did with her driving ten screaming kids home in the station wagon. She never knew what to expect from these rides. Something interesting always happened. Once an enthusiastic student was singing the new song, she'd learned at Sunday school, "Stop and let Jesus into your heart."

That prompted the little Lazarus boy to ask, "Do we have to stop and let Jesus in before I get home?"

On another day, she had me with her in the back seat, and after the kids had been dropped off, I grabbed an empty Coke bottle from the six-pack she planned to return to the A&P and hit her square on the head. She swears she saw stars.

Hey, cut me some slack! I was only two.

But today, it was much more nerve-racking than that. As she was negotiating the back streets of Cumberland, one child managed to get his corduroy jumpers wrapped around the car's back door handle, and when he tugged to free himself, the door swung open.

"Jamie's gone!" another child announced.

"Where?" Mom asked.

"'Out the door!'"

Jerking her head around, to her horror, she saw Jamie with a big smile on his face hanging from the door handle, his feet bouncing off the pavement. Mom hit the brakes and retrieved Jamie without injury, but all the rest of the way home, he kept saying, "Do it again, do it again, please!"

Looking at Dad over her scotch and water, Mom said, "Okay, tell me the whole story and what you are thinking."

Dad did, and I don't know if it was because she trusted his judgment or if it was payback for his trust when they started the kindergarten, or maybe she was too tired to argue, but she agreed.

Next stop: The Liberty Trust Company.

— The Loan —

Dad had been banking at The Liberty Trust Company for years, and they had always treated him right. Liberty Trust had provided the loan to start the kindergarten so, it was natural it would be his first choice to finance the Tastee Freez deal.

Mr. Kreider allowed Dad to use his balance sheets to prepare a business plan. It showed that he'd be able to pay off the loan in ten years, and given he had paid off a previous loan with them and had the house as collateral, there shouldn't be a problem, or so he thought. When he called to set up the meeting, Mr. Dudley, an assistant secretary in the loan department, was eager to talk with him but something changed when he showed up for his appointment the next day. Mr. Dudley was there but said little and treated Dad a bit formally as he escorted Dad to the bank president's office.

President William C. Walsh rose from his desk, shook Dad's hand, and asked him to sit in the chair in front.

"Lu, I understand you'd like to buy the Tastee Freez franchise and property on National Highway in LaVale."

"Yes," said Dad. "And I have a business plan and the deed to my home to show you how—"

"That won't be necessary, Lu," President Walsh interrupted. "I'm afraid we're not going to be able to help you in this endeavor. I asked Mr. Dudley to show you in here so I can give you a little advice."

He then spent the next fifteen minutes lecturing Dad on how foolish he was to be investing in a fast food restaurant.

"Fast food, it's a fad, a passing thing," President Walsh said. "And LaVale is too far away from downtown Cumberland. Why it can't support the restaurants there already. It's a bad deal. You need to look into other business opportunities that are more suited to your education and experience. Music, isn't that it? Aren't you a band director at Allegany, Lu? My God, boy, what do you know about fast food?"

Dad was shocked and confused as he walked to the door with President Walsh.

I'm sure he was thinking, *What happened? Why wouldn't he even consider a loan?*

The next night, Mom and Dad had drinks at the country club with their good friends Harry and Jean Butler. Dad had known Harry Butler since they were kids running around in the 1920s. The sort of "Children Playing" that motorists should be warned to "SLOW" for. Anyway, he and Harry went to school together, so Dad felt comfortable telling him about his experience at the bank. When Harry heard the whole story, he shook his head, then got up and went to the bar. A few minutes later, he returned with Hugh Shires in tow.

Hugh Shires was a Junior Manager at the First National Bank of Cumberland. Harry thought Hugh could at least hear Dad's story and maybe even help him out. Dad started his story again, but the second he said Tastee Freez and LaVale, Hugh stopped him.

"Lu, Liberty Trust is screwing with you. It isn't that you're untrustworthy or the loan is risky, you just happen to want to buy the same piece of property they want to buy."

"What in the world would the Liberty Trust Company do with a Tastee Freez?" asked Dad.

"Tear it down and build a branch office. They've wanted to put one in LaVale for years and have had their eye on either Kreider's corner of National Highway or the one across the street. Kreider won't sell to them because he loves the ice cream store and doesn't want to see it torn down, and the other lot needs to have the zoning changed before a bank can go in. I'm betting they're trying to wait Kreider out, hoping he'll come crawling back to them, and then they'll drop their price. You're not the Liberty Trust Company's customer, Lu, you're its competitor."

Harry had a big grin on his face as he slapped Hugh on the back and said, "Can First National help Lu out?"

"I don't know, Harry, but I'm damned sure we'd like to talk with him. Can you come in on Monday, Lu?" Hugh asked.

"Sure," said Dad. "Right after I close my account at the Liberty Trust Company.

Dad bought drinks for everyone, two for Harry.

Dad got the loan at First National and bought the Tastee Freez. He renamed it Uncle Lu's Tastee Freez because that was what all his nephews, nieces and most of his friend's kids called him. About five years later, The Liberty Trust Company built a branch office across the street. Dad opened a store account there but kept his personal accounts with First National.

That's how Uncle Lu got a Tastee Freez and how I got a job there. My Dad is Uncle Lu.

Chapter 4 - Help Me Make It through the Night

— My First Job —

On the morning of my fourteenth birthday, Dad took me to the Maryland Department of Labor, Licensing, and Regulation to get my Minor's Work Permit. I started work at the Tastee Freez that afternoon. My pay was 60 cents an hour. The federal minimum wage was $1.30, but it didn't apply to kids working part-time jobs. I'm not complaining; I'm stating the facts. I loved the money I made. Back then, 60 cents could buy four ice cream cones at Uncle Lu's, but I didn't have to buy them because I got them for free.

My first job was a smelly one. I emptied and cleaned trash cans. That doesn't sound too tough, but it was the middle of July and about 85 degrees outside. Inside, it was even hotter because there was no air conditioning at Uncle Lu's. Now, factor in all the melting ice cream in those trash cans, and how dairy products do not take long to spoil, and you have a pretty stinky environment. This was before plastic liner bags for garbage cans was the norm. We are talking serious gag-reflex-stimulating stink, and I had to carry each metal garbage can 40 yards away from the building to a dumpster under the trees. Then I'd scrub them out using a hose and a long-handled brush and haul them back to their proper location. My uniform was comprised of a paper red, white, and blue Tastee Freez hat and a white shirt and apron. The whites didn't stay white for long.

Two years later, I was an old hand at the Tastee Freez, and knew how to do everything: clean trash cans, wait on customers, fry hamburgers, clean ice cream machines, and even open and close the store. The Tastee Freez building itself changed too. In 1960, Dad expanded the floorplan, adding indoor seating for ten. He also expanded the menu, adding hot dogs, hamburgers, French fries, and soup.

Dad also installed a jukebox, and for a quarter, you could listen to six songs. When he would show up at night to close out the cash register, the first thing he'd do was put quarters in the jukebox so there'd be music for everyone while they cleaned the store. I remember my sister Barbara teaching me the Twist one night in front of the cash register. But it was a tiny place with only three rooms: one for storage and cleaning, one for food preparation, and one for eating. I'd estimate it was only 700 square feet total, and those square feet were jam-packed with Tastee Freez stuff. Squeezed in there were two archaic ice cream machines—each the size of a Honda Civic, a walk-in refrigerator, wall-length sink, work counters, cone dispenser, hamburger grill, deep fryer, cash register and lots more. The place was packed. Add four or five employees hustling about trying to meet customers' needs, and you've got a chaotic environment.

Service with a Smile at Uncle Lu's Tastee Freez 1964 (Syckes Family Photos)

I mentioned earlier there was no A/C, and it became a real issue in the summer. As outdoor temperatures climbed, indoor temperatures climbed higher. Adding to our misery was the heat from the motors of the refrigeration equipment, hamburger grill, and deep fryer. On top of that, a money-saving decision that Dad made when expanding the store came back to haunt him. He added five big plate-glass windows along the seating area walls; however, he didn't get ones that opened. Although the windows provided great natural lighting, they also allowed the sun's radiant heat to cook everything inside. It was hot—sometimes over 100 degrees hot—and the only way to get air moving was to open the little serving windows and place a big floor fan in the open back door. This made it easier for our other summer nemesis to come in.

I'm talking about flies—big, black, buzzing flies, and there were a lot of them. Although we had swatters, we couldn't very well be swatting flies while the customers were sitting and waiting for their food. What if a dead fly dive-bombed into the ice cream mix or onto the grill? We resorted to flypaper strips. Today I doubt anyone would eat in a place with foot-long sticky coils of flypaper hanging from the ceiling covered with dead or dying flies, but they did back then, and summer was our biggest money-making season.

This hot environment also made for hot workers, and I can remember sweating gallons while deftly gliding from flipping hamburgers to pouring drinks to dip-topping ice cream cones—my favorite just like Dad's.

When we'd get really hot, we'd take a break and step into the walk-in refrigerator. It was a big, well insulated wooden box about six-by-six-foot square attached to a refrigeration system. To open it, you pulled a levered handle on the front, and the foot-thick door would swing open. It was in here we stored all the ice cream mix and any other large perishable items like cheese and hamburger. It made the perfect place to cool off from the summer heat, but it also made the perfect place to play dirty tricks on your co-workers. To open the door from the inside, you pushed a metal plunger that would engage the handle on the outside. New employees learned quickly that if a co-worker dropped a screwdriver into a hole made for a padlock on the outside of the door, it was locked tight. As long as the screwdriver was there, whoever was in the walk-in stayed in the walk-in. Many a new employee or smart-ass old employee was trapped in the walk-in until their fellow workers felt sorry for them. I spent a lot of time in there.

— Coworkers —

We had interesting people on the staff. Let me tell you about a few of them. I'll start with the all-stars: Charlotte, Dot, and Arvada. Charlotte was about forty-five in 1971, stood five feet tall, and if she weighed 100 pounds, I'd be surprised. Intelligent, dedicated, honest, and hardworking, I always thought Charlotte could have had her pick of careers if she would have had the chance to attend college, but she was not that fortunate. She married early and raised her family, then went looking for a way to bring in extra money. Uncle Lu's was the answer, and she started working for Dad in 1965.

Dot was as hardworking, dedicated, and honest as Charlotte but was a bit on the spacey side. She always had a darting, distant look in her eyes, as if someone was calling her name or distracting her with a shiny object. She was the same height as Charlotte but twice as wide. Despite her size, Dot could move quicker than anyone in the narrow passages of the store, and she knew where everything was. These two ladies were Dad's day-shift managers, and when you were working with them, you did things the right way.

I was only a teenager and in my first job, but I was already honing my avoid-hard-work skill set, which, in later years, I perfected. The key is to appear eager and willing to take on any task, but in reality, do as little of the work yourself and allow others to carry the heaviest load. Executives call this delegating. Charlotte and Dot saw right through me although each approached solving the "Shelby" problem differently. Charlotte would check my work regularly and make me do it over and over until I got it right. Dot would get flustered and finish the job for me. I liked working with Dot.

Dad, Arvada, & Charlotte 1972 (Syckes Family Photos)

Arvada was special, and I have met no one like her since. Smart and sweet natured she was extremely shy. She was also a little girl trapped inside a linebacker's body. You see, Arvada inherited her father's build. Unfortunately, he was built like a brick shithouse. Her short stature magnified this. Wise to the world and its ways, I also think Arvada would have done well if she had been born into a family that allowed women to excel. She was not that fortunate. When she found herself trapped by an unwanted pregnancy soon after graduating high school, her family all but disowned her. This locked her into a life of entry-level service jobs from which she never escaped. My family was very fortunate when she came to work for us, and Dad gave her every opportunity.

First as a housekeeper and then as the cleanup lady at the Tastee Freez, Arvada soon knew how to do everything at the store but always remained in the back room, never wanting the public to see her. She was as good a manager as Charlotte and Dot but never embraced the job despite Dad's prodding. She only wanted to be the hard-working motor—powering all the gears.

It was these three strong women who were primarily responsible for the Tastee Freez's success. One thing they all did the same was wear their hair in tightly wrapped beehive hairdos of the fashion seen in the movie *Hair Spray*—the taller, the better.

There are only two people in the second tier of the full-time staff worth discussing: Ernie and Flora. Ernie was one of Dad's night managers and the only male member of the adult workforce. He was not impressive. In fact, I would not be surprised if Ernie's bathroom wall had a sticker reading, "Warning: Objects in mirror are dumber than they look." Let me state for the record, Ernie looked dumb. His intellect, however, far exceeded his hygiene.

His two white shirts where accented with underarms darker than dung. His pants were frayed, and his shoes looked like he buffed them with a brick. He kept his hair combed, but that was more a function of the quart of oil keeping it in place than styling. Oh, and he drove a brown Plymouth Duster—*a Duster!* Even his car was named after dirt. Despite these flaws, Ernie was honest, a hard worker and fiercely loyal to Dad. Ernie was also uncoordinated.

He once almost bled to death opening a jar of pickles. They came in gallon glass jars with oversized lids that were difficult to open with small hands. Ernie, seeing a female co-worker struggling with one, volunteered to help. First, he grabbed the jar, and with a most impressive grunt, tried to rotate the top. No luck. Then he reached for a spoon to tap the top a few times, but instead of a spoon, he grabbed a knife by the blade. Before he realized it, he'd opened a three-inch gash in his palm. This caused him to drop the jar. Lurching down to stop the jar from smashing on the floor, Ernie was too late and sliced open his other hand on the jar's broken glass. Dill pickles, broken glass, a knife, and blood covered the scene. The EMS guys thought we'd tried to murder him.

Flora, on the other hand, was something entirely different. She worked both day and night shifts and was past her fortieth birthday but dressed like a teenager. In 1971, that meant mini-skirts and low-neckline blouses. She kept her hair in a bob-style and concealed any wrinkles on her face with pounds of makeup. Her figure was nothing to write home about, but whatever she had, she displayed with astonishing frequency. It was quite normal for her to reveal herself by squatting or leaning over a counter. This did not embarrass her, but anyone with her in their direct line of sight was. In fact, whenever she did it, she always included a wink and a smile that asked, "See anything you like?"

I guess a few male customers enjoyed the show, but not me. Unfortunately, that was not all she liked to do. She'd accidentally bump into me or brush by me just close enough so I could get a whiff of her pungent perfume.

One time, I was at the grill flipping hamburgers when I felt Flora's hand slide between my legs and brush my groin. I looked down to see her arm reaching under the cabinet.

"Sorry," she said with a wink and that saucy smile as she withdrew her hand, tapping my privates again. "Gotta get some napkins."

This confused and unnerved me. Teenage boys dream of situations like this, but not, I repeat, not with women their mother's age who look like hammered dog. I did everything in my power to avoid working with her, but our paths would cross again six months later.

The rest of the workers were kids like me, somewhere in age between fifteen and nineteen. We all got along well, and it made work lots of fun. We'd do our jobs and take care of customers, but the jukebox would always be playing, and we had our serious level set on low. It was the night shifts when the practical jokes would start, and someone would find himself locked in the walk-in refrigerator.

We had another prank that was reserved for newbies on their first night shift. Before closing, the oldest among us would sidle up to the guy and say, "Hey, you've got the roof duty tonight. When we close up, come and see me, and I'll explain."

When it was time to close, the novice would find out he was to go out back to the equipment area and find a rake, a bucket, and a stepladder. Then he was to go up on the roof and rake the gravel. He was also to gather up any undersized pebbles in the bucket because we didn't want them blowing off the roof onto cars.

After inspecting his equipment, we'd tell him it was best to position the ladder near the back door, but he should start raking at the front part of the roof, up by the ice cream cone.

"Look for us when you get out there we'll make sure you're in the right spot," we'd assure him.

The neophyte would clamber up the ladder, balancing the rake and bucket, and trek to the other side. We'd all run around the building, except one of us who would go back inside. You couldn't miss the greenhorn as he passed through the blinding spotlights illuminating the "Uncle Lu's" sign and carefully stepped over the wire stringers holding it up, but it wasn't until he reached the neon cone that someone would shout to the guy inside the store,

"Okay, shut' em off."

With that, the guy inside would flip the main circuit breaker switch, and all lights both outside and inside the Tastee Freez would go out. Total darkness engulfed the beginner. It only took about ten seconds before we heard pleading sobs from the waif in the dark over our uproarious laughter. It was then we'd turn the lights back on and make sure the now veteran employee made it safely back down. By the way, there was no gravel on the roof, just tarpaper.

— Joleen & Dill —

It was near the end of a Friday night shift when I noticed Dylan Denton—who was affectionately called Dill—sitting on a stool near the jukebox. He was a friend from choir.

Yes, I was in the choir, and while we are on the subject, let me get it all out there, I was also in the Boys' Glee Club.

But back to the story. Dill was sitting there quietly, sipping a Pepsi and cleaning his glasses. I went over to say hi.

"Hey, Dill, how long you been here? I didn't see you come in. I'm in the back tearing down the chocolate ice cream machine 'cause we're getting ready to close at 11."

"Only about ten minutes. Hey, what are you doing after work?" Dill asked.

Now that was a strange question, but strange was kind of normal for Dill. Already tagged as a choir geek, he carried the additional burden of a porcine face and figure. When he spoke, you half expected to hear, "Th-th-the- th-th-the- th-th, that's all, folks!" But he was a nice guy.

Answering him, I said, "Dill, I'm fifteen years old; it's 11 o'clock at night, and I don't have a driver's license. What in the world do you think I will do after work? Hit a few bars? Dad will show up any minute to close out the cash register, and I'll ride home with him and go to bed. Why?"

"Well, I can give you a ride home. I've got my Beetle out front. Maybe we can ride around a while, and I've got something I know you'd like to see in the car."

Dill sipped his Pepsi and glanced over at the jukebox as it played "Me and You and a Dog Named Boo."

"I'll ask Dad when he gets here. Stand by," I said, then went back to my machine.

I was carefully washing the mixing blade in the sink when Dad came through the door. I didn't dare take my eyes off what I was doing because the mixing blades were deadly. If they slipped in your hand and those blades got hold of you, they'd open you up like a broken pickle jar, or worse. I took my time but yelled to Dad, "I'm catching a ride home with Dill tonight. Is that okay?"

He looked at Dill, recognized him and said, "Fine, but don't be long. You work tomorrow."

"Okay," I said and left to tell Dill.

"Great, I'll wait in the car," Dill said when I gave him the thumbs up.

He stood and crushed his wax Pepsi cup, then made an exaggerated basketball shot at the trash can about three feet away. He missed. Shrugging, he lumbered out the door.

The last of the store's lights were going off as I walked out to the parking lot and looked for Dill's VW Bug. I heard him say, "Yo, Shelby. Over here."

Off to my left, I saw Dill's Beetle, parked facing forward. Dill was standing outside it, leaning on the open driver's door. It appeared he was alone, but as I got closer, I saw someone was in the back.

Was that? Could that be…? It's Joleen Johnson.

Joleen was a natural beauty with gorgeous, straight red hair that fell to the middle of her back. She had a slim but nicely rounded figure that any boy would love to squeeze, and best of all, she was about two inches shorter than me. My five-foot-five ego cannot tolerate tall girls. Picture a young Julianne Moore with a little Reba McEntire mixed in, and you've got Joleen. Like Dill, she was a year older than me and also in the choir. I spent as much time as I could joking with her during class. She had a great sense of humor and could give as well as she could take. Our talks always included lots of double entendres, and I was sure there was a sexual tension between us, but back then I felt that way with about any female, except Flora, of course. Seeing Joleen in the car was cool, and I'm sure I had a big smile on my face when I opened the door and leaned in.

"Hey, Joleen, what are you doing here?"

She grinned and darted her eyes at Dill.

"We were out cruising around when we thought we'd come up and see if you were working tonight," said Dill.

Now that made absolutely no sense, but I didn't care. Joleen Johnson came to see me!

"Get in the back," Joleen said in a smoky voice. I pushed the front seat forward and folded myself into the back.

Joleen looked good, and she smelled even better. She was wearing a mini-skirt that barely covered the top of her light blue pantyhose and a flowered print short-sleeved top with a scalloped neckline. She was hot.

Now before I go any further, I think it is important that I let you know I was a 100% dyed-in-the-wool virgin at the time. Not only had I never gotten to third base with a girl, I wasn't exactly sure what constituted second. The farthest I had ever gone was heavy kissing with a bit of fully dressed body-on-body rubbing, but nothing more. I'd yet to hold a woman's breast or even get a good look at one in the flesh. As for what lay a little lower, I had no clue. All my experience was with myself and the Playboy Corporation, but Joleen had something on her mind, and I wanted to find out what it was.

Dill got in and started the car. You always know when you're in a VW Bug because of the motor's unmistakable sound. It's like a chain tumbling in a clothes dryer, and Dill's Bug sounded like the dryer needed oiling. We pulled out of the parking lot, and I sat there looking back and forth between Dill's head and Joleen's top.

Gosh, she's well built! Is she bra-less?

I took a deep breath, leaned up against her, and smiled.

"Wait till we get there," she said.

I slid back to my side of the seat. "Where are we going, Dill?" I asked.

"Sunset View. We'll be there in a minute."

Sunset View was one of Cumberland's suburban housing developments built in the late fifties. It was row after row of ranch, raised ranch, split-level, and split-foyer homes ranging in size from tiny to small that every town in America got after the war. Most of the houses were built with pink brick.

Have you figured out yet that I don't like pink brick?

But what it lacked in originality, Sunset View made up for in location.

Winding up the side of a hill, Sunset View faced west, as its name implies, and sat halfway between Cumberland and LaVale. The main road branched off to others. One, Forest Drive continued deep into the woods. Dill turned onto Forest and didn't stop until he was at the end of the road and looking out over its unique view. The reason it was unique was that at night, the lights of LaVale looked like a map of the United States. It was easily recognizable and even included a bright spot where Washington DC should be. That's why this was such a popular parking spot—all the teenagers in Cumberland knew about it.

The last few lots on Forest Drive were undeveloped, so, no one else was around.

This was going to get interesting.

Now as much as I was enjoying the prospects of parking with Joleen and maybe getting to second base with her, I was confused by why Dill was along for the ride. I'd be nervous enough if it was only Joleen and me, but Dill's presence made it creepy. The VW skidded in the gravel as Dill hit the brakes, and I used the jolt to "accidentally" lean on Joleen again. This time, she looked into my eyes and kissed me quickly on the lips. It was more like a bird pecking seed than a kiss, but it was enough. I wanted more.

Then Dill flipped on the car's dome light and held out a deck of cards saying, "Okay, I'll deal."

What? Cards? Did you bring me up here to play cards? You're kidding, right?

I should have said that, but I didn't. I was with Joleen in the back seat of a VW at the hottest parking spot in the Tri-State area, and I didn't want to blow it.

Sunset View LaVale - Map of USA (Fort Hill High School Yearbook)

Instead, I said, "What are we playing?"

"Strip poker," answered Joleen. "I want to play strip poker."

"What?" I stammered. "Right here, right now?"

"Yes," she said firmly. "I dare you."

Now, you might think this was a good prospect for me, but it wasn't. I'd never experienced sex, but I was pretty sure it didn't require a fat guy dealing cards. Don't get me wrong, I was all for Joleen taking her clothes off, but the last thing I wanted to do was lose a strip poker game with her and Dill. A frightening image appeared in my mind: there I was with my pants down and my dick up, and Joleen and Dill are laughing at me. No way was I going to let that happen.

"Is Dill playing, too?" I squeaked.

"No," said Dill. "I'm the referee."

Referee? What do we need a referee for?

I was glad to hear Dill wasn't playing. At least I'd be spared seeing whatever it was he had hidden under his sweatshirt. Even with it on, it was clear his boobs were bigger than Joleen's.

"Listen, Dill, can you give Joleen and me a minute alone, please?" I pleaded.

Dill looked at Joleen and got the okay. "I'll be right out here, watching," he said as he opened his door.

"Thanks, I said." When he had closed the door, I turned to Joleen and said, "I'm confused. Can't we sit here alone and talk and maybe get to know each other a little better?"

She leaned forward and kissed me again, this time with meaningful lip action. I liked this a lot, and I put my arm around her waist pulling her closer to me. Dill, seeing this, rapped his knuckles against the back window. Jolted back upright, I felt like the dog that caught the car.

What do I do now?

I leaned in again, and Dill rapped on the window again, and that was all I could stand. I had had it.

Joleen giggled, and I said, "Sorry, babe, but I have got to go. This is not for me."

She tapped her class ring on the window, and Dill jumped back in the car.

"Take him home. He doesn't want to play," she said flatly, and Dill turned the key.

That tumbling-chains sound started again, and I felt like I was in the dryer with it. The drive to my place was pretty quiet, and I could not for the life of me figure out if I'd missed an opportunity or dodged a bullet. I was going home very confused and unsatisfied but also thinking about what almost happen.

Hey, Joleen came to me. I might not be just a kid anymore.

When we got there, I started to get out, but Joleen tugged me back into the seat.

She kissed me again, this time with a bit of tongue involved, and said, "You should have played the game."

I went straight to my room to carefully reread all my Playboy Advisor columns.

Chapter 5 - Vehicle

— Driving —

The Declaration of Independence makes it pretty clear we have "certain unalienable rights," like life, liberty, and the pursuit of happiness, but the Founding Fathers did not take into account the situation of a teenage boy without his driver's license. How can you be free to pursue happiness if you arrive to pick up your girl with your Dad driving the car? That's why turning sixteen and getting a driver's license is vitally important to boys and the sole focus of their existence as they near that magical birthday. As my day neared, I knew I was ready because I'd been driving, or at least sort of driving, cars for many years.

My first driving experience was with Dad in his 1959 Buick LeSabre. That car was something to behold. It was a true land yacht with nothing but long, low lines, miles of chrome, eyebrow-arching headlights, and supernatural tail fins—the biggest ever on a Buick. The thing screamed, "Look at me!"

I'll bet when the first one rolled off the assembly line, members of the engineering staff looked at each other and said, "Oh, my God! What have we done?" because not a single one of the features listed above had anything to do with improving the car's functionality or safety.

It was all for show, and isn't that great?

Dad's 1959 Buick LeSabre Convertible (Syckes Family Photos)

It was the first car I ever drove. Well, if sitting on your dad's lap and holding the steering wheel constitutes driving, but it felt like driving to me, and I took it seriously.

My next driving experience was with go-carts. While at Ocean City, Tim and I spent many hours driving go-carts around a quarter-mile track at a boardwalk arcade. We got to know the attendant on duty so well, he would let us ride for free whenever there was no one else on the track. Every morning we'd be there when the doors opened to zoom around and around and around. It sounds crazy, but I learned a lot about how to drive a car from those go-carts. When you are racing your buddy in a go-cart that has a maximum speed of only 15 mph, you have to drive with sophistication—speed isn't enough. You're not going too fast, but when your butt is only three inches off the pavement, it sure feels fast. To add to our fun, Tim and I would each carry a plastic pellet gun to shoot at each other as we fought it out for the finish line. It wasn't until I was in Driver's Ed that I finally got to really drive a car.

I took Driver's Ed in the fall of my sophomore year, and to tell the truth; I remember little about the classroom portion of the course other than the movies. We had to watch a bunch of boring scare films with crashed cars and dead bodies lying on the road covered with blankets. They had catchy titles like *Wheels of Tragedy* and *Red Asphalt*. Now, why adults thought this would convince teenagers to drive safely is a mystery to me, given those same teenagers were paying money to see movies like *Dawn of the Dead* and *The Corpse Grinders*. Every time the 16mm projector bathed the pull-down screen with a scene of total auto carnage, someone in the darkened class would blurt out, "Way cool."

I do remember the behind-the-wheel portion of the course. It was great, and I got to drive a real car on real roads. The local car dealerships would donate to Allegany whatever models they couldn't sell. Unfortunately, they were all the dregs of the early 1970's automobile world. It was the golden age of muscle cars, with Pontiac GTOs, Chevy Camaros and Ford Mustangs running all over the place, but that's not what we got. Instead, we got AMC Hornets, Ford Mavericks, and other used dogs, the kinds of cars that put you to sleep just looking at them.

— Mr. Brooks and the Moose Curve —

My Driver's Ed teacher was Mr. Brooks, and he truly was two different men. From the waist up, he looked like a perfectly normal sixty-year-old man who hadn't bought a new suit since 1947, but from the waist down, there was something very wrong with him. He was enormous; maybe four times average size. His pant legs looked like funnels on the Titanic, and there was no transition from his top to bottom—he just exploded out from below his belt. Everyone whispered that he had elephantiasis, and from pictures I've seen of people so inflicted, I believe it. You had to feel sorry for him, especially when you saw him walking. To move forward, he sort of teeter-tottered from side to side, shifting from foot to foot as if he could not bend his hips or knees. It was Frankenstein-like.

I don't know what the reason was—whether he pissed off the principal or was just a guy with no good luck, but the Driver's Ed classrooms were on the third floor of Allegany's center section. Only a few classrooms were up there, and they had to give one to poor Mr. Brooks? That's cruel and unusual punishment, and since Allegany was an old building, that meant it had high ceilings and lots of stairs that Mr. Brooks had to waddle up to get to his classroom. That took a lot of time. If you turned in to a stairwell and saw him, you turned right around because there was no way to pass him as he slowly rocked up one step at a time. But wait, there's more! As the Driver's Ed Teacher, he had to go up and down those stairs five or six times a day for student driving, and in one final, painful irony, there were no bathrooms on the third floor for Mr. Brooks. His was a tormented soul.

It was during the last three weeks of class that students would waddle downstairs with Mr. Brooks and go for a forty-five-minute joy ride, I mean, educational driving experience. We'd take turns behind the wheel learning about the pedals, knobs, and switches, then practice our hand signals.

By the way, does anyone on the planet still use hand signals? Especially that silly left-arm-out-the-window-palm-down-facing-backwards stop signal. And if so, why?

After we had proven we could push the brake pedal, turn the wheel, and signal a right turn at the same time, we got going. Each kid would get fifteen minutes behind the wheel while the other two were supposed to be studying his or her driver's test manual in the back seat. Mr. Brooks had three or four standard courses that we would take to expose us to all kinds of driving situations. We'd drive on one-way streets and two-way streets, but all we kids wanted to do was get up on The Bridge to see how fast these family fun wagons would go. There was no second steering wheel for Mr. Brooks, but the shop class had rigged up an extension foot break he could press should the student need help. I felt him pushing on it now and then during my time behind the wheel, but not too often. I was comfortable driving. It was like a go-cart, only with doors and a roof. That wasn't the case for everyone.

Near the end of the second week of driving, Dave Thom, Debbie Smith, and I found ourselves together in the biggest of the crap-cars Allegany had in its fleet. It was a Grecian Green 1967 Chevy Impala four-door that had been rode hard and put away wet way too many times. There was one positive thing about it; it was the only car in the fleet with a V-8 engine. Debbie was one of the most gregarious girls in the school, but when she got behind the wheel, she wavered between timid and terrified. She'd creep along city streets and pause for what felt like five minutes at each stop sign looking left, then right, and then left again, over and over, but it was when it was her turn to drive on The Bridge that things got truly interesting. Dave and I were expecting her to crawl along in the right-hand lane, but as she made the turn onto the entrance ramp, Mr. Brooks told her, "Miss Smith, remember to accelerate quickly to facilitate easy merging."

With that, Debbie gripped the steering wheel like a safety bar on a roller coaster and floored it. The butterfly valves on the Impala's four-barrel carburetor opened, dumping half a gallon of high test gas into the engine as the Powerglide transmission kicked down into passing gear. We took off like a Saturn V rocket. I mean, she hit the gas so hard that Dave and I slid all the way over to the other side of the back seat as the entrance ramp curved down onto The Bridge.

Hoping for moderation once we merged, Mr. Brooks held his tongue at first, but it soon became clear that Debbie was frozen solid. The lyrics to Commander Cody's song "Hot Rod Lincoln" popped into my head: "My foot was glued, like lead to the floor. That's all there is, and there ain't no more." We merged onto The Bridge smoothly, but Debbie kept on crossing lanes as we passed through 70 mph.

Mr. Brooks said, "That's enough now. Slow it down and straighten out," but there was no response.

We whizzed by a VW Bus that barely got out of our way, and Mr. Brooks pressed on his backup brake pedal, but the Chevy's V-8 powered on through.

Debbie should have felt that, but no, she kept on accelerating. Now we were scared because the huge, blinking Moose Curve warning sign shot by as we approached 80. There was no way we would make it around that at this speed.

Cumberland's Loyal Order of Moose had a four-story lodge on the banks of the Potomac River near where it made a sharp bend north on the west side of town. The Bridge hugged the Potomac there, so it had to turn north, too. The turn was so sharp; the Interstate Highway commission demanded the speed limit be lowered from 60 to 40 mph in the curve and plenty of warning signs erected. Many a traveler's trip ended badly there, and the area became known as the Moose Curve.

Mr. Brooks shouted, "Miss Smith, slow down! Miss Smith, please slow down!" He pumped his break as hard as he could. Debbie was looking straight ahead, eyes fixed, foot planted on the gas, oblivious to everything.

Grabbing the back of her seat, I pulled myself up to her ear and said as clearly as I could, "Debbie, stop!"

I saw her head jerk as if waking from a sound sleep, and her concrete foot went from crushing the gas to smashing the brakes. A squealing erupted from all corners of the car as it nosed forward and skidded towards the Moose Lodge. Dave and I went airborne as our butts lifted off the seat, and Mr. Brooks grabbed the bottom of the steering wheel and pulled it up sharply hoping to counteract the direction of the skid. We came to an abrupt halt sideways in the service lane about an inch from a retaining wall. There was silence and relief for a few seconds until more squealing sounded as the VW Bus we'd missed earlier zig-zagged past us, just avoiding our tail end, which was now sticking out into the right-hand lane.

Dave peered up from the wheel well behind Mr. Brooks's seat as he turned off the car and flipped on the emergency blinkers. Head down, Debbie was crying when Mr. Brooks opened her door and coaxed her to slide over. The ride back to school was quiet except for regular sobs from Debbie, followed by sighs of relief from Mr. Brooks. After much counseling, Debbie was allowed to take another drive, but this time in the four-cylinder Plymouth Duster with no other students and a different teacher. We all passed the course.

— Parking at the Armory —

Although Driver's Ed was fun, the most memorable way I learned to drive a car was with Dad. At the time, it was just another outing with him, but when I look back on it now, it was one of those very special father-son times I'll cherish forever.

The Barracuda was my car of choice for these lessons and one of my favorite cars of all time. Dad started by letting me drive the car in very controlled and empty environments like parking lots and rural roads, but eventually, I graduated to city streets, and like in Driver's Ed, The Bridge. These drives were uneventful except for the occasional "slow down" command or the tug of a third hand on the steering wheel making a course correction, but it was the parallel parking lessons that tested Dad's patience to the limit. We used the National Guard Armory's parking lot for our training course and suitcases set about twenty-five-feet apart, to define the parking zone. Dad would start by demonstrating the dark art of parallel parking, and I would try to duplicate it.

These lessons turned out to be a lot like when he taught me to ride my bike. That day, the training wheels came off, and time after time, he ran beside me, helping me balance as I tried to remain upright. I often fell or put my feet down in frustration, but he'd encourage me to try again, and we'd start over. I'd re-aim my bike down the sidewalk and lean forward and push those peddles as hard as I could, twisting and turning the handlebars to keep upright long enough to get up to that perfect speed. Dad was right there holding on enough to keep me going, then *bang*, something magical happened, and I was on my own wheeling down the sidewalk, peddling and balancing, and Dad was receding behind me standing proud, arms akimbo, with a big smile on his face. Dad was helping me again but with a slightly bigger vehicle.

It was a Saturday before I planned to take my driver's test and I wanted to practice my parallel parking. Unfortunately, Dad had a tee-time in an hour and missing that was not an option. I pestered him until he agreed that we could go up to the Armory for an abbreviated lesson of only two parking tries, and I'd have to walk home to give him more time to get to his golf game.

"Great!" I said and ran to get a couple of suitcases.

The Armory was only about a mile from our house, so walking home would be easy. We pulled into the parking lot, and Dad stopped the car and threw me the keys to get the suitcases out of the trunk.

Dad was one of those guys who carried every key he owned on a ring in his pocket. He had keys to the house, keys to the Tastee Freez, keys to Allegany's band room, keys to my grandmother's house and keys to God knows what else. He could fit them all in his front pocket because he wore loose-fitting khaki pants with large, free-moving pockets. I wore skin tight jeans with narrow front pockets, so when I had his key ring in there, it was uncomfortable and awkward. If positioned right, I appeared hung like a horse, but most of the time, it looked like I had a tumor. I hated it, so I'd usually carry them in my hand. The suitcases fit neatly into the trunk, and when I put them in there, I closed and locked the trap door that separates the trunk from the rest of the car. I popped the trunk and pulled out the suitcases, then slammed it shut and turned to set up the test. It was in that second, I realized I had put Dad's key ring down inside the trunk, so I'd have both hands free to remove the suitcases. My stomach sank.

I am so screwed.

"Hey, get moving! I've got a tee time in forty minutes," Dad said.

"I stood there not knowing how to tell him we had to walk back to the house and get the spare set of keys. He came around to where I was standing and saw me staring at the trunk.

He looked at the suitcases then looked at me and saw I had no baseball size bulge in my pocket then back at the trunk. "The keys are in there, aren't they?"

"Yes. I'm sorry, Dad. I'll run home for the other set. Wait here."

Dad then used the only swear word I ever heard him utter. I did not understand then what it meant or why he even thought it was effective cursing. You see, Lu Syckes did not curse, but I had provoked him to blurt out the one terrible phrase he saved for only his most frustrating moments.

"JUDAS PRIEST! I'll miss my tee-time! JUDAS PRIEST, boy, what's the matter with you?"

Now there's an open-ended question.

Later I found out that Judas Priest was a euphemism for Jesus Christ and used as an interjection of exclamation, surprise, or dismay. Well, I get that, because if you got Lu Syckes to say it, you were at the absolute limit of his tolerance, and it was time to duck and cover. I kept quiet and put the suitcases in the backseat of the Barracuda.

I turned to walk home when Dad said, "Hey, wait for me, I'll go with you."

He'd calmed down, and we started to walk home. "I'll call Harry, maybe he can switch our tee time for a later one, but Shelby, you've got to start thinking if you're going to survive in this world."

Then he laughed and hugged me, and we walked home. It wasn't quite time for the training wheels to come off.

— Sixty-Day Card —

In Maryland, on the day you turn sixteen, you can apply for a learner's permit or sixty-day card, as we called it. It allowed you to drive a car if accompanied by another licensed driver who was at least twenty-one years old. I got my permit the second the DMV opened on my birthday.

I now had sixty days to pass the Maryland driver's test, and I planned to take it as soon as possible, but I did not want to fail. If you failed, you had to wait two weeks before trying again. ALCO Summer Band would start soon, and I had to have my license by then. If I took the test too soon and failed, Dad would be driving me to my first day as drum major of the band, and I would not let that happen. I figured it would be better to wait a few weeks to make sure I was ready for the test. It had been months since I completed Driver's Ed, and although I had done plenty of driving, I hadn't reviewed the test booklet much since then, so I waited and studied. With my permit, driving was all I thought about, and I constantly badgered everyone for the opportunity to drive.

"Hey, Mom, do you need me to take you down to the A&P for Eight-O'Clock coffee? It looks like we're down to only two pounds."

"Hey, Dad, can I drive you to the Tastee Freez this morning, please, can I, please?"

"Betsy, how about you and I go for a drive in the country? It's been so long since we've seen any horses."

Most of these ploys failed, but I never quit asking and got to drive a lot more. I also read and reread the test booklet, memorizing everything I thought was important. I even asked friends who had already taken the test to tell me what to expect. Mostly their answers were vague or unhelpful, like "Make sure you know that stuff about headlights," or "Don't worry; it's easy. I passed it on my third try."

There were two parts to the test: written and behind-the-wheel. I was more worried about the written part, but I also made sure I kept practicing my parallel parking. When I got home from picking up my sixty-day card, I used Dad's desktop calendar to plot when to take my test. I meticulously calculated a schedule that would allow me three weeks to master my parking and test-taking skills as well as create a buffer should I fail my first attempt—all before Summer Band started.

The day before my perfectly planned test taking day, I was meeting in the living room with Bob Hartman and the other band officers working Summer Band planning when Mom leaned her head through the door and said, "Honey, remember you've got to pack for next week. We're taking Betsy to the University of Maryland to get settled, then going to visit Uncle George."

"Okay, sure, Mom, no problem. Wait, we're doing what, when?!" I cried.

Mom scolded, "Shelby, I told you we have to take your sister to her new college then see George."

"But, Mom, we can't. I'm taking my driver's test tomorrow, and you or Dad has to take me," I pleaded.

"It will have to wait; we can't change our plans now," Mom said as she left through the side door.

"Judas Priest!" I hissed.

After everyone left, I went up to Dad's office and stared at the calendar. All the slack had been ripped out of my schedule, so I needed to re-plan. The earliest I would be able to take the test was the week before Summer Band.

It will have to work, and I have to pass.

There was a good side to the trip for me and that was I got to drive more than I ever had before. I drove at night and for long stretches during the day on interstates and country roads. It was great practice, but what was really cool was that I was driving the big-ass 1970 Buick Electra 225 two-door. This thing was even bigger than the '59 Buick. It was a monster. It was just short of 20 feet long, weighed in at two-and-a-half tons, and had a big 455-cubic-inch V-8 pumping out 370 hp. I doubt it got better than ten mpg whether it was going uphill or downhill, but who cared—gas was 32 cents per gallon. It had power everything: steering, brakes, windows, mirrors, everything.

The biggest difference between the Electra and all the other cars I had driven was the suspension. This thing floated along like a barge on a calm sea. Nothing phased it. You could run over expansion joints, rocks, sticks, squirrels, small children, it didn't matter. The passenger compartment was totally isolated. The downside of this was handling. You did not want to take this battleship into any hard corners, or it could get scary. It was strictly for high-speed straight-line cruising. The Buick styling department had done a full 180-degree turn since the '59 model year. The '70 Electra looked like a big polished brick with a vinyl top and white-wall tires. Out were the fins and aircraft-inspired tail lights, arched headlights, and lightness of design. In was a big, bold, blunt force trauma weapon design that had a front end like a chrome-faced battering ram.

— The DMV —

On the planned day, I showed up at the Maryland DMV in the Sears Town shopping center to take my driver's license test. I drove Dad in the Barracuda and parked near the front of the building. It was around 10 o'clock in the morning, and the place was already busy.

One reality members of the Baby Boom generation must accept is dealing with large crowds of your fellow Boomers all trying to do the same thing at the same time. Whether it's waiting to get your polio vaccination or your picture taken with Santa Claus, there's always a line. The DMV was no exception. The year I was born there were 4.1 million other kids born in the US as well (7), and it looked like a good portion of them were there that day.

When I walked through the front door, all I saw were kids sitting around, each holding a ticket and staring up at a digital now-serving sign. Seeing the ticket dispenser, I grabbed the little stub sticking out. My number was 52. I glanced up at the sign and read 20.

Crap, I thought and dropped into a chair to wait.

Dad soon came in, looked at my ticket and the sign and said, "I'm going down to Sears and look around. I'll check back with you in an hour."

I found out soon it wouldn't take that long because they called five numbers at a time. When new numbers were announced, the five lucky ones would go up to the counter, show their sixty-day card, and get a folder. In it was the written portion of the test. Then, they'd go over to the test-taking booths that lined the far side of the building. Most were filled with furrow-browed teenagers reading or filling in little circles with their pencils.

I opened up my now dog-eared test manual and read for the thousandth time, but it was futile. The words weren't sinking in anymore. Finally, I heard, "Numbers 51 through 55" squawk through the loudspeaker. I was up and moving towards the counter. Keyed up and tense, I was greeted by a glum-faced civil servant wishing she had studied more in high school.

"Name and I.D.," she droned.

"Syckes, Shelby L," I said as I removed my sixty-day card from my wallet.

"Pencils?" she asked.

I stared back at her blankly.

"Pencils. Do you have your two number 2 pencils for the test?"

"Sure, I do," I lied. "I left them in my coat on the chair. I'll get them on my way to the test desk."

"Get them now, then get back in line!" she barked.

I moved away from the counter and turned around and looked for a familiar face.

I spied an overly tall girl coming through the front door whose face had more freckles than Howdy Doody. It was Becky Byrd. She was more giraffe than girl: lean, long, and lanky. She moved like one of those fan-powered sock-goblins flailing in front of a furniture store. I got up and met her as she reached for her ticket.

"Hey, Becky, are you here for the test?" I asked.

She started to speak, but before she could, I continued, "Did I tell you your rendition of 'Blowing in the Wind' at the choir concert was far-out? Your guitar playing has really improved since I heard you last year."

Her face beamed as she looked down at me. "Thanks, I've finally mastered the *F*-barre chord, and it's made all the difference in the world. Yes, I'm here to take the test. How about you?" she asked.

"Yeah, but I forgot my pencils, so I have to wait," I sighed.

My neck was starting to hurt having to look up at Becky from my five-foot-five vantage point. She was six feet tall, but she liked to say she was five-foot-twelve.

"I've got extras you can borrow," she said as she opened her pocketbook and rummaged around. Out came five pencils wrapped tightly in a rubber band. I smiled as she pulled two out and handed them to me.

"Thanks a million, and stop by Uncle Lu's. The ice cream's on me," I said.

I think she said something about dieting, but I couldn't tell because I had turned and was dashing towards the cheery Maryland state employee. I got my folder and looked for an empty desk. I opened it to find a test booklet and an optically scannable answer sheet. The test instructions were on the first page of the test booklet, and as I read it, I learned I needed to fill in all the personal data, using only a number 2 pencil—no pens, and fill in the empty ovals without going outside the lines. This took some time given I have fifteen letters in my name. I also had to do this for my birth date, address, and Social Security number before I could flip it over and take the test.

Finished, I opened the booklet to see twelve multiple-choice questions on the left page that continued on half of the next page. The road sign recognition portion of the test filled the rest of the pages. I paused, took a deep breath, and started reading slowly. I did not want my borderline attention deficit disorder to kick in and distract me.

I should make it clear that I was never diagnosed with ADD, but that was because it was not recognized as a childhood condition until 1980, way too late for me, but I'm pretty sure I had it. Back then, kids with ADD were called brats, nuisances or fidgets, and there was no Ritalin to prescribe—just spankings, but that's okay; I figured out how to use it to my advantage. Decades later, I turned ADD into multitasking, which is a coveted executive skill that MBA programs gush about.

I worked through the twelve questions, filling in the correct empty oval next to each answer I chose. I was shocked at how easy they were, mostly focused on safety issues. One question asked, "How many car lengths is a safe following distance when traveling at 40 mph?"

Nothing to it. With one car length for each 10 mph, the answer has to be 4, right? Or was it 20 mph which would make it 2? Gulp. Answer C was 4 and D was 2. I hate it when they have wrong answers that appear to be correct.

I went with *C*, figuring the more distance, the better.

Next up was the road sign recognition section. The signs were in silhouette with no words or numbers on them. My job was to identify the sign by choosing from the multiple-choice list to the right of each one. They were all pretty straightforward, and as I flipped over the booklet to the last page, I laughed out loud. There, prominently displayed on the upper right-hand corner, was the silhouette of a rectangular orange sign with the outline of a little boy running.

Now, where have I seen that one before?

Finished, I took my folder back to the counter and was told to sit down until my name was called. I sat there waiting and learned what the next step was. There were two ways it could go: both started with an attendant carrying a clipboard calling your name who informed you whether or not you had passed the written portion of the test. Those who did were asked to step into an adjoining waiting room for their behind-the-wheel test. The others had their sixty-day cards stamped with a red *X*, indicating they had attempted the test once. I saw Becky get up and move towards the counter, so I stopped her and returned her pencils.

As I turned to sit back down, I heard "Shelly Sucks. Is there a Shelly Sucks here?"

I felt a hundred eyes on me as I walked over to the white-shirted guy with a pencil-thin tie holding a clipboard in one hand and a half-smoked cigarette in the other.

"I'm Shelby Syckes," I stated.

"Right. You passed. Here's your completion certificate. Now go wait in there." He pointed with his two nicotine stained fingers holding the cigarette.

Passed! Well, poop and push me in it. I'm halfway there.

I looked at the certificate as I walked to the next room. I had passed with an 85% score. I'd missed three questions, *but who cares, I passed.*

The new waiting room was smaller, and four kids were already there, so I settled in and spent the time occupying myself trying to figure out which of the questions I missed. One by one, other white-shirted narrow-tied men came in and called kids' names, and they'd exit the building through a side door. I only had to wait about ten minutes before it was my turn.

"Syckes," I heard.

Well, at least this guy got my name right.

I jumped up to meet my test administrator. He was on the south side of fifty and about as happy to be there as the lady behind the counter.

Apparently, DMV work is very rewarding.

He wasn't fat, but it looked like he'd tried to hide a sandbag under his shirt; only it leaked, and the sand was gathered in oddly shaped clumps that hung over his belt. He was also smoking. We forget that over 40% of men in the U.S. smoked in the early seventies (9). It was the thing to do when you weren't allowed to drink. Neither of my parents smoked, but I remember them buying cigarettes and keeping them in a lovely wooden box next to a silver lighter on the living room coffee table in case a guest wanted one; you know, like thin mints.

My tester's name was Mr. Harris, and the first thing he said to me was, "Where's your car, kid?"

I pointed to the Barracuda only a few yards away, and he walked towards it. "Come on; I got a lunch break in twenty minutes."

I followed. Mr. Harris plunked down in the passenger seat of the Barracuda. He then shared with me the rules to the next phase of the test. I could tell he was bored; my test was one more pass through the endless repeating cycle that was his job.

I listened carefully, and it all was pretty straightforward. I was to back out of my parking space and turn down the road towards the end of the mall's buildings. From there, I was to execute a right turn and proceed the full length of the Sears Town parking lot, obeying all driving rules. At the end of the lot, I was to execute a three-point turn and enter the parking test area to demonstrate my ability to parallel park.

Okay, no sweat. I can do this, let's go.

I reached for the ignition switch and realized my keys were still in my pocket. Mr. Harris grunted a laugh as I fumbled to get them out, then he took a long pull on his Chesterfield and rolled down the window. Once I had the car started, I took a long time looking over my shoulder then, into the rearview mirror, and then into both side view mirrors; then I slowly backed the car out of the parking space. I put it in drive and rolled forward keeping my speed well below the limit.

Mr. Harris was relaxed and enjoying his smoke when he said, "The test doesn't really start until you make the next turn, so you can ignore the stop sign at the end of the road up here. It doesn't count. Just go right through it."

He finished saying this as we arrived at the stop sign. I hit the brakes like it was a dog caught peeing on the carpet. Recovering from his lurch forward, Mr. Harris looked over at me with a tight smile and said, "Turn right, kid, and pick up the pace. Remember, lunch is waiting."

The rest of the test was a total breeze. I made it all the way around the parking lot without incident and slid into my parallel parking space on the first try. I returned to the DMV building and parked, and as he was opening his door, Mr. Harris said, "Congratulations, kid, you passed. Oh, and you were right to stop at that first stop sign 'cause if you hadn't, the test would have ended right then and there. When you're the driver, you're in charge. Don't take directions from the passengers. They're not the ones who will be held responsible for the mistakes."

"Thanks," I gushed. "What do I do now?"

"Go back inside and wait. I'll turn in the paperwork, and they'll print up your license."

My license! My very own license allowing me to drive on any street anywhere at any time. Free at last, free at last. Thank God Almighty, I'm free at last!.

Dad caught up with me a few minutes after I got my license, and we drove home. As soon as we pulled into the driveway, I turned to him and said, "Can I go for a drive by myself?"

"Sure, but wait a minute. I want to get something," Dad said with a smile.

He jumped out of the car and jogged into the house. A minute later, he was back with his camera and told me to hold up the car keys while sitting in the driver's seat. I did as I was told, and Dad put on his picture-taking face. You know, the one where the right side of the mouth opens, baring a few teeth, and the left eye squints shut. *Click*, he's Popeye the photo-man. With that, I was on my own. I slid the key back into the ignition and cranked the Barracuda to life. I flipped on the radio and pushed the pre-programmed button for WCUM. Then, with my foot on the brake, I grabbed the gearshift lever and dropped it down into drive. As I rolled out of the driveway, the AM radio's four-inch dash mounted speaker came to life with Paul McCartney's newest hit, "Uncle Albert /Admiral Halsey".

Perfect: my music, my car, my turn.

Shelby's First Solo Drive in the Barracuda Aug 1971 (Syckes Family Photo)

Chapter 6 - We Can Work It Out

— Leader of the Band —

Everybody liked my dad at Allegany. The students voted him the most popular teacher several times, and they dedicated the yearbook to him twice during his tenure. It was because Dad was one of the easiest going, nicest guys on the planet—competent—but easy going. His approach to teaching music was to involve as many students as possible in the music programs, and once they were committed; raise their performance capability to its highest level possible. Making music comes naturally to some people, and Dad was one of those people. Although he spent thousands of hours honing his performance skills, he was born with an intuitive understanding of how to make beautiful music.

His instrument was the trumpet, and he was a master at it. When he was in his prime, there wasn't any music he couldn't play. He could conquer even the most complicated charts in a few hours of practice. When I was a kid, he would dig out what he called "The Old War Horses" of trumpet solo music and play them for me in our living room—pieces like Rimsky-Korsakov's *Flight of the Bumblebee* or Arban's *Carnival of Venice*. Dad would stand there for an hour, rolling through piece after piece, missing few notes and making them sound spectacular.

But, that's not all he could do. He was also a gifted impromptu performer. He could deliver quality entertainment for both the highbrows and low. It was standard practice for Dad to take his trumpet with him to cocktail parties or even formal social events like Country Club dances. After the booze had been flowing for a while, someone would ask Dad to play, and he always had with him his favorite piano accompanist: my mom. Over the years, they had congealed into a near-professional-level duo, ready to bang out whatever song the audience requested. Mom carried with her a "fake book," which was a Bible of about every standard tune from the first half of the twentieth century. Her Eddie Duchin-inspired bouncy baseline style matched Dad's Harry James melodic sound perfectly. Everyone loved their music.

Dad's other great gift was teaching. I've had hundreds of people tell me how much they enjoyed learning to play a musical instrument with my dad. He did not believe in intimidation or threats, just steady, helpful encouragement at a pace the student could handle. If he felt there was real talent, he'd push a little harder and provide greater instructional guides to challenge the player. Likewise, if the student's musical limitations were obvious, he never told them to quit. He always encouraged them to try a little harder. I don't remember him ever asking someone to leave the band because of their lack of musical skills. He'd find them something else to do, like flags. Although sometimes, my fellow band officers and I wished he would dump a few kids.

He applied this same easygoing style when working with the student leadership of the Allegany Band. He did not play the all-powerful band director who requires all decisions be made by him, Dad turned over everything to us. That is, everything we could handle. He was always ready to help if we found ourselves a little bit over our heads. This made the job of drum major great fun and a tremendous leadership experience because it meant the drum major was the *de facto* leader of the band in all performance environments.

So often today, when I see marching bands perform, it isn't the drum major who's out in front of the band; it's the band director. He doesn't only direct the band, but he's also all dressed up in a frilly uniform, marching and strutting like the kids. Often, the drum major is relegated to standing on the sidelines, mirroring the band director's conducting or worse. I once saw a drum major lead the band onto the field, then run and get a stair-step like platform for the band director to direct from. For the rest of the performance, all the drum major did was steady the platform. This was not Dad's style. He never wore anything other than his usual work clothes, and he was never on the field when we performed. We were on our own. That's true empowerment, and with it, comes responsibility. You had to know what was going on and lead the band. As the new drum major, that was now my job; well, at least I thought it was.

— Ray Kline & Bob Hutcheson —

A few days before Summer Band was to begin, Dad and I were in his office talking about what music we should play for the first halftime show. Dad thought it would be smart to start off the season with marches or novelty songs we'd done before. I was about to press for something new and different when the phone rang. Dad picked up the receiver and said, "Hello." A bizarre look crossed his face. He spent the next few minutes listening, saying few words, but I knew he wasn't happy with what he was hearing.

Now and then he'd say something like, "I understand," or "Yes, I can appreciate that," but his face was saying, "I can't believe you are bothering me with this."

If the call were Tastee Freez-related, he would have shooed me from the room, but instead, he kept looking up at me and nodding or smiling a funny smile like I was supposed to understand what he was experiencing. I didn't but my hearing went into overdrive, and when I heard the male voice on the other end of the phone say the name Katie, I just about shit. I leaned my head up against the earpiece near Dad's ear and listened harder. Dad did not resist this, and it wasn't long before I knew who it was on the other end of the phone and what he wanted.

It was Katie Kline's father, and he was making a last-minute attempt to overturn the drum major decision. As any mature sixteen-year-old would do, I stood up and paced around the room, exaggeratingly mouthing "No, no, no!"

My fear was real. I was afraid my super nice-guy dad would give into Katie's dad, and I'd be out of a job—done—finished as drum major. I couldn't let that happen, but I knew I had to keep quiet. The call ended, and Dad sat quietly for a few seconds, then looked up at me and said: "That was Katie's dad. He's been talking to Bob Hutcheson, and Bob agreed to have a meeting tomorrow to discuss the outcome of the drum major competition."

I went white.

Bob Hutcheson. Robert M. Hutcheson. Holy crap, he's the principal of Allegany, and if Kline's got him on his side, I'm toast.

Robert M. Hutcheson (Allegwee 1973)

I was about to plead my case in the whiniest of terms when Dad leaned forward, touched my knee and said, "Don't worry, Son. I've got this."

I did not sleep that night.

The meeting was scheduled for 10 o'clock in Mr. Hutcheson's office at Allegany. I was up early and went with Dad to open up the Tastee Freez. I wanted to stick with him every minute before the meeting to monitor his thinking and annoyingly plead my case, but Dad was acting normal. He wasn't upset, nervous, or worried about what might happen. He was going about his everyday summer job, and this made me crazy. To calm myself, I kept listing over and over in my head all the reasons any change now would not only be unfair to the band and me but an apocalyptic catastrophe for mankind. We're talking an existential threat to the human race on a biblical scale.

On the way to the meeting, after quieting myself for as long as I could, I spoke up. "What will happen today?"

"I don't know, Son," said Dad in a kind but firm voice.

"I don't know what Kline's got or has shared with Bob, so the number one thing we both have to do is listen. I want him to say everything he has to say before I say anything. Once he's played all his cards, then, and only then, I'll show him ours. You will say nothing, absolutely nothing. Is that understood?"

"Yes, sir."

With that, we were in front of the gymnasium, and Dad pulled up right outside the front door and parked. We jumped out and went through the front doors. Our destination was the band room—Dad wanted to get something out of his files for the meeting. We walked through the lower hall of the gym that went past the art classrooms and the entrances to the locker rooms, then up the stairs to the band room. There is something strange about visiting your school in the summertime. Everything is a little unworldly, like the fact that you can park right in front of the school. No busses, no reserved teacher parking, nothing. You can park on the lawn if you want. This strangeness gets stranger when you go inside. It was hot and empty—tomb-like empty, and like a tomb there was little light. Halls were dark except for what light shown through from the windows in classrooms. It was just plain spooky.

Dad ducked into his office while I stood alone in the band room. With its thirty-foot ceiling, and chair lined tiered risers, it was a wonderful place to make music. The back wall was lined with drums and large instruments like sousaphones and bass fiddles. On the front wall was a large chalkboard, under it a small desk, and a cabinet that held all the music folders. I loved the place.

Dad came out of his office with a single manila folder. "Let's go. It's time for the meeting."

We went back down the steps and along the causeway that connected the gym to the rest of the school and passed from the hospital light-green, porcelain-faced bricks that lined the walls of the 1959 gym to the dark wood and yellowing plaster walls of the 1926 main building. They were two very different worlds. The first one felt right at home in a gas station's bathroom while the second one would blend perfectly into your grandmother's living room.

Seeing one of the many clocks that hung halfway up the high-ceilinged walls, Dad picked up his pace and said, "We're late."

We slid under the stained-glass portrait of the school's Indian mascot, turned right into the principal's office area, and then stopped dead in our tracks. There was Ray Kline, Katie's father, standing alone in the outer office. It was not a comfortable moment. Huffing and puffing a bit, Dad stuck out his hand and said, "Hello, Ray. This is my son, Shelby."

Mr. Kline shook Dad's hand and murmured, "Hi, Lu," then reached out to me.

I shook his hand and said, "Hello." Not knowing what to do, I looked at my shoes.

A shroud of silence enveloped the room. The principal's office door burst open and out dashed Flash Faherty. William (Flash) Faherty was one of those oddities high schools attract that are an amalgam of educator, administrator, coach, and janitor. He was everywhere, doing everything all the time, in a flash—get it? He was always blowing the trademark whistle he kept on a lanyard around his neck. He used it to motivate slow eaters in the lunch room or chase kids to class as the last bell sounded or herd student smokers away from unauthorized areas. Flash was always there and always in charge and always tweeting. If he ever taught a class, it was news to me.

Flash's head had the triangular shape of the guy on the cover of the *Computers for Dummies* book and his hair was a densely waxed butch cut crowned with a perfectly flat top that could have easily supported a six-pack of beer. Today he was dressed in shiny blue gym shorts, an ALCO Athletics T-shirt, knee-high white socks, and black wing tips. His whistle was in his mouth. I doubt he even saw us as he buzzed by, and he was followed by Robert M. Hutcheson, the principal.

Flash Faherty (Allegwee 1972)

"Gentlemen, welcome and come on in," he said.

Dad let Mr. Kline go first, then squeezed my arm tightly, whispering, "Remember, say nothing. I'll do the talking."

I nodded, and we went in.

Bob Hutcheson was the kind of guy who always had a smile on his face. Whether he was crowning the Camper Queen or expelling a delinquent, the smile was there. But it wasn't a "Wow, I'm happy" kind of smile. It was more a "For the love of God, please let this end soon," smile. He was a politician and had worked his way up to principal of one of the biggest schools in the county before he turned thirty-five. A graduate of Allegany, Dad had taught him in humanities class in 1949. Asking us all to sit down, Big Bob (he was over six feet tall) sat behind his desk.

He looked at Mr. Kline and said, "Okay, Ray, you asked for this meeting. How about you tell us what you want."

Kline stood and moved towards Hutcheson's desk opening a folder on it. Looking only at him he said, "Bob, as I told you two days ago, I think there has been an injustice done to my daughter. It has become clear she was not given a fair opportunity at the drum major tryouts in May. Now, I won't start with accusation, but I think after you review the information I have uncovered, you will see how the playing field was tipped in Shelby's favor."

I leaned forward about to defend myself when I felt a kick to my ankle and a cold stare from Dad.

Kline continued, "Now we all know that every single one of the Syckes children has been drum major, all three of them. The first two got the job for two years, and Shelby is lined up to do the same. Two full years, when all of the other drum majors Allegany has ever had were seniors and only held the position for one year. That, in and of itself, is unusual, but I have more. I found out that although Lu did not directly participate in the judging of the competition this year, he influenced it by hand-selecting the judges from a narrow pool of his peers. Not only are they his peers, but they are also his friends. He even mentored one of them. Now I ask you, how can you expect me to believe the three men Lu chose—all band directors like himself—all members of the same community band and all junior in seniority to him—didn't feel some kind of obligation, or at the very least, professional courtesy to vote for his boy? Well, I'll tell you what. I don't believe it."

While he was talking, Kline was also withdrawing newspaper clippings from his folder and placing them one by one in front of Mr. Hutcheson. There were photos of Barbara and Betsy as drum majors: two showing Dad and the other judges performing with the Potomac Concert Band. One was a photocopy from the 1964 yearbook showing Dad together with the band leadership. Bill AuMiller was captain of the band that year, and he was standing next to Dad in the picture. The final thing Mr. Kline took from the folder was a newspaper photo of a meeting of local music instructors taken in 1970. There were Lynn Zeller, Bill AuMiller, and Emerson Miller all standing with Dad and the other teachers. It looked pretty damning.

Mr. Kline sat, folded his arms, and smiled confidently. Mr. Hutcheson spent the next few minutes carefully looking at each of the items before him. He studied the photos, especially the one of all of the music teachers together.

Then, he said, "Ray, what would you have me do about this? It's now late August, and school starts in three weeks. The tryouts were three months ago. Why didn't you come forward with this complaint sooner?"

Kline was up again and eager to answer, "Because my girl was devastated when she lost that competition, and I didn't want to add to her misery by starting a fight. But, I couldn't let it go, so I looked into it. I wasn't at the tryout, but my wife was, and she gave me the names of the judges. Then I talked to people who know these guys, and I discovered their links to Lu. The photos you're looking at came from the library. Once I had all this information, I could not let this injustice stand, so I brought it to you."

"But what do you want me to do, Ray, what?" asked Mr. Hutcheson.

Mr. Kline leaned forward on Hutcheson's desk, "I will accept only one of two outcomes, or I am taking my complaint to the Board of Education."

I saw Bob Hutcheson's eyebrows arch up.

Speaking a little faster, Kline continued, "Either there is a new drum major tryout where Lu and I each select three judges or both Katie and Shelby are named co-drum majors for this season."

He finished. It was all there, and it was oh, so simple. Well, at least he thought so. I thought it was a nightmare come true. If they had another tryout, there was a good chance I'd lose. If I shared the job with Katie, my dad and I would be branded as cheaters. Mr. Hutcheson still had that smile on his face as the room was bathed in silence.

"Now, Ray, you're making pretty strong allegations here. For me to accept your point of view, I have to believe not only is Lu corrupt in his handling of the drum major tryout this year but that there was a conspiracy between him and the three judges. You even suggest that this corruption and conspiracy has occurred before when his daughters became drum majors. Is that right?" Hutcheson asked.

"Well, I'll let the facts speak for themselves." Ray Kline said sternly.

And with that, Mr. Hutcheson turned to Dad and said, "Lu, what do you have to say about this?"

Dad had a quizzical look on his face like he was trying to remember a telephone number. A smile broke his thought. He looked at Hutcheson and said, "Bob, do you have a piece of paper I can use?"

"Sure, Lu, here you go," Hutcheson said as he passed a notepad and pen to Dad.

It only took him a few seconds, then he handed it back to Bob along with the pen. Written on the pad were two names and dates that represented two students—other than his kids—who had been drum major for both their junior and senior years—all while he was band director. He explained this as he opened the manila folder he'd brought with him and took out a letter-sized sheet of paper with a header that read "Allegany High School Band, Cumberland Maryland." Neatly typed on the page was a single paragraph reading:

"We, the undersigned, swear to perform our duties as Judges for the 1971 Allegany High School drum major competition fairly and without bias. We will base our decision solely on the contestants' musical and marching skills as demonstrated today."

It was dated May 21, 1971, and signed by Bill AuMiller, Lynn Zeller, and Emerson Miller.

Dad handed the paper to Bob Hutcheson and then reached into the envelope and withdrew two additional papers with nearly identical paragraphs, dated May 25, 1967, and May 19, 1964. They were from Betsy and Barbara's competitions, and each was signed by the judges who took part then. One name on the 1967 document was of particular note. There, in a bold, cursive signature was the name, Robert M. Hutcheson.

Dad passed these papers to the principal as he passed the other to Kline. Then Dad went back to the folder for the final time and took out a sheet of paper torn from a yellow legal pad. At the top, in Bill AuMiller's handwriting, were two names separated by about two inches: Katie—Shelby. The number one was to the left of Katie's name, and the number two was next to mine. Below my name were two check marks that were clearly made with different pens by different hands. Below Katie's name was one check mark. It was the judges' results worksheet from this year's competition, and it showed they had split their vote. I had won by one vote. To my dismay, it did not show who voted for whom, so I'll never know who Lynn Zeller voted for.

The papers made their way around to all of us, with Ray Kline taking the most time assessing them. He paused for several seconds after reading the names on the 1967 paper. After several more profoundly quiet seconds, Mr. Hutcheson asked, "Does anyone have anything else they'd like to add?"

More silence followed. "Ray, I'm going to let the results of the competition stand. Shelby will be the drum major this year. You are welcome to take your complaint to the Board, but I caution you in doing so. You could find yourself facing a libel suit."

Mr. Kline was looking past Big Bob out the window behind his desk as if he was hoping a great army of supporters would appear and relieve him of his burden. They didn't. He was a good man and a good father doing what he thought was best for his little girl and I felt humbled by the moment. He stood, reached out to shake hands, and said "Thank you for your time, Bob. Thank you for your time."

With that, Mr. Kline gathered up his papers and left the room. We stood and after he left, Bob Hutcheson looked straight at me and said: "Shelby, you damned well better be worth it."

— Goals —

With Hutcheson's decision behind me, I turned my focus to Summer Band. I had three goals: take command of the band, prepare the band members for performance, and find a girlfriend. To achieve goal number one, I needed to get the other band officers on my side as their trust and support was key to my success. I took the direct approach and asked them at our first meeting. To my surprise, it worked, but that was only the first part of taking command. The next step was totally up to me. I had to show up at summer band and be the guy in charge.

There's a saying in the military; "When you take command, *take command!*" It's critical.

I needed everyone to listen to me. I could be the best-damned drum major on the planet, but if the band members didn't do what I needed them to do, it didn't matter. I had to wait until I was out in front of the entire band to find out if I could pull this off.

My second goal was to prepare the band for performance. I would decide what music we would play and what drills we would perform, but the hard part was training the band to play that music and perform those drills well. Summer band would determine this.

My final goal for Summer Band was a personal one but important. I hadn't had a real girlfriend, ever. Oh, I'd flirted with girls since first grade. I remember my teacher, Mrs. Mullendore, catching me in the cloakroom kissing a little girl named Michelle, but that was all innocent stuff. Before I could drive, I also had, quasi-girlfriends. We'd meet at the Hi-Land Roller Rink or a basketball game and hold hands and maybe even kiss (mostly pecking), and according to the ritual of the time, once you were seen doing this, you and the poor girl were deemed "going steady."

What in the world does that really mean? Going steady? It sounds like someone describing their regularity.

"Hey, Tom, you still stopped up like Hoover Dam?"

"No, Dave, I've been 'going steady' ever since I took that Metamucil."

I went through about ten going-steady cycles before I could drive, and I'd had enough of them. Now that I had my driver's license, all I needed was a girl who would get in the Barracuda and go for a ride with me to the movies or the Tastee Freez or maybe even Sunset View. I was determined to find one, and I figured looking for her in the band was a good place to start.

— Sedgwick Street Campus —

Let me take a moment to describe Allegany. Whoever picked out the location for the school back in the 1920s was about as visionary as a mole. Although the plot of land selected was big enough to house a good-sized building with a little room to expand, it has nowhere near the acreage needed to support a late 20th-century high school's needs. Allegany sits between Sedgwick Street and the largest and oldest public cemetery in Cumberland.

Rose Hill Cemetery is the final resting place for hundreds of residents including veterans from every American war since the Revolution. Rose Hill plateaus onto a broad plain that was used by the Union Army during the Civil War to garrison troops. It was here that the Commanding Officer General Lew Wallace got the idea to write a book he named *Ben Hur* (8).

Say thank you, Charlton Heston.

It is the soldiers' campsite that is responsible for Allegany's confusing mascot's name: the Camper.

The Camper? What in the hell is that, a Winnebago? Why they chose Camper as our mascot, and more strangely, how an Indian came to represent the word camper baffles me to this day. But, that's the way it is.

Summer Band was to take place on the football practice field on the west side of the gym that was chiseled out of a rising hillside composed entirely of shale. Well, not entirely. There were graves in there too, so the field was limited to 90 yards.

— Summer Band —

Summer Band would be divided into two parts. The first three days were for freshman band members only so they could learn the basics of marching and performance drill before integrating with the rest of the band. On day four, the other band members would join us, and we'd work on our first show. We had two big events coming up fast, and they were very different in nature: the opening football game against Martinsburg followed shortly by a competitive parade in Oakland.

A football game's halftime show is part of the ritual of high school sports in America, and ALCO was no different. First up is the band. We'd come marching onto the field playing our instruments and form some intricate pattern or spell out a complicated word like ALCO. It was our favorite for obvious reasons, and sometimes, if we wanted to be fancy, we'd write it in cursive versus block letters. Then we'd play another song before marching off the field.

A parade, on the other hand, is a very different situation. You might think it's easy because all you are doing is marching down a street playing a song. It's not because you are no longer in the controlled environment of a football stadium. You are on real streets that have to be navigated, and the band members have to follow the drum major as he navigates. It was during Summer Band we needed to learn how to do both.

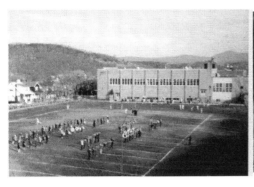

ALCO Band Practice Field (Syckes Family Photos)

Having survived A.R. Casavant's Camp, Bob Hartman and I decided to base our training of the freshman on it. When the twenty-five freshmen showed up on the first day, we had them all stand in line and count off to form smaller squads. Over the course of the three days, we trained, drilled, and badgered our flock of newbies until they could march down the football field hitting the five-yard markers perfectly every eight steps ("Eight to the bar," we called it). There was frustration in overcoming inevitable challenges, but there was also great fun in seeing the kids become seasoned marchers.

It was on day four that I hoped to fulfill goal number two: taking command of the band. I was behind the wheel of the Barracuda while Dad drove in the Buick so he could leave early for golf. The weather was on my mind. It was going to get hot fast but, despite the heat, I was not wearing shorts.

Maybe it's the name, but I have never liked shorts.

I wanted my 65 inches to appear as tall as they could, and shorts didn't do that, so I had on my best skinny jeans and a button-down loose-fitting shirt. Just for luck, I also wore my gold suede tennis shoes from tryouts.

When we arrived at school, kids were already gathering around the band room door, but since we were going to be focusing on marching and not music that day, we had them move to the practice field and form a single line facing the steeply sloped shale hill dividing ALCO from the graveyard. Dad, Bob Hartman, and I clambered up the narrow path that led to the top of the hill. It provided a commanding view of the field below and was perfect for communicating with the band while they practiced.

Dad had with him his bullhorn, which made it easier for him to be heard by all 120 band members. It had a leather lanyard that allowed him to hang it around his neck, so he didn't have to hold it all the time. Dad planned to get the band's attention, introduce Bob and me, and then go to the golf course.

The man had his priorities.

He wanted them to know we were in charge of the band now, and they shouldn't come running to him to overturn decisions made by the band leadership. I was a bit worried because I had no idea how many of the kids knew about the Ray Kline/Bob Hutcheson affair, but some of them had to know. There were lots of rumors flying around, especially since Katie did not show up for practice. She had quit the band.

Dad flipped on the bullhorn, and after it crackled to life, he said, "Welcome, members of the Allegany High School Band. We've got a great season ahead of us, and I want to introduce the leaders who will get you through it. First, we have our new band captain, senior Bob Hartman."

Dad tapped Bob's shoulder as he waved. There was a smattering of applause, and then it was my turn. Finally, I was assuming leadership of the band. It was my time to *take command,* and I was ready. I had a speech all prepared that I had practiced using my best command voice in front of my mirror. I was very pleased with it because it was all adult and business-like.

Bob stepped back, and Dad squeezed the bullhorn's trigger again and proclaimed, "Leading you on the field this year is Shelby Syckes, your drum major."

Hoping to hear a little applause, I stepped in front of Bob and reached for the bullhorn. I grabbed the rim of the horn as I felt a piece of shale loosen and slide forward under my right foot. My heart stopped as I surfed down the face of the hill. Gripping the bullhorn's bell with both hands, I arched across the face of the cliff, scraping my side along the way. Dad's grip on the lanyard was the only thing stopping me from tumbling all the way down to the field. Suspended in mid-air like a third-rate trapeze artist who missed the catch, I dangled there helplessly. Bob dropped to his knees, grabbed my belt, and pulled me up. I heard a gasp from the crowd below, followed by guffaws and giggles. Well, so much for my *take command* moment. I scrapped the speech.

Shale dust covered me from head to toe, and my shirt had a large rip down the side. Oh, and the slide ruined my gold suede tennis shoes.

What a way to start!

But, I still had to start, so I swung the bullhorn up to my lips, pulled the trigger and said, "Well, I'm glad that's out of the way. I'll try not to do that at halftime." More giggles from the band as the full weight of the embarrassing moment swept over me. "Let's get to work," I barked, then turned and signaled Bob to follow me.

"A.R. would have loved that," cracked Bob.

"Bite me," I sneered.

— Patty —

Like every other boy born in the 1950s, I had a crush on Annette Funicello. She was everywhere during my first ten years. She was on TV in *The Mickey Mouse Club*, on the radio singing "Pineapple Princess," on the newsstands in *Teen Magazine*, and at the movies in *Beach Blanket Bingo*. To me, she was scrumptious—petitely perfect. It was in her beach movies that she stole my heart. By then, her big round mouse ears had migrated a bit south making her the perfect girlfriend prototype.

Why am I telling you this in the middle of a story about Summer Band? Because I thought I saw Annette Funicello standing in line with the other freshmen on the first day of practice. Honest to God, there she was, this super cute little girl with a great figure, big dreamy eyes, and a perfect pixie-like nose. The only difference was that her name was Patty. She was the cutest thing ever, with long, dark hair and a big, happy smile. I made her candidate number one to be girlfriend number one, and I went to work fast.

Although I spotted her because of her Mouseketeer looks, I was sure I knew her. It took me a while, but after looking at the roster of freshman names, hers rang a bell, and eventually, I put things together. She had been two classes behind me at Mount Royal Elementary school, and we had a mutual interest in Rat Finks.

Now, I'm betting you didn't expect me to say Rat Finks.

Rat Fink was a cartoon character created by artist Ed "Big Daddy" Roth that appeared in car magazines like *Hot Rod* in the late 1950s. I didn't become interested in them until they showed up as little plastic Rat Fink statues in bubble gum machines around 1963. They came in a variety of colors, and I collected as many as I could. It turned out Patty liked them too, and we had talked about them on the school playground whenever we could. I remember we were both on the lookout for the most coveted color Rat Fink of them all—turquoise. I moved on to junior high school and forgot all about her until she showed up in my freshman band class. Rat Finks gave me an in to start a conversation with her; now all I needed was an opportunity.

The freshmen had done well, and on the third day of summer band, we had them all line up on the field to test their eight to the bar marching skills. Bringing them to attention, I ordered, "Forward, march!" and they all stepped off.

They did a good job of keeping the line straight while hitting the yard markers every eight steps. The band officers were running up and down the line looking for errors as everyone was yelling, "1, 2, 3, 4, 5, 6, 7, hit it!"

I barked, "Squad halt! Okay, let's try it again, only this time with your eyes closed."

This may sound mean, but in reality, a marching band's members need to hit the line without looking because they're playing instruments and reading music while marching. I gave the "Forward march" command again, and as they passed through ten yards, I made the intentional error of standing right where Patty would plant her last step.

Crash! She slammed right into me, and I did my best-exaggerated pratfall, making sure she didn't hit me too hard.

The whole line erupted in laughter. Looking up at her from my posterior pose, I smiled and said, "Sorry, Patty, all my fault. You take the 'close your eyes' thing seriously, don't you?"

I was expecting her to blush and try to help me up, but instead, she looked at me suspiciously. I winked at her and smiled. As the practice ended, I tracked her down and found her talking with a friend.

"Hey, Patty. I want to apologize for bumping into you. I wasn't watching what I was doing."

"That's okay," she said.

Then her friend interjected, "You did that on purpose, didn't you?"

"No, I didn't," I insisted. There's no way I would do that. Hey, Patty, are you still looking for that turquoise Rat Fink?"

"Oh, yes, you did," said the other girl. "It was obvious."

A bit frustrated, I smiled and asked her, "I'm sorry, do I know you?"

Wide-eyed and leaning forward while batting her eyelashes at light speed she said: "I'm Connie. Don't you remember me from Mount Royal?"

"Oh yeah, sure," I fibbed. "Patty and I used to talk about Rat Finks there."

"You're kidding?" said Connie.

It took a second, but I saw a light come on in Patty's eyes, and she said, "Oh yes, I remember that. You liked those little plastic rats, didn't you?"

"You mean you didn't?" I asked, trying to hide my dejection.

"I had a few my brother gave me, but I wasn't obsessed with them like you were." She laughed and looked at Connie as they both started to giggle. My confidence dropped, but I pressed on.

Looking straight at Patty and turning my back as much as I could to Connie, I asked, "Do you need a ride home?"

"Sure, we do," Connie said as she spun me around by the shoulder.

Okay, I've got a stubborn one here. I can't say no to Connie and yes to Patty.

"Great, let me finish up in the band room, and I'll meet you back here in a few minutes."

Connie Kent was a pretty girl waiting for her body to catch up with her height. There was no way anything was going to catch up with her mouth. It moved at the speed of heat.

She and Patty were best of friends and lived only a few houses away from each other. I knew where Patty lived having found her address on the band roster. Connie's address was a mystery, but I had to figure out a way to drop her off first so I could be alone with Patty. This was going to be tricky.

Patty and Connie were waiting for me near the front of the gym.

"This way," I said. "Where do you guys live? I know it's somewhere up by the armory, isn't it?"

"Yeah," Connie said, "I'm on Brown Avenue, and Patty's on Van Buren.

I was hoping Patty would sit in the front seat so I could chat with her on the way, but Connie got to the car first and opened the passenger door. She then pulled the seat forward and directed Patty to get in.

Damn.

Connie was talking a blue streak as we pulled out of the parking lot. I interrupted and asked: "When we reach the overpass which way do I turn to get to your house, Connie?"

"It's best to take Patty home first. That way when you loop around to drop me off, you'll be pointing in the right direction," she insisted.

Well, that was helpful.

I needed to think fast. Looking at her in the passenger seat it hit me: *She's up front, and this is a two-door car.*

Patty still hadn't said a word, and as we drove onto the overpass, I said, "You can see my house over to the right there." I was hoping this distracted Connie as we approached the turn.

"Oh, you live in the Dingle, don't you? What does Dingle mean?" Connie asked.

"It's a long story and honestly makes no sense," I said as I started the left turn on to Connie's street.

"Wait! You're making a wrong turn," Connie bellowed as if I'd stolen her purse.

Accelerating, I said, "Connie, you're the one in the front seat and this is a two-door car. It makes sense you be the first one out." She huffed in deep frustration and dropped her arms into her lap. "Oh, I get it. I know what's going on. You want to be alone with Patty, don't you? Don't you?!"

"Which house is yours?" I asked in the sweetest voice I could muster.

"It's this one right here," said a timid voice I hadn't heard since we got in the car.

Hallelujah, Patty was helping me.

I pressed on the brakes, and before I could say, "See you tomorrow," Connie was up and out of the car.

For the first time since I met her, she did this without saying a word. The door slammed, and I heard a giggle from the backseat. "She's something, huh?" Patty laughed.

"I'll say," I said as I looked at her in my rearview mirror. "And so are you."

That was the first of many times I'd take Patty home, and we'd always go past Connie's house. It was our little joke.

The rest of Summer Band could not have gone better. Everyone was in great form and learned the music and drills quickly. It paid off to select songs we'd used before because it saved a great deal of practice time. We decided on "Red River Rock" and "St. Louis Blues March" for the first halftime show. Both are real crowd pleasers the band knew cold, and to make our lives even easier, we picked "St. Louis Blues March" for the parade as well.

If I had to give myself a grade on how I accomplished my goals, it would be a B+. Taking command was a stumble but preparing the band was much better, and I definitely earned an A on the girlfriend front. Patty was my girl, and I was elated. Connie didn't talk to me for a month.

Chapter 7 - Joy to the World

— This Is Dating? —

My junior year was starting off great. I was the drum major, and the band was ready for the performance season, and more importantly, I had my driver's license and a girlfriend. Next up was lots of fun driving with Patty on dates. Well, that's what I hoped for, but I didn't factor in her mother, or as I came to call her "Queen No-Way-In-Hell."

I'd take Patty home from school almost every day, but I regressed in my making-out impulse. I don't know why, but I guess I liked Patty so much I didn't want to do anything too forward to cause trouble in our relationship. At first, I'd only drive her home. We'd chat about what went on that day, but when we got to her place, she'd open the door and say goodbye.

About a week after I first took her home, I asked if she wanted to see the movie *Willy Wonka and the Chocolate Factory*. It was playing at the Strand Theater, and I figured we could catch an early show Saturday and be home before 10 o'clock. She said she would ask her mom, and I drove home confident my first date was set.

The next day after band, I approached Patty as usual for our ride home, and she said, "I can't go."

"You can't go home? What's going on? Do you have field hockey practice today?" I asked.

"No, I can't go to the movies with you. Mom says I'm too young to go out on dates," Patty pouted.

What? Too young to date? What are you talking about? You're fourteen. Girls in Africa are married with three kids by fourteen.

These were the irrational thoughts that ran through my head, but instead what I said was, "Darn, that's a bummer."

I had to think of a way around this. My first step was to push the envelope on the drive home routine. Going out to a movie was important but what I really wanted was to break through my regressed make-out motivation. So, if she couldn't go out, then I needed to go in—her house that is. It was going to be tricky because Patty's mom came home from work around four-thirty, and she didn't want boys in the house without her there. But, Patty was sending signals it might be okay, so as we pulled into her driveway, I said, "How about you give me a tour of your house?"

She looked at me mischievously. "All right, but you need to be gone before Mom gets home."

"Absolutely," I promised. *Yes! I'm through the door.*

After my quick tour, *sans* bedrooms, she walked me to the door holding my hand. I opened it to leave, then turned around and stared into her big brown eyes. *Kiss her, you idiot. Kiss her!*

But I didn't, and as I turned to go, she pulled me back, leaned in and kissed me right on the lips. So softly, so warmly, I melted. That was the best drive home I ever had.

— The Uniform & Mom's New Job —

When I got home, there was a big package waiting for me. I opened it to find my new drum major's uniform. It was gorgeous. I inherited the uniform the previous drum major had worn, and it didn't look right on me. When Mom saw it, she immediately took over the job of replacing it. She contacted the Camper Club and got it to authorize funds for a new one. Then she went to work on the design. Armed with my measurements and a book on military uniforms, she came up with a winning look.

Mom had changed jobs and was now in the fashion business. She was the manager and buyer at Peskin's Department Store in downtown Cumberland. Peskin's was one of only two high-end department stores in Cumberland that catered in women's ready-to-wear fashions. Lazarus was the other, and they had dominated the market for years. When Mort Peskin inherited his parents' department store, he was determined to change that, and he hired Mom to make it happen. They had been friends for years, and Mort noticed Mom was always well dressed, so he hired her to apply her fashion sense to his business.

Within a few weeks, Mom had given up her teaching career and had become a manager of a fashion department store and responsible for buying all the store's clothing. It required her to fly to New York City once a month and select and purchase thousands of dollars of women's clothing hoping the ones she picked would sell. This was new to her, but that didn't deter Mom. She was already a successful small business owner, so she tackled the job with the same determination and intelligence she'd applied to Br'er Rabbit, and succeeded.

Peskin's women's fashion floor became a rival to Lazarus and started to make Mort Peskin money, which is why I trusted Mom to design my drum major's uniform. On her next trip to New York, she visited a tailor she knew, and he turned Mom's design into reality. The principal fabric was a creamy white gabardine, but what made it really stand out was the bold rank insignias on the sleeves and a large gold stylized "A" that sat on a brilliant blue breastplate. When I tried the uniform on, it fit perfectly and looked spectacular. To make me stand out even more, an eighteen-inch white fur Busby hat, crowned with a six-inch gold plume topped off an already eye-catching outfit. To add to the glam and glitz, I wore white buck shoes swathed in gold spats. I couldn't wait for Patty to see me in it.

New Drum Major Uniform 1971 (Syckes Family Photos)

— Jesus Christ Superstar —

Having broken the ice with a first kiss and an in-house visit, I was invited into Patty's house almost daily from then on as long as I was gone before her Mom came home. We spent our time practicing our kissing, but we decided that if we were ever going to get to go out on a date, I had to meet her mother.

There was a lot riding on this. I really wanted to take Patty out, but I didn't want to anger her mother.

Who knows what the woman was capable of?

On that day to delay getting to Patty's place before her mother did, we drove around Cumberland listing to music. We arrived at Patty's just as her mom did. I was on my best behavior with lots of "yes, Ma'ams" and "no, Ma'ams," but it didn't matter. I asked if I could take Patty to a matinee movie and got the same answer; "No."

Deciding not to push our luck, Patty and I retired to the living room and turned on the TV. It was on that day we found what became our favorite afternoon show, Julia Child's *The French Chef.* We loved it, not because we were trying to make the perfect beef bourguignon, but because we found Julia hilarious. We couldn't believe anyone took this woman seriously.

That voice, those mannerisms. Come on, it's a gag, right? Look at her! She's gotta be six-foot-three, and what's with that hair-helmet?

From then on, we made sure we had the TV on every day for Julia—*bon appetit.* While watching, we tried to think of ways to convince her mom to let me take Patty out. We listed different venues like friend's parties, roller-skating, or school plays she might accept, but none seemed workable.

Patty made the crack, "You could be the Pope, and she wouldn't let me go out at night with you."

"That's it," I said.

"You want to be the Pope?" Patty quizzed.

"No, but Popes spend a lot of time in church, and there are a lot of churches here in Cumberland. We have got to be able to find a church function that your mom will accept," I said.

Well, the good news was Patty was Lutheran, and she and her family went to Reverend Manning's church, so the next time I talked with Mrs. Rudd, I told her what good friends I was with the Mannings. I failed to mention that Reverend Manning had to bail me out of jail a few months earlier, but I did tell her how much time I spent with his son working in the church's Cafe-Gym-torium.

Ha! Working!

When I got home, I called Mike and asked what events were coming up at his church that coming week. He went and asked his dad and then told me the Homburgs and two of their music students were performing songs from *Jesus Christ Superstar* in the Cafe-Gym-torium this Saturday.

"Perfect." I grinned.

How can Patty's mother turn down Jesus at her own church?

Before I go any further with the story, let me introduce you to JoAnn and Al Homburg.

— JoAnn, Al & The Arrowettes —

Hurricane Homburg blew into town in 1964, and nothing in Cumberland was the same for the next nine years. JoAnn was a force of nature the likes of which I've never seen since. Al, on the other hand, was a farce. I can say with sincerity that JoAnn changed people's lives, while Al changed jobs and partners. Now, I'm being a little too nice to JoAnn and maybe too rough on Al, but whatever the truth is, they were unique.

JoAnn was born in Cumberland and graduated from Allegany in 1950 but moved to Oklahoma after finishing college. From a distance, she was attractive, but when you got closer, you'd see she was a mixture of *That Girl* and Popeye's girlfriend. She had Marlo Thomas's style but Olive Oyl's profile. Al was from Kansas with a barrel-like build and a set of chubby cheeks to go with it. Somewhere along the line, someone told him he looked good in a Roy Rogers cowboy outfit, and from that point on, he wore one for every singing performance.

They must have been kidding him.

Before they got to Cumberland, Al studied music at college then tried to be a country and western singer but never got the break he wanted. He often bragged of performing with Johnny Cash, Loretta Lynn, and Jerry Lee Lewis at the Grand Ole Opry. This may be true, but I never saw much proof of it. He once showed me a photo of him standing next to Johnny Cash, but it looked more like Al was getting an autograph than singing a duet. Even if it was true, by the time he got to Cumberland, all his musical talents got him was a job singing under the plastic grapes at Warner's German Restaurant in his clown-colored rodeo outfit.

Al's voice was a deep, resonant baritone, but his presentation was overly operatic. His favorite song was "They Call the Wind Mariah," and he had a 45-rpm record cut of it, which he passed out with much fanfare if you caught his act. It was about as good as Warner's pizza which—like Al—was oily. Al didn't like working much, and over the course of his nine years in Cumberland, had many jobs. None of them lasted very long. He also sang at the drop of a hat whether you wanted him to or not, and he had the bad habit of chasing other men's wives.

JoAnn & Al Homburg (Allegwee 1971 - Syckes Family Photos)

JoAnn was completely different. She was extremely hard-working, dedicated, and driven. You did not want to get in her way. Accepting a job as the drama teacher at Allegany, she moved quickly to create something that no one in Cumberland knew we needed: a high-kicking, all-girls performance drill team. Modeled after the Kilgore College Rangerettes of Texas, JoAnn named them the Allegany Arrowettes. This snappy homonym was the word arrow, which represented the weapon of our Indian mascot, followed by the diminutive suffix "ette." Well, let me tell you, the Arrowettes were anything but diminutive. What she created was more, much more than just another girls' dance team: it was a lifestyle where applicants had to prove their worthiness before joining.

Allegany Arrowettes (Allegwee 1965)

Only after passing a rigorous assessment of their dance talents, good looks, height and weight standards, popularity, and elegance did JoAnn let them join. To stay in, you had to maintain a total subservience to all Arrowette rules, rigorous daily training, and complete devotion to JoAnn. It was more religion than drill team, and like religion, it did about as much harm as good. Trying out for the Arrowettes was a mixture of *The Bachelor*, *Miss America*, and *Survivor*. It all culminated one late summer night in an orgy of performance, pageantry, and pathos.

While a live band played, one-by-one the applicants would parade across the stage in different outfits. First in performance-like uniform (so we'd know how they'd look on the field), then in appropriate school attire (knee-length skirts—pants were *verboten*), and finally formal dress (prom queens on parade). Then they'd rigorously perform all the required Arrowette dance skills. The most critical of these was the ability to high kick. High-kicking required the girls to stand with their arms outstretched over the shoulders of the girls beside them and throw first their left and then their right foot up over their heads. Note: To do it right; you needed to be in perfect time to the music, in rhythm with your teammates and to not bend your supporting leg. If you've seen the Rockettes of Radio City Music Hall, you know what I'm talking about. It is not a natural act.

This round of the competition would end, and the judges' scores would be presented to JoAnn. She would accept or reject them, and then a few girls were voted off the island, and another round would begin. Once pared down to a magic number that only JoAnn knew, all the remaining contestants would be lined up on stage. As a drum roll sounded and a spotlight followed her, the royal anointment would begin. JoAnn would walk down the line with a bouquet of long-stemmed roses. She would pause in front of each girl, looking them over one last time, and—then and only then—give them a rose signifying they were part of the team. Not everyone got a rose—it heightened the drama. This was followed by an outpouring of cheering and crying and group hugs for all the winners while the losers stood in the shadows and watched. I'll give her this: it was one hell of a show, but for those girls not chosen, whether it was because of their high-kick skills, body shape, or fashion choices, it was devastating. JoAnn just went too far.

— Success, Prep & Date Night —

Speaking of going too far, the thought of listening to Al Homburg sing the then cutting-edge rock opera hits of *Jesus Christ Superstar* was just weird, but Al was my one chance to get Patty out on a date, so I didn't care if he got nailed to a cross in his Dale Evans fringe—we were going to the show.

Mike got me a copy of the church bulletin that had a notice in it announcing Al's performance, and I had it with me when I took Patty home the next day. I showed it to her, and she said, "Let me handle this. I know how to get my mom to say yes."

When we got to her house, we waited outside until Mrs. Rudd's car pulled into the driveway. Patty got out first and walked over to talk to her mom. I pretended to check the air in the front tire. I saw Patty with the church bulletin, giving it everything she had and then, miracle of miracles, her mom nodded in agreement. She opened the back door of the car and reached in for her groceries. I exploded off the pavement like a track star hearing the starting gun and got to Mrs. Rudd as she swung around with a bag of groceries. Face to face, I said in my most saccharine voice, "Let me help you with that, please."

She clutched the bag tightly at first then relinquished it as if to say, "Okay, I give up."

"Mom says we can go to the concert," Patty chirped.

"But only the concert—after that you need to come straight home," said her mom, sounding a lot like one of the policemen who pulled me from under the pine tree.

"Yes, Ma'am," I said, following her to the door and winking at Patty.

Praise the Lord. Jesus saves.

The day before the performance, I cleaned the Barracuda to within an inch of its life. I also got my hair cut for the first time in months. Somewhere in the middle of my sophomore year, I stopped going to the barber as it was the Age of Aquarius, and I wanted to fit in with the hippie style. Just letting it grow out with no trimming made me look like a cross between an early-Beatle mop-top and a shaggy dog—it was uneven. The solution was Jack's Barbershop.

Plopping into one of Jack's big, red, vinyl chairs with chrome-plated arms, I scanned the magazine pile for something worth reading.

Damn, no Playboys. I'll have to settle for a Popular Science.

It was late Saturday morning, and Jack's was packed with Cumberland's finest: railroad men and Kelly Springfield workers on their lunch breaks, a cop who looked annoyingly familiar, and a couple of other kids my age. It was going to be a wait, but not a long one because Jack could clip hair faster than rabbits mate. There were no scissors involved, nothing but electric clippers of varying cutting lengths. The guy before me wasn't in the chair more than a minute when Jack asked, "How's that look?" and he was up, paid, and gone. It was my turn.

Men of the day didn't let more than two weeks go by without a cut, so there wasn't much for Jack to do. He was in his late forties and always wore a tight-fitting, white barber's tunic that was covered in clipped hair and cigarette ash. He looked at me with great suspicion and said, "What do you want, kid?"

He punched the word "you" like it was a burglar breaking into his house. Remember, I hadn't been to a barber shop in over six months, so I didn't look like one of his regular customers. As far as he knew, I could be part of the Weathermen Underground. He started gesturing at me with his clippers as the lit cigarette dangling out of the side of his mouth bobbed up and down, emphasizing every word.

I swear he could drink a glass of water and that thing wouldn't fall off his lip. Was it super glued there?

"You want a butch cut, kid"? Jack laughed.

"No, sir. Just a trim please, around the sides and off the back. Leave the top alone," I said.

"But, boy, that's where all your hair is. You're not going to get your money's worth if I don't cut that," Jack replied.

"No thanks, just the sides, and back." As I finished saying this, the front door squeaked open and an African-American boy, maybe three or four years younger than me, entered.

He started for the chairs when suddenly Jack erupted, "Get the hell outta here, I ain't cuttin' no nigger wool, it gums up my clippers. Git!"

The air turned cold. I seized the arm of the chair as the boy turned and left the shop. The other men in the store smirked and looked at each other then smiled at Jack. I felt terrible but did nothing. I wish now I'd have gotten up and thrown the apron at Jack and walked out, but I didn't. It was wrong, but it was Cumberland in 1971.

I spent a lot of time deciding what to wear that evening because I wanted to strike the right balance between Ricky Nelson and David Cassidy. All the moms loved Ricky from *Ozzie and Harriet,* but all the girls loved David from *The Partridge Family,* so I put a sports coat on over my T-shirt and jeans.

Patty was ready to go when the door opened, and I was hoping we could make a clean getaway, but no. "Tell Shelby to come in for a minute," sang out from the living room.

"Okay, Mom," Patty said. "You better come in; I'll try to make it short."

"No problem. Gee, you look great."

Patty had on a long-sleeved turtleneck sweater dress that fit her perfectly and accentuated all her curves without revealing an inch of skin.

Damn.

I enjoyed following her into the living room, but as I raised my head from staring at Patty's beautiful butt, I found myself looking right into the face of her father.

"Hi, I'm Patty's dad," he said.

"Yes, sir, hello, I'm—" I started.

"I know. You're Shelby," he interrupted. "Are you going to take good care of my little girl tonight?"

How do fathers expect boys to answer questions like this?

I could have said, *No, Mr. Rudd, I've got three sailors waiting in the car for us with some heroin. They tell me it makes things easier.*

Of course, I didn't, but his question was silly. I guess he had to ask me something. He wanted me to know he understood my motivation because he too was once a sixteen-year-old horny boy but more importantly, he wanted me to know that if anything should happen to his precious daughter, he would personally remove my eyes with his thumbs.

"Yes, sir. Yes, sir, I will. I promise. You know, sir, I'm good friends with Walt Neff's boy Walter. I think you play in his poker club," I diverted, hoping to show a mutual acquaintance.

"Oh, you know Walt Neff?" he asked.

"Yes, sir, his son and I have been friends since grade school and are acolytes together at the Emmanuel Episcopal Church," I added.

That was the one time in my life I used my job as an acolyte to polish my halo. The truth was Walter and I were almost thrown out of acolytes for shooting "the bird" at each other during services and drinking leftover wine, but Mr. Rudd wasn't interested in those boring details.

"Dad, we've got to get going. The show at the church starts at seven," Patty interjected.

"Okay, have fun and come straight home. Your mom and I will be waiting," said Mr. Rudd.

Mrs. Rudd was getting up off the couch as Patty jerked me by the arm and spun me towards the door. I grinned and waved as she pulled me out of the house. I opened the passenger-side door for Patty, and she got in the Barracuda, and then I went around and dropped into the driver's seat. She leaned over and gave me a big kiss—I mean a real kiss. I'm talking a Joleen Johnson kind of kiss.

Okay, this is starting off well.

— Jimmy, Garrett, & Jesus —

It was strange to be entering the Lutheran Church's Cafe-Gym-torium without a Frisbee, but I didn't let it phase me. There were seats set up for 200, and I was amazed at the number of people there. Who knew a country and western version of a British stylized interpretation of Christ's betrayal and death would be so popular in Cumberland? It was a crazy way to spend a Saturday night, but I was out on my first date with Patty, and that's all that mattered. I saw friends of mine, and we went over to sit with them.

Garrett Sweet and Jimmy Eaton were a very interesting pair of guys. I'd been good friends with Garrett a long time, and I'd come to know Jimmy through him. Garrett was tall, dark, and easygoing. Jimmy was short, puffy, and acerbic. They'd be the last people you'd think would be friends, but they were, and they both played bass fiddle in the orchestra. I will have much more about them later, but tonight they were here to mock and ridicule Al Homburg for daring to sing the music of Andrew Lloyd Webber.

Garrett and Jimmy had been huge fans of Webber's rock opera since it came out in 1970 and turned me on to it soon after it was released. They hadn't met Patty, so I introduced them, and we waited for the show to begin.

"Are they going to do the entire 90-minute album?" I asked Garrett.

"Beats me," he replied.

"Fuck, no," added Jimmy. "Homburg can't go that long without a drink."

Patty's eyes opened wide, and I looked away pretending he really hadn't just said "fuck" in her church.

"He's such a ham. I bet he sings all the big songs himself, including Mary Magdalene's 'I Don't Know How to Love Him'", Jimmy belittled.

Patty snorted, then laughed so loud the people sitting in front of us looked around. She was turning bright red when the house lights went down, and a spotlight lit up the stage. Out came JoAnn in a white, bell-bottomed pantsuit with a colorful scarf tied around her neck. From our distance, she looked more *That Girl* than Popeye's girlfriend tonight.

"Good evening, and welcome to a night of music with Al Homburg and friends," she chimed. "Tonight, you'll be hearing an original interpretation of music from the rock opera *Jesus Christ Superstar*. Now, let's give a warm welcome to Al Homburg, John Steel, and Cathy McDougal."

"John Steel," groaned Garrett. "He's a jock. Does he even know how to sing?"

"No, but he knows how to keep JoAnn's toes curled," shot Jimmy.

"Shush," I heard from the row behind us.

It had been a long-standing rumor that while Al was pounding out songs at Warner's, JoAnn was getting pounded by the varsity football team. I doubt this was true, but it made for great gossip around the school lockers.

Al walked out from the other side of the stage holding a twelve-string guitar. John Steel was carrying a stool, and Cathy McDougal had a mic stand. Al had a smile big enough to drive a truck through. He had on one of his cowboy suits, but it was a subdued brown color with black tassels. To make it fit better with the subject matter, he had a huge wooden crucifix around his neck. Both John and Cathy were wearing crimson, floor-length capes that made them look a bit monkish. You could tell John wanted to be somewhere else, but Cathy was more effervescent than Lawrence Welk's bubble machine. The stool went down, and Al climbed on it as Cathy took the mic from JoAnn and attached it to the stand.

"Is that all the instrumentation they're going to have?" Jimmy asked. "Christ, there's a full orchestra and twenty rock musicians on the album. How are they going to produce that sound with one lousy guitar? I want my money back."

"Shut up, Jimmy, the concert's free," hissed Garrett.

"Exactly," Jimmy said louder. "They should pay us to be here."

That last crack caught JoAnn's ear, and her eyes burned on us like Superman's X-ray vision. Patty grabbed my hand and whispered, "Who does he think he is, Don Rickles?"

"Yes, he does. He also thinks he's God's gift to classical music, but he's wrong on both counts," I answered.

Al strummed the guitar and made a few last-minute tuning adjustments, then rolled into "Heaven on Their Minds." This worked, given it's a song with lots of guitar accompaniment on the album. John and Cathy stood behind him trying their best to look like they were really rocking out, but it wasn't working. In spite of Al's excellent guitar work, it was still his "Saturday at the Met" baritone voice with its Kansas twang. It was going to be a long night.

Cathy was an Arrowette and was also in the choir. Unfortunately, her high kick was better than her voice, but she made it through "Everything's Alright" in workmanlike fashion, but John was totally over his head when he tried to sing "This Jesus Must Die." It sounded like he was killing cats instead of the King of the Jews. It was right in the middle of this that Jimmy stood noisily, made his way to the center aisle, and walked out. Garrett sank into his seat, and I put my arm around Patty and leaned away from him as if to protect her from any collateral damage. JoAnn peered out from the side of the stage and shot another look of death at Jimmy, but realizing she'd been seen, smiled a big smile and disappeared. Thank heaven intermission was next. Patty and I shuffled with the rest of the crowd towards the door. She leaned on me and said softly, "Let's get out of here."

We went straight to the car, and as we drove out of the parking lot I said, "How about some ice cream? I know a place that makes a great dip-top cone."

Patty leaned across the metal console and kissed me on the cheek as we drove to Uncle Lu's. I pulled up to the back door when we got there, and as I jumped out, I said, "Wait here. I'll be back with the cones in a minute."

As I opened the door, I saw Ernie—the night manager with a quart of oil in his hair—down on all fours dangling a piece of cheese near the space between the storage shelves and the walk-in refrigerator. In his other hand was a hammer. I was about to ask what was going on when I saw three of the teenage staff standing in the corner with their fingers up to their lips and mouthing, "Quiet." They looked like they were about to bust a gut from laughing.

Ernie looked up and said, "Keep back! I think I see him."

That's when Diana, a flute player in the band, grabbed me by the arm and pulled me into the hallway.

"Karen told Ernie she saw a mouse run under there, and we convinced him to lure it out with a piece of cheese and kill it with a hammer. He's been at it for a half hour." Diana laughed.

I knew what was going on and slipped past Ernie to the ice cream machine. I finished the cones, and as I closed the door behind me I heard someone yell, "There he is!" and the thud of a hammer hitting concrete.

This was followed by uproarious laughter.

It was a slow night at Uncle Lu's.

As much as I'd like to tell you that Patty and I drove up to Sunset View and made passionate love while looking out at the map of the United States, we didn't. We ate our ice cream while laughing about the concert we'd endured with both of us agreeing Jimmy's kibitzing beat anything we heard from the singers. Then, I drove her home.

It was a marvelous night.

Chapter 8 - Spinning Wheel

— Hey, Lookie Here Now —

With a creak and a groan, the school year started like a rusty carousel: slowly at first, then faster and faster with each rotation. ALCO's building was alive again as everyone scrambled to adjust to the new-old routine. The surroundings were the same, only the teachers' and the class locations had changed. It took a while for each student to plot the fastest route from class to class, but by the middle of September, things were running smoothly.

I was eager for the first Friday night football game where I'd take the field in front of the band and lead it in our performance—but classes came first. Never one to push myself academically, I signed up for the easiest required classes to stay on the college-bound track. My two electives were band and drama.

The week of sixth-period band classes before the first game went as well as Summer Band, and we continued to hone our musical and marching skills in preparation for our debut. One difference was now we were practicing with the Arrowettes. Up until this point, they practiced in the gym to recordings of their dance music, but as the first game drew near, we had to integrate the two groups. The Arrowettes did not perform to a wide variety of music, which made the band's job easier. They would take the field to "Hey, Look Me Over," and then do their high-kick routine to "Everything's Coming up Roses."

The first few times we worked together, there were rough spots. The band knew the music, and the dancers knew their steps, but the drum major had trouble getting the tempo right. I had a bad habit of directing the music faster than the Arrowettes could handle. It made throwing their legs up over their heads even harder than it already was. I worked on it, but before I got it right, there were lots of nasty looks from extremely tired high kickers.

JoAnn, as a kind and understanding person, walked over to Dad during one of my poorer efforts and yelled, "What the hell is going on Lu? Tell him to slow down."

But I figured it out, and from then on things went smoothly, that is, until the day before the first Friday night game.

I showed up at the band room a few minutes before class to find Dad, JoAnn, Bob Hutcheson, and Al all chatting in Dad's office—yes, Big Bob, the principal who saved me from Katie's dad, and Al Homburg of *Jesus Christ Superstar* fame. I knew something was up. JoAnn was talking to Dad, and he had a tight-lipped look on his face. Whatever it was she wanted, he did not seem happy about it.

Oh, my God. Don't tell me JoAnn and Al want me out of the drum major job too. Come on. I didn't play, 'Hey, Look Me Over' that fast, and it wasn't my fault Jimmy Eaton walked out of Al's performance?

Upon seeing me, Al said, "Shelby, come in and join us. This concerns you."

My sphincter slammed shut, and I felt a little stomach acid squirt up into my throat.

"Mrs. Homburg and I have an idea of how we can make the introduction of the Arrowettes special," Al beamed.

"We talked to Mr. Hutcheson, and he's willing to give it a try, but we need your help."

I looked at Big Bob. He had his standard smile on his face; only I sensed he'd already been overwhelmed by the Homburgs and was looking for the easiest way out. That was JoAnn's modus operandi—badger until beaten. I looked at Dad.

"Mr. Homburg has written alternative lyrics to 'Hey, Look Me Over' that are especially for the Arrowettes, and he wants to sing them as they take the field for halftime," he said.

Okay, I'm not going to lose my job. That's good. My butt relaxed, and I swallowed sourly.

"How will that work?" I asked.

Al had a big voice, but there was no way he was going to be heard over the hundred-piece ALCO band down on the football field.

"Mr. Homburg will be up in the announcer's booth with me, and I'll turn the microphone over to him when it's time. We're going to try it out today at practice only using the bullhorn instead," Dad said.

I knew this didn't have a damn thing to do with the Arrowettes, and Dad and Bob Hutcheson knew it, too. It was another one of Al Homburg's promotional stunts. He and JoAnn would do anything to get his fat face and feeble voice in front of the public.

Who knows? Maybe there would be a Capitol Record's A&R guy in the stands Friday night who would finally recognize Al's talents and make him an international recording star. Ha! I doubt it. But, I didn't have any good reason to argue against it. He'd have to follow the band and me, so what the hell.

"Sure, it sounds like fun," I chirped.

With that, JoAnn and Al exited Dad's office, and I told Dad I'd get the band ready to hit the field.

Mr. Hutcheson nodded at Dad and brushed by me on his way out the door, "Thanks, we're even," he said.

Out on the practice field when it was time for the Arrowettes to make their entrance, Al was standing about twenty feet from me holding the bullhorn and looking up at Dad and JoAnn on the cemetery hill. I started the band and the familiar introductory strains of "Hey, Look Me Over" filled the air. After four bars, I heard the *click* of the bullhorn's on switch, and Al's Midwestern Pavarotti bellowed out the most inane lyrics ever written:

"Hey lookie here now,

What a nice surprise,

The Allegany Arrowettes,

Stepping up to size.

They're quite a group now,

As you can see.

The Allegany Arrowettes,

Here for you and me."

It went on for two more verses. When it was done, there was silence except for JoAnn, who had stuffed her clipboard under her arm and was clapping like Nixon just finished the State of the Union. The deal was done. Tomorrow night, Al would debut his song at the opening football game.

— First Performance —

School on Friday was a blur, and I don't remember anything about it other than I was focused 100% on the upcoming show. After school, I drove Patty home and told her I'd have to skip our date with Julia Child because I had to get my uniform ready, and we all had to be at the stadium for pregame practice by six. She kissed me, and I took off for home.

I needed to try on my uniform and make sure all the pieces were there; then disassemble it and put it in a hanging bag to take with me to the stadium. I would not put it back on until right before the pregame show. I didn't worry about this much when I was one baritone player wearing the same uniform as everyone else in a sea of 120 other band members, but tonight, I'd be alone, out in front of the band, wearing a brand-new, ivory-white, drum major's uniform with every eye in the house on me. I had to make sure I didn't forget to bring something. I went over every piece of my uniform three times before I zipped the bag shut and laid it out flat in the back seat of the Barracuda. It was time to go. I grabbed a Pop Tart as I ran through the kitchen and ate it on the way to Greenway Avenue Stadium. The stadium was getting old. The home team side was constructed in the 1930s and was made completely out of concrete. Later, wooden bleachers were added to the other side for the visiting team's fans.

I arrived wearing a pair of jeans and my new leather bomber jacket. The sun was starting to set, and the stadium lights came on, creating a netherworld between day and night. A bit of magic occurs at American high school football games every Friday evening in the fall. The air is energized with anticipation that transforms kids into combatants. Whether it's helmets and cleats, pompoms and megaphones or Busby hats and horns, they come armed and ready for battle. No matter the outcome, memories will be made.

ALCO, as the home team claimed, the original 1930's bleacher side of the field, leaving the open-air wooden bleacher side to the opponents. Housed in the cave-like passage underneath the concrete seating area were snack bars, bathrooms, locker rooms, and ticket counters. During pregame and halftime, this area was a sea of human beings ebbing and flowing like a magnified view of blood cells in an artery.

I was forming the band up on the quarter-mile track that ringed the football field as Dad arrived. Seeing me, he moved my way.

"Are you ready?" he asked.

There's that damn "Are you ready?" question again.

"Yeah, I'm going to run them through the beginning of pre-game then shift to the halftime lineup. Hey, are we going to practice with Al Homburg using the amplification system here?" I asked.

"That's up to him. If he shows up in time and wants to run through it, then we will. If not, too bad." Dad smirked.

I went back to forming up the band but was surprised by Dad's smart-ass answer.

The practice was not good; everyone was out of sync. The drums kept missing my "roll-off" command, and the trombones made a wrong turn and slammed into the clarinets, damn near decapitating one of them. We shifted to the halftime show, but before we could finish, the two football teams took the field for warm up, and we had to retreat to the stands.

Al Homburg was nowhere in sight. Seeing JoAnn in the stands talking to the Arrowette Captain, Terri Kaneko, I went over to ask about Al.

"Excuse me, Mrs. Homburg, is Mr. Homburg going to sing with us tonight?" I asked.

JoAnn didn't answer. She kept chatting with Terri with her back to me. I waited a half a minute, then gave up. I needed to change into my uniform—time was running out.

The ALCO band uniforms were dark blue with gold and white accents and—because they resisted the elements—most of the members came dressed in them, ready for performance. Mine, on the other hand, was all white, and I didn't want to expose it until the last minute.

I waded through the mass of humanity flowing into the stadium and found the exit. Then, I ran up the street where I'd parked the Barracuda. Gathering my uniform, I turned back towards the stadium. "Hey, where am I going to change?" I asked out loud. I hadn't thought about this before.

There was no way I would go into the football team's locker room. They'd be coming in off the field as I got there, and who knows how they would react to a Band-Fag putting on his girly-girl suit. I did not want to find out, so the only other option was the men's room.

The bathroom was not a pleasant place to change. Although the wall of toilets had dividers separating them, there were no doors. On the opposite wall was a row of four-foot-tall urinals that were cleaned at least once a year. In the center of the room was an enormous circular sink that looked like it was designed to water cattle. The ambiance was a mixture of ammonia bottling plant and abattoir. Surroundings aside, what made it especially memorable was the constant flow of men and boys that came in, crapped, peed, and spat while I changed. It became my dressing room for most of the season.

I managed to get my uniform on quickly and swam back through the high tide of humanity to the band's seating area. Stepping up the ladder-like metal railing that separated the stands from the field, I locked my legs around the top bar and blew my whistle.

"Ten minutes until show time. Get your instruments ready, and check your music," I commanded.

Looking into the faces of the band members, I realized this was the first time they had seen me in my new uniform. I liked the look in their eyes.

I jumped back down and turned to see if the football teams had left the field. That's when I saw Al. I felt my whistle fall out of my slack-jawed mouth as I beheld, in all its splendor, Al Homburg's outfit. His bright white pants were tucked into blue and white cowboy boots, and his shirt was an orange cream color that looked to be made of self-illuminating satin. He was a Dreamsicle. Standing at the end of the bleachers, he was suggestively snuggling up to Toni Dixon, the beautiful, forty-something, former Miss America contestant. It was clear Al had his hooks out in case any fish were biting tonight. Apparently, they weren't, because he quickly turned my way. I was about to jump down from the railing to the track three feet below as he got to me.

"Shelby, I need to coordinate my entrance with you." Al radiated.

"Entrance, what entrance?" I asked.

"Before you start 'Hey, Look Me Over,' look back at the stands. I'll be sitting here when your dad introduces me, then start my walk up to the announcer booth. When I get there, I'll wave to the crowd. That will be your signal to start the song."

My eyes said, "Are you for real?" but my mouth said, "Yes, sir." I pushed off the bar and dropped to the ground.

Our pregame show was not complicated, and we did not change it from last year's. The band formed a rectangle of five rows of twenty band members each at Allegany's end of the field. Four sousaphones were in the rear, each sporting a letter on a cloth stretched across their bell to spell out ALCO. The flag squad was on the band's flanks, and the majorettes were out in front, all sparkling and twirling in unison. I called the band to attention and made sure they were all aligned properly. Turning around for one final look before kicking things off, I glanced back at the sousaphones and read *C-O-A-L* instead of A-L-C-O. I waded through the center of the band, and after spell-checking the sousaphones moved back to the front.

Then, I marched out about ten yards and took my place as the leader of the band and waited.

I heard a click, the sound of fumbling, then a loud, amplified, feedback squawk followed by an announcer's voice.

"Ladies and gentlemen, welcome to the first game of the 1971 football season, with a matchup between the Allegany Campers and the Martinsburg Bulldogs."

After listing both the school principals' and coaching staff's names, the announcer said, "And now, let's welcome the Allegany High School Band, led by Drum Major Shelby Syckes."

I did an about face, and before calling the band to attention, I caught Patty's eye, who was standing with the other flute players in the front row. I smiled, winked, and then yelled, "Atten-hut."

Executing another about-face, I gave the horns up command, forming a "V" with my upstretched arms.

This is it. Everything I've done for the past nine months is culminating in this moment.

In front of me stretched the beautifully mowed green grass and perfectly aligned white chalk stripes of the football field. It was bathed in a celestial bright light that shone down from an inky black sky. The light towers were like great eyes staring down at me, and the bleachers looked like outstretched arms holding back the large crowd. Strangely, I felt calm. I was completely focused on my next action. I blew four short whistle blasts, and all one hundred and twenty of us stepped off the line with the first note of the "National Emblem March."

I have no idea what it looked like from the stands, but from my perspective, it was magnificent. The band sounded spectacular, and we moved down the field in absolute unison, hitting every five-yard marker with our right foot precisely on count number eight. As I crossed the fifty-yard line, I did a crisp left flank and marched straight for the home team bleachers. The majorettes did the same as the band split into two equal groups. After a few more sharp maneuvers, the band formed a rectangle again with everyone facing the grandstand. Then, the band members all marched toward the stands with their horns tilted up for effect as the majorettes took their place in front of them again.

The band stopped, and I stepped up on the football team's bench and directed the rest of the march. When it ended, I spun around and saluted, and the ALCO crowd erupted in cheers. It was deafening. The speaker system squawked again, and I swear a filling in one of my back teeth vibrated loose. "Please rise and join in the singing of our National Anthem," the announcer said.

With three tweets on my whistle, we waltzed our way through "The Star-Spangled Banner" with no trouble at all. The only disturbing thing was despite the five thousand people in the stands; I swear I could hear Al Homburg's voice deliberately holding each note a second longer than anyone else.

The ALCO Band Takes the Field (Syckes Family Photos)

With that over, I gave the roll-off command, and the drum section exploded with a flourish of paradiddles and ratamacues while each line, in turn, did a left face and marched off to form a tunnel at the goalpost. I followed them, and once they were all in place, they turned to face me. We then rolled smartly into "'Tis Allegany," our school fight song. As the song reached its climax, the football team ran into the tunnel and burst through a paper wall held up by the cheerleaders and painted with encouraging slogans like "Go Big Blue" and "Kill 'em dead." Then, the football players started throwing footballs around or doing jumping jacks or anything else they could think of to look as manly as humanly possible. What a totally American ritual and what great fun.

The game started, and it was a close one. As halftime approached, neither team had an advantage. I passed the word through the band that we'd be moving down onto the track at the two-minute warning. Having kicked off the season successfully with our pregame show, everyone was feeling confident that halftime would go as well. I was confident too, but still worried about Al Homburg's singing stunt.

As the gun sounded the end of the first half, I signaled the band members to move forward from the quarter-mile track and take their place in two long lines on the ALCO sideline. I had them face toward the field so their horns would be pointing away from the stands. The fifteen-member flag team was positioned in the center of the field facing the band. The five majorettes were in a line behind us. I stepped out in front of the band and called them to attention. I gave the Horns-Up signal as Dad's voice came across the loudspeaker systems, thankfully without the feedback this time. "Ladies and Gentlemen, the Allegany High School Marching Band of Cumberland, Maryland."

I tweeted my whistle four times, and the band stepped off the line and started playing the initial measures of "St. Louis Blues March." It begins with a unison rhythmic melody of *Dum, Dum, Dum Dum Dum*. As we started marching towards the center of the field, the flag team stepped off too, heading in our direction. Aligned just right and with a little luck, the flag team passed right through us, and we exchanged places with them on the field.

Dramatic.

Exactly at the eighth measure of the march, as the trumpets come in with an unforgettable sustained high "A" whole-note followed by a descending arpeggio, the entire band swung around with a sharp to-the-rear move and blasted the stands with the nostalgic sounds of Glen Miller's music. The flag team peeled off to the left and right and started whirling their banners in circles in time to the music, adding eye-catching motion to the sides of the band.

Halting and marching in place with the majorettes now in front of them, the band rolled into the jazzy center section of the song. This was the cue for the majorettes to go into high gear, throwing their batons skyward as the drum solo section hit. Catching them in unison, it was the brass's turn to finish the song. Our drill was simple but powerful and accentuated the grandeur of the march. We finished, and I turned around. With one blast of my whistle, the entire band bowed at the waist. The fans loved it.

We then played "Red River Rock" and spelled out the word ALCO on the field in block letters. With that, our part of the halftime show was over, and it was the Arrowettes' turn to take the field. I ordered "Forward March," and the word ALCO collapsed as we entered the end zone.

I moved out in front and looked into the stands. I heard Dad's voice again as he introduced Al Homburg, "And now, ladies and gentlemen, it's time for the Arrowettes, led this year by their Captain, Terri Kaneko, to entertain you with their synchronized high-kicking dance routine. But, in addition, we have a special guest with us tonight. Mr. Al Homburg, singer, musician, teacher, and star performer at Fred Warner's German Restaurant every Thursday evening from 7 to 9 p.m. will debut his original rendition of the Arrowette theme song. Let's give him a big hand."

"How much did Fat Al have to pay for that?" cracked someone from the trumpet section.

Lots of low-level smirking followed, but I kept my eyes on the stairs leading to the announcer's booth. Suddenly there was Al, up and flowing and jiggling like a walking lava lamp.

Oh my God! Does the man not own a mirror?

The Arrowettes had formed up in two diagonal lines on the ALCO side of the field, and I saw Terri Kaneko—all four feet, ten inches of her—standing with the rest of her officers in front, proudly ready to take the field. As Al got to the top of the bleachers, I saw Dad hand him the microphone through the window of the announcer's booth. Al waved his hand signaling me. I turned to face the band, and with four whistle blasts started "Hey, Look Me Over."

Now, physics is a bitch. No matter how smart or funny or pretty you are, you must operate within the confines of its laws. There are no exceptions, not even one for overweight, loudly dressed losers like Al Homburg. When he decided to sing his new lyrics to "Hey, Look Me Over," standing more than 100 yards away from the band using the stadium's amplification system, he did not take into consideration the time it would take our sound to reach his ears. Even though our music was traveling at 761 miles per hour, the delay was enough to throw Al off, and he was doomed to be behind the beat and out of sync with us no matter how hard he tried.

Despite the band playing the four-measure introduction to the song perfectly, Al's booming baritone voice came crashing in a half beat behind us on the chorus. There was nothing I could do. For every right note we played, Al sang a different and wrong note, usually the one we had just stopped playing, creating a yoyo-like effect of dissonance and disorder.

It was gawdawful.

There was a loud murmur in the stands as the fans all turned around to see what was causing the ever-worsening echo chamber effect, and all they saw was the oversized Dreamsicle singing away, oblivious to the problem. I could not see him, but I'll bet Dad had a big grin on his face. Did I tell you he minored in Physics at Oberlin?

As painful as this was for the people listening in the stands, it was more painful for the Arrowettes. Although they got a clear downbeat to start their marching when the band began the song, the second Al started singing, nothing was clear. There were girls marching in rhythm with the band, and girls who switched over to Al's late beat. It was total chaos. No one was in step, and Arrowettes exchanged frantic looks in an attempt to synchronize. Instead of them taking the field like prancing Lipizzans, they looked more like Clydesdales plodding through mud.

The song ended, and Al Homburg looked out expecting to see an ocean of adoring fans applauding his magnificent performance. Instead, he was greeted with the stricken faces of Arrowette family and friends, politely clapping and shooting him the evil eye.

JoAnn came bounding up the stairs and grabbed the mic out of Al's hand before he had a chance to flip the off switch. "Gimme that thing, you jerk," screeched JoAnn's unmistakable voice through the loudspeakers. Then in controlled dulcet tones, she introduced the next part of the show.

The Arrowettes had somehow managed to make it to the center of the field and were aligned single-file, ready for their high-kick dance routine. The band rolled into "Everything's Coming up Roses," and the girls did a spectacular job. How they took the field was forgotten as their top-quality performance dazzled the crowd. You had to see it to believe it. Seventy beautiful, young women, all in a line stretching from goalpost to goalpost. They interlocked arms and kicked their feet over their heads much farther than God ever intended possible.

It was unforgettable, and when they finished with their signature rolling-wave bow, the stands went wild. I cued the band, and we joyfully played "Hey, Look Me Over" again as the girls proudly marched off the field. JoAnn would not relinquish the microphone back to Al, and we were all spared another round of tonal torture. We won the game 14 - 12, and it marked the beginning of one of the greatest winning streaks Allegany has ever had.

Next up was the parade.

Chapter 9 - Are You Ready

— Parade Prep —

Every fall, the city of Oakland sponsors a competitive parade as part of their Autumn Glory Festival. We won last year, and I wanted to win again, but it would be tough. Fort Hill didn't compete last time, but they would be there this year. So, we had to be good. Staying with our keep-it-simple plan, we decided to play "St. Louis Blues March."

Every day during band, we'd march up and down the street in front of the school practicing. I wanted to recapture the dramatic beginning of the song we used to great effect at the halftime show but to do this in a parade would be a challenge. Getting a band to play loudly is easy. It's the nature of the beast, but getting it to play softly is a chore, and getting it to play softly consistently at the start of a song is damn near impossible.

I wanted "St. Louis Blues March," to begin with a very low volume and then gradually get louder and louder until the big high-note trumpet entrance. We had achieved this on the field with the band facing away from the stands, muffling the sound, but I couldn't have the band march backward down the street and then spin around as we did on the football field. Dynamics were key, and we worked on it a lot.

Oakland's was a competitive parade, and they're different from non-competitive ones. In a non-competitive parade, you march the band down the street and play your song whenever you like. In a competitive parade, there is a specified section of the route called the judges' zone, and it is in this zone that the judges do their thing.

Every band starts with a perfect 100-point score. Judges reduce that for every infraction identified. In the judges' zone, you find the grandstand filled with the mayor and city officials, the Autumn Glory Festival Queen (usually the Mayor's daughter), as well as the head judge. There are other judges on the street walking alongside the bands analyzing everything going on. They're looking at the straightness of the band's lines, the uniformity of marching style, the players' uniforms, their instruments, their dental records, everything. Oh, and they're listening to the music, too — not only to what you are playing but to how well you are playing it, and more importantly, how you are presenting it to the crowd. Do you have pizzazz? When you get to the judges' zone, you are expected to begin playing your march and complete it before you exit. Points will be deducted if you start early or end late.

— Drummers —

Allegany's drumline was a good one, and Cody Radcliffe was drum captain. Cody was tall, with dark, wavy, hair that draped over the right side of his face, obscuring a good portion of it. I remember watching him in the back of the band room practicing an intricate drum riff on his snare. Exactly every thirty seconds, he'd whip his right hand up to his face and push his hair out of the way. He did this without missing a beat. How he avoided putting his eye out with his drumstick is anyone's guess. He was a senior, and I don't remember ever hearing him say more than two words. No matter the subject or request made, all Cody ever said was, "Got it," with absolutely no expression.

Drums have been around as long as mankind, but it wasn't until men started organizing other men to kill their fellow man that drums found their niche. Early military leaders discovered it was helpful to have a few of the guys rhythmically beat on drums to motivate the others to continue moving towards certain death (10). History records that as early as 684 BC in ancient China, at the battle of Changshao, the use of drums to organize the attack significantly contributed to the State of Lu defeating the State of Qi.

Now, I do not know if the State of Lu was an uncle and owned a Tastee Freez, but I'd like to think so.

Despite a band's dependence on drummers, they get a bad rap—pun intended. They always bear the brunt of jokes like, "What do you call a drummer with half a brain? Gifted."

Research suggests that drummers have innate problem-solving skills and a positive impact on communities. Researchers in Stockholm found that, after playing a series of beats, drummers who had better rhythm scored better on a 60-question intelligence test (11).

It gets even crazier; when drummers make errors in beat, they're tapping into a natural rhythm found all over Earth. A Harvard smarty-pants discovered that a drummer's internal clock doesn't move linearly like a real clock, but rather in waves. This wavy rhythm is found in human brainwaves, sleeping heart rates, and the nerve firings in felines' ears (12). That means that when a drummer slips up, they're actually matching the elemental beat of the world.

ALCO Marching Band Parade Rehearsal (Allegwee 1972)

Isn't that frightening?

When a band is marching in a parade with the drums playing a marching cadence, there needs to be a way to signal the band it's time to play the song. This is called a drum roll-off. To start it, the drum major raises his right arm and blows a single, sustained, eight-count whistle blast. This is the drummer's signal to start the roll-off, which in turn signals the band members that at the end of the eight count roll-off, they are to be ready to play. It also is a great way to catch the ear of the crowd, so it focuses on your performance instead of the clown cars.

I've talked about drum roll-offs before, and you may be a bit confused by exactly what they sound like. The truth is, if you've ever seen a 20th Century Fox movie, you've heard a drum roll-off. Every one of its films opens with a scene of the 20th Century Fox logo with a drum roll-off playing in the background, followed by heralding trumpets.

We practiced roll-offs a lot in the weeks leading up to the parade to make sure we could effectively make the transition from marching to playing "St. Louis Blues March" then back to marching. With the drums at the back of the band, it was up to me to blow my whistle loud enough for them to hear me, but I had reviewed all this with Cody, and he had his ear tuned for my whistle.

— Parade Day —

Since Oakland was only an hour's drive from Cumberland, we organized carpools to get the band members there instead of using buses, so on parade day, Allegany's parking lot was buzzing. Parents were either dropping off kids to be picked up by others or loading their cars with kids and band gear.

The rallying point in Oakland was the parking lot of a liquor store north of downtown. The parade route was only about a mile and a half long with the judges' zone near the end of it in front of the Garrett County District Court. Dad and I drove in separate cars so we could carpool more kids.

Well, that's how I sold him on the idea.

All I really wanted was to drive Patty and her friends in my Barracuda without a chaperone. It was great fun loading up all my gear and picking up Patty, Connie and another flute player and driving to Oakland, my first road trip. We had the radio blaring, and I remember we all were singing along to Cher's new hit, "Gypsies, Tramps & Thieves."

Appropriate, wasn't it?

When we arrived in Oakland, the parking lot of the liquor store was a zoo. It was a big lot that served not only the liquor store but an adjacent strip mall, so it attracted cars from all of the participating schools that day. I saw kids in Fort Hill band uniforms making their way to the front of the parade. As new entrants, Fort Hill would be the lead group.

As I got out of the car, I saw Dad escorting our star trumpet player, Sam Nutter, out of the liquor store. Apparently, Sam went in to buy a Coke, and while the counter clerk was counting his change, two Southern Comfort miniature bottles accidentally fell into his band uniform pocket.

It could happen.

Dad was summoned, words were exchanged, and the liquor store was off limits to all other ALCO kids.

I put on my uniform jacket and hat and herded the band members to our designated spot on the road to assemble in a parade formation. Parade formation was a big rectangle with the drums and sousaphones in the back. In front of the band, two flag team members carried the Allegany High School banner, and the rest of the flags were in a line behind them. The five majorettes were next in line, and finally, I marched between the majorettes and the band.

Dad took off to sign us in with the judges, and I looked over the band members to make sure they had everything they needed and were ready to go. I started with the flags and worked my way back through every row, inspecting the uniform of every member. I was with the trombones when a guy with a clipboard tapped me on the shoulder and said, "Ten-minute warning," then disappeared down the road to the next group.

Turning to continue my inspection, I was startled by Mark Jenson, the trombone section's first chair, who said, "We have a problem. Chucky forgot his spats."

Crap. That's one of the easiest ways to lose points from the judges, and since our uniforms were dark and the spats were white, the missing pair would stand out like a clown's nose.

I followed Mark down the row to find Chucky Grainfield sitting on the road with his trombone in his lap. His face was the Greek mask of tragedy.

"Chucky, get up," I said.

"Why? Mark says I can't march without my spats."

"Does anyone have any extra spats?!" I yelled already knowing the answer.

There was no response.

"Okay, Chucky, let's not give up. We need you in the parade, or our lines will be unbalanced, and that will cost us more in deductions than the missing spats."

Chucky Grainfield was not the brightest bulb in the box. He was a big kid with sandy blond hair, and you could see in his eyes that the wheel was spinning, but the hamster was dead. He had an average face, but it was decorated with creative clusters of acne concealed behind a large pair of nerdy, black glasses carefully mended with surgical tape. He was my age, but this was his first year in senior band. Believe it or not, he had endured two full years of junior band before Dad felt so sorry for him he promoted him to senior band.

Remember how I said the other band officers and I wished sometimes Dad would ask people to leave the band because they couldn't cut it? Well, Chucky was one of those people. He played the trombone and could move his slide into all seven positions, but the sound he produced was not what you'd expect. Instead of Tommy Dorsey, you got dinosaur death rattles.

When I looked back down at Chucky, he had his head between his knees and was rocking back and forth. I noticed he was wearing white athletic socks under his dark blue band pants. A light turned on in my head.

"Hey, does anyone have a pocket knife?" I yelled.

Sam Nutter tugged my sleeve and handed me a switchblade. "Here ya go, kid. Don't hurt yourself," Sam chuckled, and I swear I got a whiff of Southern Comfort when he said it.

"Chucky, take off your socks," I ordered.

"Why?" Chucky mumbled.

"Take them off, and I'll show you."

The next few minutes were disturbing. Not since I was scrubbing the spoiled ice cream out of the Tastee Freez garbage cans have I had to work while wanting to retch. Chucky's white socks were only white from the ankle up. From there down they were a crusty shade of yellow and brown, and as he handed them to me, I swear something fell out of a hole in one of them and scampered away before anyone could step on it. The odor was overpowering.

"Mark, hold the bottom of these," I asked.

"No fucking way," Mark deadpanned.

"Okay, then take the tops, but hold tight," I said knowing the clock was ticking.

I grabbed the moist toes and sawed through the fabric right at the ankle bend.

"Chucky put these back on and then your shoes. Then pull the socks down over your shoes where your spats would go," I said with more compassion than I was feeling. "Please, we're running out of time."

Mark figured out what I was trying to do and told me he'd make sure they'd look as good as they could. I told him to put Chucky in the center of the trombone line as far away as possible from a judge. Then tossing the closed switchblade back to Sam, I ran to the front of the band. As I got there, Dad was talking to the head majorette.

"Sandy, please be careful when throwing the batons, we don't want them coming down on any spectators."

"Yes, Mr. Syckes," Sandy nodded as she pulled down on the side of her thigh-high sequined majorette's uniform that appeared to be painted on her hourglass body. She was gorgeous and graceful and could kill a charging elephant with one blow of her baton. You did not mess with Sandy.

"Dad, how much time do we have before we start?"

"Not much, but I found out how to tell when you're getting close to the judges' zone. There will be an ESSO station on the left followed by one more cross street. As you pass that, the zone starts and—" Dad was interrupted by a loud whistle blown by the man with the clipboard running down the street towards town.

He had a walkie-talkie up to his face, and he yelled into it, "Start 'em up, move 'em out, Rawhide!"

A parade is like a train with bungee cords connecting its cars. When the engine pulls out, the bungee cords stretch, but the second car doesn't move until the cords are pulled tight. When that happens, the car jerks forward, catching up quickly to the engine, then stops again until the slack is once more taken out of the cords—repeating itself over and over with each car in the line creating a paddle ball-like effect. We were car number sixty-seven in that train—the last band because we won last year—and no matter what the guy with the clipboard said, we couldn't go anywhere until the group in front of us moved.

Not all groups participating in the parade were bands. In fact, most of them weren't. They spaced the ten competing bands over the length of the parade so that their music would not interfere with each other. Along with bands, there were church groups, Shriners in tiny cars, Boy Scout troops, veterans in ill-fitting uniforms, fire departments in their cleanest of clean trucks, and prom queens in their daddy's convertibles. I had not paid any attention to who was in front of us until I took my place at the head of the band. It was the Garrett County Saddle Club, all fifteen of them and all on horseback. I was watching a beautiful Appaloosa mare as she finished pinching off a bread-size loaf of shit when the rider spurred her side and they shot forward. It hit the pavement with a splat, and I looked down at my freshly polished white buck shoes and grimaced.

"We're off!" I yelled at the flag team holding the banner and turned around to face the band.

I glanced back, relieved to see that the sousaphones' spelling was on the mark today. I blew my whistle twice and yelled, "Band, Atten-hut!"

I could see that they all didn't hear the command, so I ran down the side of the band and gave the command again.

This was going to be challenging.

Back at Allegany, there had been no one around, and the only thing my voice and whistle had to compete with was the birds. The road in front of me was crowded with hundreds of people talking and clapping. The other parade groups were making lots of noise, too. I heard engines revving, sirens wailing, and the clopping of the sixty horse hooves right in front of me. I was going to have to get creative if I was going to be heard.

Seeing that everyone was at attention, I stayed on the side of the band, and with four, short whistle blast, I started the drum cadence and the band marking time. *Da dum da da dum, da dum da da dum.* Moving back up front, I saw the flags and majorettes had already started marching, so I threw my arms forward and tweeted once again, and the front row of the band stepped off. As each row saw the one in front of them move, they followed, and suddenly we were all marching in step down Oakland's main street.

Dad came up to my side and said, "Watch for me. I'll stay even with you on the sidewalk to your left."

"Thanks," I said, but I'm not sure he heard me because he had already darted back into the crowd.

I figured we'd better find out if we could play our song and march in this very different environment from the quiet streets of Allegany, so I turned around, and while marching backward, pushed my right arm straight up in the air and blew my whistle louder than I ever had before. I held the blast for a full eight counts, then prayed it would be followed by a roll-off. It was. With the same perfect timing Cody displayed when flicking his hair out of his eyes, his drummers shifted smartly from their monotonous marching cadence to the beginning of the 20th Century Fox sound. Simultaneously, all the band members brought their horns up, and a beat after the drum roll-off ended, the rhythmic thumping of "St. Louis Blues March" started in nice and soft, as we practiced it.

Hey, this isn't so hard after all, I thought as my left foot came down solidly in the middle of a horse pie.

Shit! and I mean that literally. I'll bet the Fort Hill Band Director put those ponies in front of us.

He did not want us to win two years in a row, and his was the only band that had a chance of beating us. My band sounded great though and as it swung its way through the smooth sounds of Glen Miller's march, I was having a great time watching the rear ends of the majorettes swishing and swaying as they tossed their batons into the air.

The crowds lining the street were getting thicker as we approached the downtown. I kept seeing Dad moving along and jumping up every now and then. He had his whistle around his neck, and every time he'd jump into the air, it would rise over his head and then slap back down on his chest. I did not want to play the march too many times before we got to the judges' zone because the trumpet players' embouchure only had so many high A's in them, and I wanted to save their best one for the competition.

We rounded a bend, and I heard the band about five groups ahead of us finish their march, so I decided to give "St. Louis Blues March" one more practice round before we were judged. Like the first try, it all went swimmingly. My eight-count whistle blast was clear, Cody and his drummers slammed into the roll-off perfectly, and the swelling sound of the march began low and built to a crescendo as we planned it.

Squish. I felt another pile of water, oats, and hay splash out from under my foot.

The next horse I see, I'm kicking, I said to myself as the song ended, and the drums smoothly transitioned back into the marching cadence.

I saw the flags stop, and I almost ran over Sandy, the head majorette.

"Sorry," I said as she pranced forward to get out of my way.

I slowed and shot my left hand down by my side with the palm facing backward to warn the band of the coming stop as the wave of deceleration washed over us.

Hey, what do you know? I used the stop hand signal from Driver's Ed. Go figure.

Bunching up, I found myself marking time in the flute section. This was not all bad given I had made sure Patty was positioned right behind me in the front row. I gave her a little nudge and then moved back out a step or two in front. Continuing to mark time, the slow-down gave way, and the band reformed into its well-spaced rectangle like a spring recoiling after compression. That's when I saw my first judge. It was a forty-something, pear-shaped woman with her graying hair pulled back in a ponytail.

Oh, my God, I know what comes out from under those.

She was standing by the curb with her clipboard gripped in her left arm as she captured her impression of the band she'd was judging. We were close to the zone.

I looked to my left and saw a big red, white, and blue ESSO sign over the heads of the spectators. Glancing down, I saw Dad's head pop up, and he was pointing at the sign. I nodded and strained my eyes forward, looking for the white painted line that would mark the beginning of the judge's zone. The horses blocked my view. I noticed two male judges on the right-hand side in a more relaxed state of mind—they could have been waiting for a bus. I figured this was my last chance to look over the band and make any corrections I could, so I turned around and moved across the columns looking down them using my hands to encourage band members to move left or right. I was still marching backward when I saw a bright line of white paint pass under my feet.

Jesus, Mary, and Joseph—we're in the zone.

— The Zone —

Hopping to the center of the band, I knew I had to get that roll-off started quickly, or we would be out of the zone before we finished the song, and that would be the end of our chances to win. Facing the band and throwing my arm up, I was about to let wail a roll-off whistle blast when a fire truck siren cried out over the crowd. I turned around to see where the siren was coming from, keeping my arm in the air. I also held in the enormous breath I had taken for the whistle blast, hoping the siren would die down fast. It did, and I let that air go with all my might. I felt my eardrums push out as my cheeks inflated, and I was afraid I was going to spit my whistle into Sandy's heart-shaped ass. When I was done, I listened for the beautiful sound of the drum roll-off, but there was nothing—total silence—not even the drum cadence that was playing before.

They stopped! Why in the world have they stopped?

All I heard was the *tap, tap, tap* of the band member's feet hitting the pavement as they continued to march forward in silence. I was counting in my head—

1,2,3,4. Trying not to panic, I knew the only thing I could do was wait the full eight counts before trying again.

Realizing I had not faced the band when I blew my whistle, I spun around with my arm still over my head. A blur of motion caught my right eye. I turned my head slightly and saw Dad break through the spectators on the curb and shoot to the back of the band. He saddled up right next to Cody, and I saw him put his whistle in his mouth about an inch from Cody's ear—5,6,7,8—Dad and I together blew our whistles for a second eight-count roll-off command. Cody's head bent hard to starboard from the force of Dad's tweet. One beat later, the most beautiful drum roll-off ever played exploded from our marching silence, and then the band began, with almost baby's breath softness, the march's introduction.

Without a doubt, it was the best rendition of "St. Louis Blues March" we'd ever played, and I could see by the faces of the crowd they loved it. People like to clap their hands to music, but this group was listening and drinking in every aspect of the performance they were witnessing. The trumpets hit their high "A" and then glided down that arpeggio like a skier schussing an icy run. The lower brass banged out the bass, and the woodwinds wailed the boogie-woogie echoing beat to bring the band to the climactic slow-building finale. Starting softly again, everyone knew this was the big moment to hold our fire until the very end—and we did. As we passed by the reviewing stand, I turned the upper portion of my body, so I was facing them and saluted as the band crescendoed the end of the song like a tidal wave hitting a beach. As the drums shifted to their march cadence, I glanced down to see the end of the zone's white line pass beneath my feet.

We made it.

I wanted to talk with Cody and find out what in the world was going on back there, but there was still a little marching to do. We turned left, and I saw Dad walking back to the reviewing stand to find out how we'd done. We'd been the last band to perform, so the results would be announced soon. I knew the parade was over when I saw Sandy slam into a pony's rear end as we started stacking up with the group in front of us.

I gave a halt command, and the band stopped marching for the first time in an hour. I yelled "At ease!" and told everyone to relax until Dad got back with the results.

I was spent, but I still wanted to talk to Cody, so I made my way to the back of the band. He was sitting on his snare with his chin resting on his clenched fists. He looked up and saw me coming and got up slowly, but before I could open my mouth I heard Dad yell, "We won!"

We both turned to see Dad trotting across the courthouse lawn.

"We won? How'd we do that?" I said to Cody as Dad bounced up to us.

"You're not going to believe it," he said as he handed me the piece of paper he was carrying. "Read it. You're not going to believe it."

It was a summary of the judge's results. We had indeed come in first place, but it was how we got there that floored me. Our technical score was 86 out of 100, but that was the same score Fort Hill's band received. Under normal circumstances, we should have tied, but the judges gave us five bonus points for our outstanding musical interpretation and performance. They specifically noted our dramatic silent marching prior to beginning our song.

Ha! Like that was planned.

Passing the paper to Cody, Dad laughed and said, "Kid, I don't know what you and your drummers were doing back there, but whatever it was, it's why we won."

Cody looked up from the paper, pushed the hair out of his eyes and said, "Got it."

Chapter 10 - Superstar

— ALCO Spirit & Walter —

Things settled into an orderly process; I'd drive to school each day with Dad, suffer through my classes, then work with the band on the upcoming halftime show. The football games were on Friday, and the band would take the field and strut their stuff. The team was going gangbusters, beating every school they faced, which meant that the only thing standing between us and a perfect season was Turkey Day. Fort Hill was having a good season too, having lost only one game. That meant Turkey Day was stacking up to be a true battle of the champions, and Cumberland was alive with the prospect.

Not all residents in Cumberland put up decorations for Christmas, but for Turkey Day they do, or at least it looks that way. Signs, placards, bunting, colored streamers, buttons, corsages, hats, lights, T-shirts. You name it, and you'd see it as Turkey Day neared. If you were alive, you had to let everyone know whether you were for Big Blue or Big Red. Even businesses boasted whether they wanted an ALCO or a Fort Hill victory although there were a few of them that hedged their bets and had displays supporting both teams but in different parts of the store.

For the first time, I decided to contribute to this lunacy and produce a sign of my own, but I didn't want a little pep rally-sized sign. No, I wanted it to be big. Big enough to be seen by everyone on Turkey Day. To do this I needed a large canvas for my masterpiece, so I turned to the Tastee Freez.

The cake cones we used to serve ice cream came in cardboard boxes that stood four feet tall and were three feet wide on each side. When emptied, cut and folded out flat, they formed an area twelve by four feet. Over the course of a month, we'd go through about three of these, so it wasn't hard for me to get two of them. On the Saturday before the game, I took the boxes and cut them into four, equal-sized rectangles of six by four feet each. These would form the foundation of my Turkey Day sign, and as you might guess my sign would spell out ALCO. They would be big, but I wanted them to be bold as well, so I painted my cardboard placards dark blue and added one letter to each one in bright white paint. They were spectacular. I then reinforced their back with flat pieces of wood so they could withstand the rigors of any mounting location. My signs were ready. Now all I needed was to figure out a place to put them in the stadium.

Since Turkey Day was a battle between two schools in Cumberland, each year one was designated the visiting team, and in 1971, it was Allegany's turn, so we would occupy the wooden bleacher side of the stadium. From a sign standpoint, this was not ideal because there was less display area on that side.

The conventional wooden bleachers of the visitor side started at ground level and climbed up an excavated hillside until they reached a brick building housing bathrooms and the radio station's observation deck. There was a railing at the base of the seating, and small signs could be hung here but could not block the fan's view. The brick building was off limits. Knowing this, I decided to drive up to the stadium to investigate my options. It was a risky proposition for a true-blue Allegany student to venture into enemy territory this close to the day of battle, but I needed to do it. Luckily, my red and white Barracuda provided excellent camouflage.

I don't know why my father bought a red and white car, but my bet would be it was the cheapest one on the lot. Even though it was the right color for a drive to Fort Hill, it still had a problem—a huge, blue Allegany decal on the back window. After putting on the only piece of red clothing I owned—a University of Maryland sweatshirt—I got Dad's duct tape and covered up the decal. Then I was off to pick up my good friend Walter Neff who was serving detention at Allegany. Flash Faherty had caught Walter standing suspiciously near the entrance to the girl's locker room. The rumor was that if you stood in front of the art classroom across from the girl's locker room door, you could see all the way into the showers if you tilted your head just right. You had to wait for the door to swing wide open and then peer through the crack on the hinge side of the door.

Well, that's what I was told, but I never saw a damn thing.

The roads to Allegany were safe territory. Everywhere I looked, I saw ALCO signs nailed to trees and telephone poles or hanging from front porches. As I turned on to the school's street, there were life-size cut-out plywood statues of football players in varying football poses. Ones like where the player has the ball tucked under one arm, and his other arm is sticking straight out, palm up and his knee is pulled up tight covering his groin. He looks like he's fending off a tackle or has just seen a mouse. *Eeek!*

Each of the cut-outs was painted blue and white and had a player's team number on it. It was customary for the girlfriend of each player to paint kiss impressions on the cheek of the cut-outs with their lipstick. Even now, decades later, I'm shaking my head at this silliness.

I saw Walter sitting on the two-foot wall that ran along the outdoor covered walkway connecting the side of the gym to the rest of the school. He was talking to Donna Diamond one of the most vivacious cheerleaders. I beeped my horn and skidded to a stop.

Teenagers must always make noise with their car when stopping or pulling out—it's the law.

He ran over, jumped in, and we were off to Fort Hill.

Walter was just figuring out that he was a really good looking well-built guy. He was heavy as a child, but by sixteen, he was nearing six feet tall, his baby-fat had burned off, and he was lifting weights. Suddenly he looked like a young, Burt Reynolds. That meant girls started noticing Walter, and Walter started catching girls. His confidence soared.

"What's the plan?" asked Walter.

"I will park near Brown's store about three blocks from the stadium. I figure it's better to walk to the field instead of driving, to keep to a minimum the chance of any Fort Hill asshole seeing my decal. You know they've got delinquents up here serving detention like you were," I said.

Walter's palm hit the back of my head. "You turd! Detention isn't all that bad. Flash made me push a broom around the basketball court, and I got to watch the cheerleaders practice while I was sweeping. Did you see me with Donna Diamond? She's as hot as a gas griddle."

I was passing over the railroad tracks at the far end of downtown when a sense of unease filled the car. We were in the demilitarized zone between Allegany and Fort Hill. The second we turned right in front of the YMCA, we were in the world of red. Nothing made the danger more apparent than the uniformed effigy of an ALCO player lynched from the limb of a big oak tree. It swayed in the breeze, noose cinched tight around its neck, with a tortured face painted on the head. A sign was pinned to its chest reading, "You're in Sentinel Territory." The Sentinel was Fort Hill's mascot, and it made much more sense than ALCO's Camper. The Sentinel was a Revolutionary War soldier in full battle dress, equipped with a musket.

Walter Neff (Syckes Family Photos)

As we continued, we saw hundreds of signs like the ones near Allegany, but they were all red and white now. Fort Hill plywood football player cut-outs appeared attached to every tree lining the street. Walter flicked his half-spent Winston at one of them, and I saw the red-hot ash burst as it struck a red helmet.

"Shit, Walter, you want to get us killed?!" I yelled.

"Screw 'em. What are they gonna do?" Walter boasted.

At the top of the curvy hill, we found ourselves at Brown's store. I pulled into a parking spot on the side of the building, turned off the car, and looked over at Walter.

"Please be cool. We don't need to start anything we can't finish," I whispered.

"Right. What do you want me to do?" Walter asked.

"When we get to the stadium, we'll circle it and look for good places to put my signs. You go right, and I'll go left, and we'll meet on the other side. I need to know what equipment to bring to put them up. Remember, I want them somewhere they'll be seen, and they need a load of space, over 80 square feet."

"You know you're nuts, right?" Walter laughed as he opened his door and searched for another Winston.

He lit it with his favorite Zippo and asked if I wanted one. I almost said yes, thinking it might be smart to have a cigarette hanging out of my mouth, to look as tough as I could, but then I remembered how I had hated smoking when I tried it at church camp. We walked up the street to Fort Hill. It would be the most dangerous part of our trip to the wrong side of the tracks because we had to walk in front of the high school before we got to the stadium.

Walter was the second of my two best friends growing up. Tim was the other, and like Tim, sometimes Walter and I were inseparable, but there were also times when we didn't see each other for months. That was when I was with Tim. We all lived in the same neighborhood, but Tim and Walter were never friends. Walter had one advantage over Tim, though. Whereas Tim was the oldest of seven children, six of them boys, Walter only had an older sister, and she was something special indeed.

Kathy Neff was beautiful—I mean drop-dead gorgeous—and this was not just my opinion. She had been crowned Miss Frostburg State College and was on her way to the Miss Maryland pageant soon. She won and went on to finish in the top five of the Miss America pageant of 1972. She was still living at home, and so as an over-sexed, underfed teenage boy, spending time at Walter's house was a lot more fun than going to Tim's.

— Saved by The Bell —

Fort Hill was well-named. It sat on a hill, and it looked kind of like a fort, but I always thought it looked more like a prison. Larger in all aspects than Allegany, Fort Hill was a smartly designed high school and provided enough space for all desired activities.

Things were quiet as we strolled by the main entrance and hurried down the hill to the front of the stadium. As we approached, we heard the football team practicing on the stadium's field. I told Walter, "We have to be extra careful; they'll be watching for ALCO spies trying to learn their playbook."

As we got to the edge of the concrete bleachers, we split up. In designing my sign, I figured the easiest way to display it would be to attach the letters, side by side, to the front of a fence or wall, but as I made my way around the stadium, I saw I was late to the game. Every square inch of the ALCO side was papered in blue and white signs. I found out later that the day before was "decorate the stadium day," and everyone was allowed to put up their signs unmolested. There was a lot of open area on the hillsides of the wooden bleachers, but I knew many fans would be there on Turkey Day.

The two sides of the stadium had a seating capacity of 6,000, but for big events like Turkey Day, they sold non-bleacher seats. The fire marshal's approved total capacity was 8,000 however; the fire marshal was always on paid vacation on Thanksgiving so the number could swell beyond that. That made the hillside a poor choice. Walter and I rejoined at the far side of the visitor's bleachers, and I asked him if he saw any good places for my sign.

"No way, unless you attach them to the hedges to the left and right of the scoreboard," Walter offered.

I looked at the scoreboard and contemplated what it would take to attach my letters to the bushes. It would be tough, and again, there would be hundreds of people standing, sitting and jostling in that area, so the likelihood of anyone seeing my work was slim.

"Hey, you should rent a helicopter and fly them over the stadium?" Walter joked.

I looked up and that's when I saw it. Over Walter's smoke-encircled head was the perfect place for my signs—one of the six 100-foot-tall lighting towers that had created the impression of eyes during my first pregame show.

That's it! Instead of attaching my letters horizontally, I'll go vertical.

"Hey, you kids," I heard a man bark from the base of the bleachers. "What are you doing up there?"

Startled, I whispered to Walter, "Let's beat it."

He smiled and waved to the guy then yelled, "Fort Hill sucks!"

The guy said something to the other people nearby him then started running up the bleachers.

"Jesus, Walter," I squeaked as I ran back around the stadium the way I came.

He followed me after thrusting his right hand up at the attacking horde with his middle finger displayed. We had an advantage given we didn't have to climb up bleachers, but it wasn't that much of an advantage. Instead of going all the way back around to the front of the stadium, we ducked into a walkway that ran beside the Fort Hill gymnasium. It led to the front of the school and cut our time to return to the car in half. We looked back to see how near death we were and saw nothing, no charging multitude of foam-frothing Fort Hill bullies, nothing, so we slowed and started laughing as we approached the store.

"I'm going to get some smokes," Walter said as he turned in to Brown's.

"Please, remember to be cool," I pleaded, and I decided to wait in the car.

We had already tempted fate too much today, and I needed to get back home and figure out how I would attach my signs to that tower. I turned in to the parking lot on the side of the store and saw, to my horror, three Fort Hill thugs sitting on the trunk of my Barracuda. One of them had a ball of wadded up duct tape in his hand, and I could see my Allegany decal was again visible on my back window.

"This your car, dick?" the one with the duct tape snarled.

I felt my primordial fight-or-flight response kick in. There was no way I would let fight win, so I backed up slowly.

"Hey, stop, or I'll take a brick to this back window, so I don't have to look at this pussy blue sticker anymore," he said as he slid off the trunk of the car.

I kept backing up until I heard Walter's voice whisper from behind me, "Keep them busy for a minute, I can fix this."

Say what? Keep them busy! How? Let them beat on me until you figure out how we get away?

I smiled and stopped. "Listen, guys; I've got no quarrel with you. I was over here picking up medicine for my sick grandmother. She's got the flu and needs Vic's Vapor Rub for her chest," I babbled until interrupted.

"Oh yeah, then why in the hell did you cover up your ALCO decal. Get over here," my tormentor ordered.

This cannot be happening. I had maybe ten feet between me and three slope-headed losers, and Walter wanted me to keep them busy.

"You guys on the football team?" I whimpered.

The other two boys slid off the trunk. All three of them were moving towards me when I heard a loud bell ringing. It was like the bells at school for changing classes, but this one kept ringing. I was pushed forward by a lady who was holding a wet newspaper over her head. Following her were several others who were also either damp or soaked to the bone. That's when I saw Walter at the back of the building, waving to me. The three guys were looking at each other in an obvious attempt to muster enough brain power to decide whether they should stay or go. Apparently, go won because they darted away from my car as we all heard a new sound. Well, it wasn't a new sound for me, but unlike the last time I heard it, this time I was glad. It was a police siren.

No, wait. That's not the police—it's the fire department!

I slid along the wall to my car, popped open the driver's side door, and started it up. Before I was sure the engine had caught, I slammed it down into reverse and hit the gas. The back end of the Barracuda shot across the parking lot and started to climb a six-foot hedge before I could get it into drive and spin the wheel enough to clear the fender of the car parked on my left.

Walter was running towards me. I leaned over and pulled the door handle, letting it swing open as I turned left onto the road that wound its way behind houses before popping out back on the main drag. Only slowing enough for Walter to dive in, I made the turn, and we accelerated down the brick-paved street. Walter was clutching the center console and squirming to right himself in the seat while laughing hysterically. I reached over with my right hand and grabbed his belt, stopping him from sliding out—he felt like a wet dog.

"Did you see the look on those assholes' faces?" he belched. "They didn't know whether to shit or run naked."

"What did you do, pull the fire alarm?" I asked as I spun the steering wheel hard right to negotiate my entrance back onto our road to safety.

The back end of the Barracuda hopped around the turn. Walter managed to close his door and sit upright in the seat. He pulled his Zippo out of his front pocket and flipped it down in one smooth motion. As the top swung away from the satin-finished lighter body, a bright, warm flame enveloped the wind-protected wick.

The smell of lighter fluid filled my nose as Walter boasted, "Nope, but I found out if you accidentally put your lighter too close to a fire sprinkler head, the whole damn system goes off. I almost drowned before I could get out of that little window in the bathroom." We were about to reach downtown when Walter shouted, "Stop the car!"

I slid into a parking spot in front of the Methodist church as Walter reached into his other pocket.

"Look what I found on my way to the bathroom," he said.

He had three Cover Girl lipstick tubes in his hand as he popped open his door and dashed across the street. After checking for any pursuing police or Sentinels, I looked to my left to see what he was up to. He was busy at work on the plywood cut out of Fort Hill's star quarterback, Mark Manges. His statue was standing, legs astride, resembling the Colossus of Rhodes with a football cocked back in his right hand, ready to throw a Hail Mary. Walter was focused a bit lower down, and I had to get out of the car to see what he was doing. Using the bright red lipstick, he outlined big bright lips around Mark's naughty bits, and he signed it, "Love ya big boy, Coach."

I knew we had to get out of there fast. If anyone saw him, we'd be dead.

I swung a hard left into traffic and pulled up beside Walter. He was standing and was stepping back to admire his work when I screamed, "Get in the goddamn car!"

Slowly returning the cap to the top of the lipstick, Walter sauntered back to the Barracuda and dropped into his seat. I hit the gas and ran a red light as I turned onto the avenue that led to The Bridge. I would have to wait and take my signs up to the stadium on game day. But, how in the hell was I going to climb up that light tower holding four six-foot signs and a roll of duct tape? I had to go up at least thirty feet, or the last letter wouldn't be visible.

— The Pep Rally —

The day before the big game was pep rally day, and as wild as things had already been, today the crazy meter would be pegged. It was mandatory to wear some blue clothing, and senior guys were going around checking compliance and providing painful noogies for those found wanting. Many a boy saved himself by pointing to the blue line on the waistband of their Fruit-of-the-Loom underwear. The entire afternoon was dedicated to glorifying everything Allegany and denigrating everything Fort Hill.

Classes were canceled, replaced by two hours of speeches, endless cheers, introductions, skits, musical numbers and dance performances. I, of course, was right in the middle of it all. Along with my drum major responsibilities, I organized a small group of juniors to make fun of the Fort Hill band. Each class had to put on a skit at the pep rally, and my group would represent the juniors. We planned to dress as hillbillies, stumble around the gym floor making horrible sounds on our instruments, and encourage the student body to mock and ridicule us.

It's the American way.

My last class before the pep rally was Gary Durr's social studies. With only ten minutes left, I was studiously drawing pictures of the dashboard of my Barracuda, trying to figure out the best place to install an 8-track tape player. I had been lusting for weeks after a Mad-Man-Muntz unit on sale at Sears but didn't have the $45 needed to buy it. I was using my ruler to check my measurements when I heard Mr. Durr ask, "Shelby, can you tell me what we call the first ten amendments to the Constitution?"

Was that my name?

"Shelby, are you with us?" Mr. Durr asked.

"Yes, sir," I blurted.

Gary Durr was about six-foot-four and weighed maybe 135 pounds. In his brown three-piece suit, he looked like the stick the janitor used to squeegee the school's second-floor windows from outside. He'd been a basketball player and did not think much of the hoopla surrounding football. I was not making his teaching life that rewarding, either.

"Balance of power," I said with no confidence, hoping the first thing that popped into my head was right.

"No, that's between the branches of government, Mr. Durr said, shaking his head.

The bell rang, and Mr. Durr's face acknowledged the futility of trying to make me a better citizen. Saved by the bell again, I jumped up, grabbed my books, and ran straight for the band room. The quickest way to get there was to go down to the ground floor. As I entered the stairwell, I saw Eddie Deezen cowering in the corner of the landing below me. Surrounding him were three senior boys demanding he recite the words to "'Tis Allegany" correctly or they'd stuff him in a locker. I felt for him, having endured this trial myself as a freshman. Eddie was a skinny, geeky, class clown trying to survive his first year of high school.

I'm sure today those bullies wish they'd treated him better—he's one of only two movie stars Allegany High school has produced. After graduating, Eddie was discovered on *The Gong Show*, then appeared in some of the biggest hit movies of the next three decades. Films directed by Steven Spielberg and Robert Zemeckis, like *1941, Grease, War Games*, and *Polar Express*. Despite his fame, I'm sure he still remembers all the words to "'Tis Allegany." For the record, the other movie star who graduated from Allegany is William H. Macy.

Eddie Deezen (Allegwee 1972)

I exited the ground floor doors planning to cut left and run to the gym. I didn't have my coat, but it hadn't been too cold that morning, maybe 44 degrees. When I pushed open the outside door, I felt a stiff, decidedly cold, wind that felt no warmer than 35. The sky had that winter gray look, too, but so what?

It was late November in the Appalachian Mountains—it's supposed to look like that.

A lot of the other band members were already in the band room when I arrived, and it didn't take long for the rest of them to show up. I blew my whistle and said, "Make sure you have all your music, including tomorrow's halftime show, in case they ask us to play more songs; then head to the gym."

Like the football team, the band was having a great season. With our successful first halftime performance and the win at the parade, we cautiously increased the complexity of both the songs and the drills at each of the following games, but the band took it all in their stride. Each week, we got better and better, and now we were ready for the Turkey Day Game with two hot-off-the-presses Broadway show tunes that all the Baby Boomers could relate to. Oh, and Al Homburg would love them too. We were playing the theme song from *Jesus Christ Superstar* and another number from the rock opera called "*Hosanna.*"

The gym looked as if we were preparing for a human sacrifice. Signs covered all the walls and dangled from strings over the basketball court. There was also a fake bonfire in the center, and cheerleaders dressed as Indians with war paint streaked across their cheeks danced in a circle around it doing war whoops and cheers. Adding to the drama, cardboard cut-outs of fearsome-looking Indians were placed at every corner of the court. Black pots filled with water and chunks of dry ice created clouds of billowing smoke.

I kicked things off by having the band play "Red River Rock" as the principal and front office staff took their seats. Everyone was standing and clapping along with us, and as we finished, there was a reverberating echo in the room from the crescendoing force of the sound. The gym's amplification system turned on, and Bob Hutcheson stepped out on the court with a microphone in his hand, but he only got about four feet before the mic's cord caught on the edge of the bleachers and jerked him back like a running dog reaching the end of his leash.

Thunk! echoed through the room as the mic hit the floor. This was followed by a roar of laughter as Flash Faherty shot out from under the far end of the bleachers and made a beeline run for the mic. He was squatting as he ran, under the impression that if he sunk low enough to the floor, we wouldn't see him. He scooped up the mic, untangled the cord, and thrust it up to Big Bob with one hand, his body never rising higher than three feet. There was more applause as Flash skittered back under the bleachers, and Mr. Hutcheson continued his walk to center court. The cheerleaders were kneeling in front of the fake bonfire, and the principal stopped right in front of them, creating an uneasy tableau, more Sermon on the Mount than high school motivational speech.

"Good afternoon, students and teachers of Allegany High School, the only high school in Western Maryland to have an undefeated season so far," Hutcheson said with great gusto.

ALCO Band Turkey Day Pep Rally 1971 (Syckes Family Photos)

The stands erupted with cheers and applause that lasted thirty seconds. Turning in my direction, Big Bob said, "Now, let's all stand and join the band in singing the national anthem."

I led the band in "The Star-Spangled Banner" as the flag squad marched the American and Maryland flags around the gym. I knew next up would be the introduction of the coaching staff and then the football team, and I planned to play "'Tis Allegany" as the cheerleaders formed a tunnel for the players to parade through, but I wanted to do something more, something different and special, so I whispered to the front row of the band, "Before we play "Tis Allegany,' play the first eight bars of 'Superstar.'"

There were a lot of blank looks, but I saw Sam Nutter flipping through his music, instinctively knowing what I wanted to do. Sam Nutter was a gifted musician and one of the finest trumpet players ever to play at Allegany. But, Sam had other gifts. He was a gigolo and a pirate, which I came to appreciate later.

— Sam, Mixing Music, & High Kicks —

From an early age, Sam had only one goal in life: get laid by as many girls as possible. I don't know what the body count is today, but he amassed a pretty large number when I knew him. Adopted into a respected home, both of Sam's

169

parents were teachers in the Allegany County school system. His dad, Bob Nutter, was a music teacher who traveled to all the elementary schools in the county teaching beginner's wind instruments. After my father, he was my first music teacher, and he was great with his students: kind, patient, and understanding. Bob Nutter's instruction was a great way to learn how to play an instrument.

Unfortunately, he displayed none of these characteristics in Sam's musical education. He was a total tyrant. Every day after school, Sam was expected to practice his trumpet for three hours and then do his homework. That was every weekday—no exceptions. Sam told me later how he longed to go out and play, but he could not. He was also not allowed to participate in organized sports or other groups like Boy Scouts. It was all music all the time. This determination on Mr. Nutter's part paid off in two significant ways. Sam became the best trumpet player in Allegany County as well as a borderline juvenile delinquent. Whenever he was set free from his practicing, he would go wild and make up for all his lost play time by causing as much trouble as possible. Sam's other gift was inbred. He looked a bit like Paul Newman and had strong independent sex appeal as well. Girls liked Sam, and Sam knew how to talk to girls, which meant that Sam succeeded in getting into their pants most of the time.

Sam on The Make (Allegwee 1972)

Having found his copy of "Superstar," Sam stood and moved through the band, instructing everyone on what it was I wanted them to do. He told them that if they didn't have the part or didn't feel confident enough to play it right to sit out the intro and come in on "'Tis Allegany." I helped Sam organize my plan as the coaching staff said a few words of encouragement.

As I stepped off the bleachers, Head Coach Stimmel was striding to the microphone wearing a full Indian headdress. As the mastermind of ALCO's winning season, it was his turn in the spotlight. I cued the drummer to play a tom-tom beat as Coach Stimmel acknowledged the cheers of the students. Waving his arms like he was fanning a fire, he encouraged the crowd to quiet down so he could give his prepared speech.

Coach Stimmel carefully unfolded a piece of paper from his suit coat pocket and preceded to stumble through the dullest summary of the strategies he applied to beat each of the teams we'd faced that season. This included the sequencing of plays and the players running them. He apparently misplaced the second page of his speech, so he ended abruptly halfway through the fifth game. Bob Hutcheson saved him by clapping him on the back and grabbing the mic and saying, "Let's hear it for the finest football coach in Allegany High School history!"

Big Bob looked at me, and I cued up the music for the players' entrance. Looking at the band, I scanned them all, nodding and mouthing "'Superstar' then 'Tis Allegany.' 'Superstar' then 'Tis Allegany.'" I got mostly positive nods back, so I was hopeful.

Mr. Hutcheson spoke again, "And now the moment we've all been waiting for. Let's welcome the undefeated Allegany Campers' football team!"

The cheerleaders were in two lines leading from the side entrance to the gym floor as I started the band. Bursting from it came the unmistakable quarter-note, eighth-note, half-note descending-third chords of the opening bars of "Superstar" followed quickly by four pounding sixteenth-note drum beats. This repeated four times as the undisputed royalty of the school sauntered onto the court.

When teenage football-loving boys in men's bodies are worshiped as gods, they tend to take on an attitude of slouching coolness that is hard to describe. Instead of standing tall and accepting the adoration of their worshiping masses, they walk with a drooping shuffle that is a mixture of John Wayne and Stepin' Fetchit.

I don't know; I guess that's what cool looks like on the move.

The "Superstar" intro caught a lot of students off guard because most of them were staring at the band instead of the football players, and at the end of it, the band broke into "'Tis Allegany." I saw Sam wince in pain, and I knew why. Although the "Superstar" intro provided the grand opening effect I was hoping for; I had not foreseen the dissonant clashing of the different musical keys of the two songs. "Superstar" was written in a different key than "'Tis Allegany," and so it sounded like someone had accidentally sped up a reel-to-reel tape player in the middle of a song. It was jarring. Fortunately, the crowd was too entranced by the pageantry and didn't notice much. As the football players finished their parade around the basketball court, they sat on a row of chairs the cheerleaders had quickly aligned in front of the main bleachers facing the court. It was time for the floor show where each class would put on a skit appropriate for the occasion.

First up was a group of freshmen who read a poem they had composed about the football team. Eager to miss this groan-fest, I joined my group of juniors to get ready for our mock Fort Hill band parade. There were eight of us, and most carried an instrument that was either damaged or badly configured. Only one of us had a fully functioning horn, and I encouraged him to play it as loud as he could. That was Chucky Grainfield.

The sophomores were finishing their Indian-themed skit when it was time for us to take the floor. Dressed as hillbillies, we wore an assortment of long underwear, torn shirts, or dirty overalls as we lined up to march. Mr. Hutcheson introduced us with great formality, saying, "Wanting to be fair and balanced, we welcome the Fort Hill Marching Band to perform for us today."

With that, we made a lot of bad music as we marched around the court. It was hard for all of us except Chucky. The students booed and jeered us, and several items flew in our direction from the stands, including an algebra textbook. I went to the band room and took off my costume, and by the time I returned, the seniors were ending this portion of the pep rally with a presentation to Coach Stimmel of a plaque listing his victories.

In retrospect, the next part of the pep rally can only be classified as sexist exploitation of young women—it was the Arrowettes' turn to perform in front of the team. I gave the horns up signal and started the band. Two long lines of the drill team came prancing onto the court from opposite ends. JoAnn was on the microphone to introduce her pride and joy.

The Arrowettes formed a long line in front of the football team, and as the song came to an end, they executed their rolling-wave bow. Trying to keep things moving, I had the band play "Everything's Coming up Roses," and the Arrowettes did their high-kick routine a few feet in front of the thirty-five member football team.

Now That's Entertainment (Syckes Family Photo)

As the girls kicked their legs high over their heads, the enjoyment of the football players was obvious. You'd have to pay a $10 cover charge with a two-drink minimum to see this kind of entertainment anywhere else, but today, it was just for the conquering heroes of ALCO High.

The pep rally was coming to a close when I glanced up to my left at the long bank of windows running the full length of the gymnasium, and I saw it was snowing, and I mean snowing hard. Mr. Hutcheson was back on the PA, telling everyone to be safe driving home and that he'd see us all at the game tomorrow. The pep rally was over.

— Donuts —

"Patty," I said catching her as she stood up to go. "Do you need a ride home?"

"Yes, please, but can you take Connie, too? She's stuck here waiting for her mother," Patty answered.

"Sure, meet me in front of the gym in five minutes," I said and went to pick up my hillbilly costume in the band room.

There I found Dad, whom I hadn't seen all day. He had his camera and had been taking pictures of the pep rally. Dad and I met the girls in front of the gym, and we all were surprised at the density of the snowfall.

"Look at that, it's really coming down fast," I said.

"It can't keep that up for long; a heavy wet snow usually means it will be over quickly," Dad shared.

"Good," I said. "We don't want to be marching in snow tomorrow."

I drove Dad home first, then took Connie to her house. The roads were still clear of snow, but it was starting to accumulate on the grass. I stayed at Patty's until *The French Chef* was over, then went home to get my uniform in order as well as finalize my plans for securing the ALCO sign to the light tower.

The snow continued, and it started to cover the roads. On my way home, I tried to think of how to get those signs up that tower without killing myself. I knew I would need help, so I'd enlisted Walter again as my wingman. He'd be critical in giving me a boost up to the first rung of the ladder on the tower's leg. The first rung was ten feet off the ground to discourage idiots like me from climbing it, but that part didn't worry me. What I was worried about was having to go up and down that tower more than once. How could I avoid attaching my letters to the tower one at a time? There would be police at the game, and I was pretty sure climbing the light towers was frowned upon.

There must be a way to get them all up there at once.

Sliding a bit as I rounded a turn, I saw an American flag snapping in the breeze at the top of a pole, and I thought of Dad's Oberlin bicycle prank. Remember, Mom's story of Dad running a bike up a flagpole? I realized: *That's how to get those signs up there! I'll hook them all together and pull them all up at once with a rope. Hell, it might work.*

When I got home, I spent the next hour modifying the signs so they could be hoisted up the tower together, then I left with Dad to have dinner with Mom downtown. It was the day before Thanksgiving, and Peskin's was staying open late for a Turkey Day sale.

By the time we finished dinner, there were three inches of snow covering everything, and the temperature was dropping. The digital thermometer on the First National Bank read 30 degrees.

Dad looked around as we walked to the car, and I asked, "Will they cancel the game tomorrow if this keeps up?"

"I have no idea. It's never happened before. By the way, I need you to close up the Tastee Freez for me tonight because I have to pick up Mom from work. I don't want her driving home in this," Dad said.

"No problem," I said with the maximum amount of calmness I could muster while I was jumping for joy inside. Dad was asking me to drive the car in the snow, and every teenage boy in America knows what that means.

Donuts!

In a ritual carried out for decades on the first of December every year, Dad would take our cars to Smitty's ESSO station and have snow tires put on them. In the world before steel-belted radials, cars needed extra traction if you wanted to get anywhere in the wintertime. It was only November 24th, so when I'd venture out tonight, I would be rolling on the Kelly Springfield bias-ply blackwalls Dad had on the Barracuda. I might as well be on Billy Kidd Skis. This may sound frightening to you, but to me, it was a new adventure. When nine o'clock rolled around, I was out the door to brush the latest inch of snow off my windshield and slide the Barracuda down the driveway.

The Dingle roads were a bit slick, but the heavily traveled streets were just slushy, so it wasn't too tough making my way up the interstate ramp. When I got to the Tastee Freez, most of the evening-shift workers had gone home. It didn't take me long to close out the cash register, and as I opened the door returning from depositing the money in the bank, Ernie—the Tastee Freez's resident idiot—was on his way out. He had on his winter coat, and a camouflage hunting hat with the ear flaps pulled down and cinched tight under his chin. He looked like Ernest T. Bass from *The Andy Griffith Show.*

I saw two Morton Salt containers tucked under his arm as he handed me a quarter and said, "Tell your dad I took these in case I get stuck in the snow."

"Ernie, do you think you can live on salt until the rescue crews find you?" I asked.

"Nah, silly. I'll use the salt to melt the snow under my tires." He laughed and continued to his dirt-colored Duster.

After locking up the store, I hopped into the Barracuda and fired up the engine. I turned on the radio to hear John Lennon's latest monster hit single, "Imagine." Looking out at the vast, empty, snow-covered asphalt parking lot of the Tastee Freez, I smiled as John Lennon sang;

"You may say I'm a dreamer.

But I'm not the only one.

I hope someday you'll join us,

and the world will be as one."

I hit the gas and turned the wheel as hard as I could, spinning in lovely concentric circles around and around.

— Meanwhile —

About two thousand, three hundred miles northwest of Cumberland, cruising at approximately ten thousand feet, a Northwest Airlines 727 was en route from Seattle to Mexico City with a lone highjacker onboard. As I was doing donuts at the Tastee Freez, D. B. Cooper lowered the airstream passenger steps integrated into the tail of the plane and jumped out with $200,000 in cash, never to be seen again (13).

It's nice to know I wasn't the only one having fun that night.

The snow was still coming down as I drove home creeping along the road to the interstate eastbound ramp. Spread along one lane was coal ash providing me needed traction, so negotiating the hills and turns was reasonably easy. Finding myself at the bottom of Dingle hill, I knew getting up there was going to be tough sledding. There were only a few tire tracks plowed through the snow, so I backed up a bit to get a running start. I was going about 40 mph as I passed the stone towers that guard either side of the entrance to the Dingle, and although my traction was tenuous, my momentum made up for it. I didn't touch the breaks until I was sure I'd get to the top of the hill and before I knew it, I breezed past my house. I hit the brakes and turned the wheel to park in front of the neighbor's house but felt the car's weak grip on the snow give way.

I slid sideways towards Judge Shear's front lawn. I felt the car jump as it hit something solid, and I knew I'd vaulted the curb. After my abrupt stop, I got out and surveyed my parking job. No big trees or small dogs were hit, so I declared it successful. I looked up and could see the snow had changed from the dense wet flakes of this afternoon to tiny crystalline specks almost salt-like in appearance. The sky was a ripple of dark chocolate as I passed through the shine of the harsh street light reflecting off the snow. Snowfall has a magical way of amplifying the silence of a dark night, and as I walked across my front lawn, I could hear the exaggerated crunch of each of my footfalls. I thought of all that had happened today and wondered what tomorrow would bring. There were at least six inches of snow already and no sign it was going to stop anytime soon.

Looking up at the sky, I said out loud, "There is no way we will have the game tomorrow. No way at all."

Chapter 11 - Signs

— WTBO —

"**W**ell, it looks like I lose again," Joleen Johnson said as she spread her cards on the counter at the Tastee Freez.

"Your straight beats my pair of aces; I guess I'll have to take off my shirt."

She pulled her sweatshirt over her head, and as her pair of aces slid out and bounced a bit, Dill Denton said, "Do you like what you see, Shelby?"

The sweatshirt was off now, but it was Dill's head talking on Joleen's body.

What the hell? I thought as a shiver ran down my spine. "Brr," I buzzed as I glanced down.

Shit, I'm naked!

My eyes shot open, and I realized I'd been dreaming.

"Good morning, Cumberland, and happy Thanksgiving! You're listening to WTBO, and we'll be covering today's top story. We've got eleven inches of snow out there, and nobody knows how it will affect the Turkey Day game," my clock radio sang.

Sitting up, I thought, *Oh, man, Joleen is so hot.*

I had set my radio's alarm, and it had turned on at 8 a.m. to Cumberland's oldest radio station, WTBO. The station was a fixture of the city's skyline with fifteen-foot-high letters blinking in red neon light on a hill overlooking downtown. You could not miss them if you wanted to and the joke every third grader told was, "Do you know what WTBO stands for? Why tubes burn out."

The sun was shining into my room as if it were a midsummer's morning, but when I looked out the window, all I saw was white. Everything and I mean everything, was covered in Uncle Lu's soft-serve ice cream. Yard landmarks, bushes, and rocks were bumps in the creamy carpet. Even Dad's big Buick looked like a frozen goiter on the neck of the driveway.

The WTBO announcer reported, "The Cumberland Valley Athletic League reconvened its meeting this morning at 7:30 a.m. after adjourning last night without a decision on whether the football game should be canceled. Members of the coaching staff of both Fort Hill and Allegany were asked to attend and be prepared to make recommendations."

You mean they haven't canceled the game yet? They've got to be kidding. It looks like a Yeti wonderland out there.

"But, there's good news in the forecast for today, folks," the announcer continued. "It's already 33 degrees, and the weatherman is predicting a high temp of forty by this afternoon. That means we will see this snow melt and melt quickly. But it will take time for that, and the game is going to start in less than five hours. If they go forward, it will be more like mud wrestling than football."

Oh my God, what will happen to my beautiful white uniform?

I jumped out of bed and for no good reason, ran to my closet and checked over my uniform.

The phone rang, and answering, I heard Walter's sweet voice say, "Wake up, you homo, the game is on."

"How do you know? WTBO says the CVAL meeting is still underway," I asked.

"They don't know dick. I talked to a member of the team, and he's been told to report to the stadium for pre-game warm-up at 11," Walter boasted.

The radio was playing Jerry Reed's hit song "When You're Hot, You're Hot" when the announcer bumped his microphone and interrupted, saying, "We've just received official word that the Turkey Day game is a go. It will start as scheduled today at 1 p.m. in Greenway Stadium. I have a request from the president of the CVAL that students and all interested parties are encouraged to help their staff clear the snow from the stadium. The gates are open, and if you want to help, please bring your own snow shovels."

"Did you hear that?" I asked.

"Yeah, that's what I was calling you about. Are you still gonna put up those signs?" Walter asked.

"You bet your ass I am."

"Okay, there is no way you will make it up here; the road's a mess. I'll walk down to your place," Walter said.

"Okay, when will you get here?" I asked a dead phone line. Walter hangs up when he's done whether the other party is finished or not.

The radio announcer continued, "Here's what we know about the CVAL meeting: The president of the league left the decision up to the head coaches, and Fort Hill's Coach Lattimer said he'd accept whatever Coach Stimmel decided. Stimmel's answer was, 'My boys are ready today, and they can beat Fort Hill in anything: snow, mud, anything.' Whatever the outcome, he'll have to answer for why the game went forward. So, keep tuned to WTBO with our full pregame coverage starting at noon. But, let's get back to Jerry Reed and—"

Flipping the radio off, I thought about what to wear. I needed to be ready to shovel snow and climb a light tower.

— Getting There —

By the time I got dressed and dug my snow boots out of the closet, Walter was at the side door.

"Wait out there. You have snow on your boots, and Mom will kill me if you tramp it in here," I told him.

"Bite me!" Walter barked as I slammed the door in his face.

I turned around to see Mom with a cup of coffee in her hand. "Where are you going, sweetie? I need you to pick up Nanny. I can't fix Thanksgiving dinner without her."

"Mom, the Turkey Day game is on, and I've got to be at the stadium now to help remove the snow," I pleaded.

"Christ on a cracker! They're having that goddamned game today even with a foot of snow?" Mom cursed like a seasoned sailor. She did not share Dad's shyness.

I put my boots on and zipped my bomber jacket to my neck, then grabbed a stocking cap and gloves and went out the door. Walter was waiting with a snow shovel over his shoulder. I told him where the Barracuda was and asked him to see if we needed to dig it out. I went to the basement to get the four-piece ALCO sign. I also got duct tape and the clothesline I'd need to hoist the letters into place.

Walter was back, saying, "Your tires did a bad, bad thing to the lawn."

"Okay, let's see what we're dealing with," I said as I handed two letters to Walter.

Getting off the judge's front yard was a snap with Walter pushing from the front. We covered the deep ruts my tires had dug into the lawn with snow, but as we bumped down off the curb, I saw Judge Shear in his bathrobe standing on his front porch with his hands on his hips. Walter waved, and I touched the gas to start us sliding forward.

I had to deal with freshly fallen snow covering packed icy snow that forced me to turn the car's steering wheel left and right then left again like I was balancing on a high wire. The sun was shining, and there wasn't a cloud in the sky, making yesterday's dark gray dump-fest all like a bad dream.

The main streets were a mixture of snow, slush, ice, salt, and coal ash, so as we drove, it sounded like a sandblaster was on high and aimed at the underside of the Barracuda, but I had traction, and we were navigating our way to Greenway on the same roads Walter and I took the other day but, things looked very different. All the signs lining the roads were either covered in snow, unrecognizable from their paint running or torn down from the weight of the frozen mix. It was even a struggle to see the plywood football players. A few were face-down in the snow, but most looked as if the Mafia had fitted them with concrete overshoes in preparation for throwing them in the river. I parked on the visitors' side of the stadium to be as close to the light towers as we could get.

Gathering up the gear from the back of the Barracuda, Walter and I trotted across the Fort Hill practice field to the radio building atop the visitors' bleachers. I told him to wait there while I scoped out the situation.

Reaching the tower, I was at the top of the bleachers and I looked out over the football field. There, I saw a most unnatural sight: the gridiron looked like a chocolate sheet cake covered in white icing with hundreds of ants devouring it one bite at a time. Half the field was untouched snow while the other half was a mix of dirt, mud, and slush. The ants, or should I say shovelers, were crews of kids working in fire-brigade style, filling their shovels with snow, then moving to the side of the field to place it on ever-growing piles on the running track.

In the stands, others were digging or pushing their portion of the cake's icing off the soon-to-be packed football fans' seating. It was a fantastic sight. What made me smile the most was all of the signs that had been so carefully put in place three days earlier were either destroyed by or covered in snow. My big ALCO sign might end up as the only team spirit display that anyone could see—if I could get it into place. Turning my attention to the job, I walked over to the tower. Not seeing any police, I ran back to Walter, and we shouldered the signs to our work site. Once there, we positioned the letters in the proper order.

I had embedded eye screws to both the top and bottom of the wood frames on each letter. This allowed me to loop the rope through them starting with the top of the *A*; then I attached the top of the *L* to the bottom of the *A* using garbage bag twist ties. I repeated this for the *C* and *O*. I hoped that when the rope pulled them up, they'd unfold like a Chinese fan, but they were going to be an enormous fan. I inspected the tower and confronted—for the first time—the complexity of my task.

— The Tower —

I've always been a climber. I have never shied away from a tree that presented itself for assault. Also, as a Baby Boomer, I knew how to negotiate the challenges of playground jungle gyms or firemen's ladders, so I figured a little light tower would be a breeze. What I didn't realize was how exposed I would be climbing the ladder that ran up the side of the tower's leg and how high I would have to go. I also didn't take into account my perspective of the height once I started climbing. The tower sat at the top of the hill forming the bowl of the stadium. That meant, when I started my climb at ten feet off the ground, it would look like it was forty feet down to the field.

This was going to be hairy.

Checking the rigging of the signs one more time, I put the roll of duct tape in my coat pocket and signaled Walter to give me a boost up to the first rung. Mistake number one was not putting on my gloves. I had taken them off to attach the signs together, and when the unprotected skin of my hands grabbed that ice-cold metal rung, I knew I was in trouble. I pulled myself up and locked my legs around the tower and called for Walter to throw up my gloves.

Then, it was time for the rope, and I got it on the first try. Pulling up about thirty feet of it, I looped it around my arm. Next, I started to climb the ladder. I avoided looking to my left at the football field to delay any dizzying effects I knew were coming. Reaching what I thought was about forty feet up, I looked for a crossbeam to throw the rope over and lower it down into the center of the tower for Walter to pull. There was one about ten feet below me, and five feet above but not where I felt was the best location. I continued climbing.

At its base, the tower's four legs were about fifteen feet apart, but at the point I had reached the legs had narrowed. I didn't have to move far off the ladder to get to the center, but when I took that first step out, I could not help but see the field about seventy feet below me. I felt like Jimmy Stewart in the opening scene of the movie *Vertigo* where he is chasing a crook across a rooftop, and the policeman in front of him tries to jump from one roof to another—Jimmy watches him fall to his death. Like Jimmy's, my vision zoomed in and then out like the lens of a camera slammed from near to far focus.

Gripping the metal crossbar with all my might, I closed my eyes until no longer disoriented. Then, I inched out further and pushed the rope over the top. The loops released and fell to Walter's waiting hands, but before they reached him, I saw him dart a look to his right, back up at me, and then he scrambled out from the tower's center.

Where in the hell is he going?!

I moved back to the safety of the ladder. The rope was down, but Walter was gone. Starting down the ladder, I heard Walter say in a voice intentionally loud enough for me to hear, "Excuse me, officer, have you got a light?"

Officer!

I froze and twisted my head to look in Walter's direction. I saw him with an unlit cigarette approaching one of Cumberland's finest in his dark blue winter uniform. The cop was about thirty feet from the far leg of the tower, looking out over the mass of humanity moving more snow than any backhoe could in the same amount of time. The cop turned hearing Walter's request, but Walter walked in front of him, blocking his view of me, and continued to his other side. The cop turned with Walter as he reached into his pocket and took out a lighter.

Okay, so what am I to do? The sign is ready, the rope is in place, but there isn't anyone to pull it, and I've only got about one more minute before I'm arrested.

Moving down slowly, I got back to the first rung. Walter was still talking to the policeman, and I saw him take his wallet out of his back pocket, open it up and hand it to the cop.

Oh, Christ, he isn't trying to bribe him, is he? They will lock us away until next Christmas.

As the cop took Walter's wallet, he looked up at me and jerked his head in an upward motion. I wasn't sure what he meant, but I figured I only had a few more seconds, so I moved off the ladder rung and onto the crossbar to the center of the tower. I stood there keeping one hand on the tower's leg and reached out into mid-air to grab the dangling rope. On my first try, my foot slipped, and I thought the next thing I would feel was the hard concrete base of the tower splitting open my skull, but my right hand hung on enough for me to regain my footing.

I grabbed the rope on the second try and pulled on it. The signs lifted off the ground below me. Pulling in about fifteen more feet, I looked over to see how Walter was doing. The officer was handing Walter's wallet back to him, and Walter gave me that head jerk again, so I figured I better do something fast.

Thinking out loud I said, "What the hell?"

I grabbed the rope with both hands, balanced for a second on the crossbar, and jumped. I heard the sliding sound of the clothesline running over the top of the crossbar and a loud *thud* and *squish* as my boots landed in slush at the base of the tower. I hit hard, and I felt the wind push out of my lungs but going up the tower as I was going down was my four-panel ALCO sign which luffed into place like the jib of a sailboat in a stiff breeze.

The slush helped me bounce forward, and I somersaulted towards the back leg of the tower. Upside down and soggy, I could see my ALCO sign was where I wanted it to be. I was reorienting myself as Walter grabbed my arm and helped me up saying, "Nice dive, douchebag. What took you so long? I thought for sure that cop would blow me off and see you."

"Did you bribe him?" I asked.

"No, idiot! How stupid do you think I am? I recognized his name. He was in school with Kathy, so I asked if he wanted to see her Miss Frostburg State photo. I've got one in my wallet. I think he'd have given me his gun if I had one of her in a bathing suit," Walter bragged.

"That's good, I guess, except the part about you carrying around a picture of your sister. I don't even like being in the same room with pictures of my sisters. Let's tape the sides of the sign down and forget about the top. We need to get out of here," I said.

We did that and were quickly back in the Barracuda without ever having dug one shovel of snow.

The Sign (Syckes Family Photos)

— The Snow Game —

The temperature was rising, and the snow was melting, but it would not be a typical Turkey Day. There had been a major snowstorm only hours earlier, and ninety percent of that snow was still exactly where it landed—on lawns and roads, cars and parking lots—and the city hadn't mobilized its snow removal workforce.

It was Thanksgiving, for God's sake!

Although a couple of hundred crazy kids got to the stadium and pushed the snow around a bit, what would happen when 8,000 people showed up for the game?

There were signs of asphalt peeking through the tire tracks on the road home, so I skied the Barracuda all the way to the top of the Dingle and let Walter out at the bottom of the hill behind his house. Avoiding going anywhere near Judge Shear's front lawn, I parked in a driveway across the street and ran to the side door. Changing my clothes, I gathered up my uniform and went back downstairs to clean off my bomber jacket.

Dad came into the kitchen and asked, "Are you ready to go?"

"Yes," I answered. "The football team's practice should be over by noon, and then we can run through our routine once on the field."

"I don't know if we should try that or not. Let's wait and see what the field looks like," Dad cautioned.

With that, we were off to Greenway Stadium. Parking was crazy, so Dad dropped me off in front and then spent forty-five minutes looking for a spot. I went in the home team's side main entrance and walked around the track to the visitor's side. The place looked like a Salvador Dali painting. I recognized things, but there was something odd about them. There were no melting faces or pocket watches, but there were melting mountains of snow checkered with dirt surrounding the field with walkways cut through them now and then so people could enter and exit. I had to jump up in the air to see over the mounds to find out the two teams were practicing on the field, but what I saw was more Chicago stockyard than pregame workout.

Everything was covered in slushy cold mud, including the players. If the ball touched the ground, a coach would wipe it clean with a towel, but the towels were losing. The backdrop to all of this was a group of joyous youngsters sledding down the hill in front of the scoreboard. It was bizarre.

I carried my uniform bag over my head as I made my way around the track. Most of the band members were already there as many of them had stayed after helping clear the snow away that morning. I saw Bob Hartman and asked him to do a headcount. As I turned to walk up the bleachers to where the band would sit, I saw to my delight my beautiful blue and white ALCO sign standing tall on the light tower at the far left end of the stadium. It was clean as a whistle—unlike all the other signs. Before the game started, the cheerleaders showed up with new, hastily produced signs, but they couldn't compare to my masterpiece.

Bob gave me the headcount, and we decided we'd do only a little practicing given the poor conditions. We wanted none of our band members stumbling and smearing their uniforms with mud. We had a great show ready to perform, and I felt confident the band would pull it off despite the mess.

The pregame would be different than others this year because both the Fort Hill and Allegany bands would be on the field at the same time. Each band was to form a tunnel at their goalpost and play their fight song as teams took the field, but the Fort Hill band would play the national anthem because it was the home team. I was okay with that, the less exposure, the better. I wanted to preserve my uniform until halftime.

I took my uniform bag and climbed the bleacher steps to the men's room in the brick radio building behind the stands. Compared to the home bleachers' bathroom, this one was a palace—so I took my time. As I emerged, I saw that despite the snow and the terrible road conditions, the stadium was filling up fast.

By the time I returned to the band, we needed to form up on the track for the pre-game show. This was not as easy as it sounds because there was less room for us to maneuver. There were hundreds of football fans searching for seating and avoiding the muck. Only the bleachers were available with the hillsides still buried in snow. I formed up the band into smaller than normal squads so we could navigate our way through the crowd.

Marching to the nearest entryway, I halted the band and told them to break up and reform on the other side. This made us look more like a diaspora of blue and white uniformed kids leaking onto the field instead of the organized marching unit we represented. I looked out on the field, and what I saw was disturbing.

Gone were the beautifully manicured lawn and crisp white chalk lines of my first pregame—in their place was the tortured battleground of cold brown and white. The stadium was one giant, dirt Slurpee. Across from us was the enemy— the Redcoats—the Fort Hill High School Band—and it was its job to get the pregame show started. Using the time I had left, I walked along the band and checked members' alignment. Despite the conditions, we looked good. With the sun now shining and the temperature hovering near forty, the weather was cooperating.

The stadium's amplification system came to life with its usual screech of feedback, and the announcer's voice said, "Welcome, one and all, to Turkey Day 1971, that will be unofficially known from now on as 'The Snow Game.' It's because of the super support from fans like you we can bring you the epic battle of the two best football teams Allegany County has ever produced. So, let's first give ourselves a big round of applause for battling the elements and coming out to support our teams."

There was a thunderous roar throughout the stadium as everyone rose at once and cheered. The fans really believed just getting there deserved an attaboy.

The Snow Game (Syckes Family Photo)

The announcer continued, "But the true heroes we all have come here to see do battle are the undefeated ALCO Campers, with their head coach, George Stimmel, and the nearly undefeated Fort Hill Sentinels, with their head coach, Charles Lattimer. Now, let's all join the Fort Hill band in singing the national anthem."

I heard the distant yet familiar sound of the Fort Hill band marching onto the field. "The Star-Spangled Banner" began, and it sounded darn good. I glanced left and right down the line, making sure my band was ready for our entrance. I saw Sam Nutter holding his trumpet under his left arm as he carefully compacted a dirty white snowball. "Nutter, you idiot, put that down. We don't want to start a fight!"

Sam looked at me like I was a bothersome fly, then hurled his slushy projectile at me. I ducked but almost fell from the shifting weight of my eighteen-inch, white Busby hat strapped to my head. Keeping it balanced up there was a full-time job, and when its center of gravity shifted, I had to move fast to counteract it. The music stopped, and the announcer said, "Thank you for that great patriotic sound. Now it's time to welcome the boys who will do their duty for their schools and decide which team will forever be known as the Turkey Day champs of 1971."

I kicked off "'Tis Allegany," hoping to be first to get a fight song started. Two lines snaked forward from the center of the band, forming the tunnel for the football players, and I led them as we arched to the left so the tunnel's mouth would lead to the team's bench. The Fort Hill band was only seconds behind us in starting its fight song, and I'm confident folks in the stands couldn't distinguish "'Tis Allegany" from "Hail, Fort Hill," but they sang along no matter.

Leading the right line of the tunnel, I was only feet from the Fort Hill band doing the same thing in the opposite direction when I heard a *thwack* and felt my head lean hard to port as cold, wet ice crystals showered over my right shoulder and down my neck. A snowball—more ice than snow—had struck my hat near the top.

My first thought was, *Nutter, you bastard*, but it couldn't have been Sam, given where he was in line.

A Redcoat had attacked me. Propelled by the momentum of my marching, I keeled over as my bombarded hat began to pull me down to the left. Like a calf with a rodeo noose around its neck, I was no longer in control. Only seconds from my white uniform becoming a soiled piece of toilet paper, I felt the strong hands of one of our saxophone players, catching me inches above the muck. Others joined in to right me as I saw Sam Nutter, trumpet under his arm again, retaliating against the passing Redcoats. *Attaboy Sam!*

A few others joined in, but to my surprise, a full blown snowball fight did not break out. I doubt anyone in the stands knew this was going on, but I needed to stop it before it spun out of control. We were still playing the fight song, and the football team was entering the field through our tunnel, so I passed through the right wall and stood between the two bands as they whirled past each other like two disconnected cogs of a vast, dirty machine.

The football teams burst through the paper walls the cheerleaders were holding, and the songs ended. Pre-game was over. I saw the Fort Hill band's drum major, only a few feet away from me. I moved over to her and said, "You go left, and I'll go right. Let's get them as far away from each other as possible."

She nodded and started her band marching toward their end zone. I did the same, but as I turned to go, I bent down far enough to grab a handful of snow. Squeezing it tight, I tossed it over my shoulder towards the Redcoats like spilled salt. I didn't bother to see if I hit anyone, I only wanted to make sure I was part of the fight.

The game started slowly as if the two teams were trying to avoid getting dirty. The kickoff was clean, but that was the last time the ball was distinguishable from the mud. Led by Fred Kreiger, star quarterback and team captain, ALCO tried in vain to advance the ball with running plays and ended up punting it away. Fort Hill also failed to make headway, and it was clear a ground game was not the way to win. The first quarter ended with neither team scoring, and as they shifted to the other end of the field, I had the band play a few bars of Cliff Noble's "The Horse."

Allegany abandoned the ground game, and the first pass connected, and the receiver crashed through the end zone for a touchdown. A slippery ball denied us an extra point, and the score was six to zero. Fort Hill fumbled the ball after kickoff, and ALCO recovered it at the Sentinels' 26-yard line. Krieger connected again for 14 yards, but a personal foul moved the ball back. Reverting to the running game, we had our second touchdown in two more carries. Another failed extra point made the score going into halftime Allegany 12—Fort Hill 0.

As the band moved back down onto the field to perform the halftime show, we all looked like we'd been dipped in Uncle Lu's chocolate dip-top. There was nothing but mud from our knees down on everyone, including me. The slush was overpowering, splashing up on our pant legs as we marched. Our halftime show started with the band lined up from one end of the football field to the other on Fort Hill's out-of-bounds line. We were all facing the ALCO stands, and I alone was out in front.

— Halftime —

I heard Dad's voice over the loudspeaker say, "Good afternoon, I'm proud to introduce the Allegany High School Marching Band as they present inspirational sounds from *Jesus Christ Superstar*."

I threw my arms up and tweeted my whistle and like at the pep rally, long before the first snowflake fell, the clean, clear, sounds of "Superstar" pulsed outward towards the stands.

The majorettes were first to move off the line as they emerged from the solid wall of blue-and-white uniforms twirling and tossing their batons into the air as they high-stepped forward. Next were the flag team members, looking as if they were piercing their way through the band, flag tips forward jousting-style. As soon as they were free from the ranks, they lifted their flags in a splash of color, tossed them into the air and caught them by their poles. As the flags passed me, I signaled the first group from the band to move out.

Assigned a number between one and four, each band member stepped off one at a time, staggered every four counts. This formed a diagonal pattern from the fans' point of view and made the band look twice as large as it really was. Despite the miserable conditions, we all were at the top of our game and had the confidence of our team's 12-point lead on the scoreboard to back us up.

We then played "Hosanna," and the four lines that had formed as we entered the field turned in opposite directions and marched away from each other. After going ten yards, they did a to-the-rear-march and moved back to their starting points. This made the band look as if it were expanding and contracting like an accordion. Turning to face the stands as the song ended, we all went down on one knee as the majorettes threw their batons in the air and the flag team dipped the tips of their poles in a salute to the stands. The applause was strong, and our part of halftime was over, so I marched the band off the field and had it turn around and prepare to play "Hey, Look Me Over."

The Arrowettes were up, and all of them made it onto the center of the field without falling, but when they did their high kick, it looked like a farmer's disk tilling machine in high gear. Each time a leg lifted from the ground on its way over a lovely girl's head, a sizable clod of mud came up with it and flew farther than most of the passes in the first half. As the foot came down, it would splash an equally sizable quantity of mud up onto the leg of the girl on either side. It was dirty work but fun to watch. Now it was the Red Coat's turn, and the music sounded top drawer. The Fort Hill Band was a strong and well-practiced group, and like the football team, they were having a great year. We were just having a little greater one.

— End Game —

As we all feared, Fort Hill came out of the locker room for the second half charged up and ready to change the game. The third quarter was a tug of war that ended with neither team scoring, and many thought the ALCO team looked tired. Fort Hill's team reversed the tide in the fourth quarter, putting together a tremendous drive down the field that got them to first and goal. Nobody thought they'd be stopped except the fired-up ALCO defense. Fort Hill tried three times and failed, and going for a touchdown on fourth down, the Sentinels hit a blue brick wall and had to relinquish the ball. That's when it was our turn to feel some pain.

On the very next play, Fred Kreiger fumbled the ball, and Fort Hill recovered it on the one-yard line. This time, the Sentinel's star, Mark Manges, ran a quarterback sneak and rammed through to the end zone, putting Fort Hill on the scoreboard for the first time. After a successful fair catch on the kickoff, Fred Kreiger showed Fort Hill he wasn't finished and completed a 74-yard pass that was run in for ALCO's third touchdown. The extra point missed again, and as the fourth quarter ticked away, the score stood at 18 – 7. But, it only took five minutes for Fort Hill to push back with a 35-yard drive to score again, cutting the Campers' lead to only 4 points. If the Sentinels could do it again in the remaining seven minutes, ALCO's season, no matter how spectacular, would end in defeat.

Kreiger couldn't capitalize on his momentum and had to punt the ball back to the Reds with two minutes left on the clock. The Fort Hill team knew what they had to do and set up two running plays followed by a pass downfield intended to catch us sleeping. But, it was intercepted, and Kreiger took a knee on the next play to run out the clock.

We won!

The place went crazy. Hats filled the air, everyone was hugging, players and coaches rode on shoulders, and I led the band in "'Tis Allegany" at least three times.

There was a long-standing tradition that the winning high school's team, cheerleaders, drill team, band, and their fans would march through downtown after the game and—despite the weather—I intended to make it happen. As soon as things calmed down and the players left the field, I got the band member's attention and told them to do what they needed to do with their personal belongings and form up for a parade in front of the stadium. The Arrowettes got the same direction, and with a little coaxing, Coach Stimmel let the football team join in. In one more great team spirit display, The Snow Game ended with well over two hundred people marching down the winding, snowy Cumberland Streets led by the ALCO band on our way back to Allegany. No snowballs were thrown.

I didn't get home until after 5 p.m. and awaiting me was a full-course Thanksgiving Day dinner. *Thank you, Nanny.*

The march downtown was the last one an Allegany band would ever lead on Turkey Day because there were only two more before the Thanksgiving Day tradition was ended and ALCO lost them both. An earlier season homecoming game replaced Turkey Day.

As I was leading the band on that final march home, I wasn't thinking about the snow or the game. I was thinking about taking Patty to the Victory Dance.

Last ALCO Band Turkey Day Parade 1971 (Syckes Family Photos)

— Victory Dance —

On the Saturday night following every Turkey Day game, there was a dance at ALCO. If we won, we called it a Victory Dance. If we lost, we called it the Turkey Day Dance. I wanted to take Patty, and I figured I'd needed to plead my case to Mrs. Rudd to have any chance of pulling it off. Patty and I had been going together for three months now but not really dating. Except for the Al Homburg "Superstar" fiasco, her mom had not allowed me to take her on any other dates. Even though I was getting more than enough necking time while watching *The French Chef*, I wanted a girlfriend I could take out to the movies or parties. I wanted to show her off to my friends. In other words: I was not happy.

The week before Thanksgiving, I told Patty my plan. She wasn't sure what her mom's reaction would be, so I figured I had nothing to lose. We didn't watch TV on the day I planned to ask and listened for Mrs. Rudd's car to pull into the driveway. When we heard it, we jumped up and went to the back door, pretending I was on my way home.

As I was hoping, Mrs. Rudd had groceries to carry in, and I immediately came to her aid. After setting the last paper A&P bag on the peach colored linoleum countertop, I took my shot.

"Mrs. Rudd, I want to take Patty to the Turkey Day Dance next Saturday night. It's a school function held in the gym, and I promise to have her home by ten o'clock sharp. Can we go, please?"

"Sure, no problem," she said.

Wait? Did she say, 'no problem'?

"We'll see you there," Patty's mom continued. "Mr. Rudd and I volunteered as chaperones for the dance figuring you two would want to go. What took you so long asking?"

Shit, did I just win or lose? Please don't tell me it will be a double date.

On dance night, I picked up Patty at seven o'clock, and she was home alone. Her parents had left early to help the other chaperones at the dance, so we had her place all to ourselves. Although I was excited about the night, I still felt cheated. I wanted more. Where were my nights roller-skating with my girl on my arm during the couples-only songs at the Hi-land Roller Rink or snacking on popcorn in the back seat of my car at the drive-in theater?

All I was doing was watching Julia Child debone chickens. I was feeling pretty sorry for myself, and I didn't do a good job of hiding my feelings. Patty looked great—as always—this time wearing a velvet blue mini-skirt and matching top with a choker-collar necklace made of the same material. I had on dark blue pants with a lighter blue shirt topped with a blue-and-gray-pattern sports coat—all of it made from polyester.

I'm surprised I didn't spontaneously combust. Oh, and the knot of my tie was bigger than my head.

When Patty opened the front door, she said, "Do you want to come in? Mom and Dad aren't home, and I can show you my room."

Now, that's the kind of offer every boy wants to hear, so what did I say given my piss-poor mood?

"Nah, we better get to the dance. I'm sure your parents are waiting for us."

And that's pretty much how the rest of the night went. Every time I saw Patty's parents, I'd get angrier.

Now, before you say, "Shelby, you idiot! Don't you realize what a great deal you had there? You were dating a beautiful girl who liked you. All you had to do is wait six months, and her parents would most likely let you take her anywhere you wanted."

Don't bother; I have said this to myself a thousand times since that night. Give me a break. I was sixteen and stupid. It's part of God's little game. He gives us all the hormonal energy when we're sixteen, but no wisdom. By the time you've got the wisdom, the hormones are gone. He must spend a lot of time looking down and laughing at us.

We danced a few times and tried the punch, but I felt like we were on display and that her parents were monitoring our every move. I'm sure I was wrong, but that's how I felt, so when I took Patty home, I walked her to the door and said good night without kissing her.

What a fool!

Patty & Shelby Turkey Day Victory Dance Nov 1971 (Syckes Family Photos)

Chapter 12 - Wild World

— The New Tastee Freez —

"Y ou're kidding?" The manager of City Cleaners questioned in disbelief.

"No sir, don't you clean uniforms for free?" I asked.

"That's not a uniform, that's a Fudgsicle with stripes. What in the hell did you do in that, boy, slop hogs?"

"No sir, I wore it for the Turkey Day game, but now I need it cleaned. Can you do it?" I pleaded.

"Listen, kid, I can clean anything, but I can't guarantee the fabric ain't stained for good, and I'm not doing it for free. I do that for military uniforms only," the manager said while using a yardstick to push my uniform into a laundry bag marked special.

"Okay, when will it be ready?" I asked.

"Give me a week," he replied. "But, I might need a month."

It was the Monday after the game, and the reception I got at the cleaners was not a surprise. When I got home from the game, I had dropped my uniform in a pile in the corner of my closet and hadn't touched it since. I left City Cleaners and drove to LaVale to meet Dad. Pulling into the store's parking lot, I saw him with his camera, snapping pictures of the building from the far side of the lot.

"I thought I should get photos of the old girl before they tear her down. Friday, we close for a week; then we'll open in the new building. Doesn't it look great?" Dad said, pointing at the new Uncle Lu's that was nearing completion.

It had been under construction for the past three months, and Dad was worried about whether it would be completed on schedule. Luckily, the contractor was able to bring on more help to meet the mid-December opening date. This was the only good news Dad had gotten since the whole thing began.

Nine months ago, he'd committed to a new Uncle Lu's. The old store was no longer practical and could not compete with the new fast food restaurants popping up on the interstate. With indoor seating for only ten, no air conditioning or public restrooms, it had reached its maximum earning capability long ago. We needed something new and modern with much greater floor space.

The Tastee Freez Corporation had updated store design a lot since its founding in 1950, and our new building was to use that new design. Out were the concrete block, low-roofed single story shacks, and in, was modern architecturally exciting designs with high walls of plate glass on three sides topped with a wavy, prestressed, concrete roof that looked like a lady's fan viewed from the top. In fact, Tastee Freez provided a "build to" design package any competent contractor could handle, avoiding the high cost of architects and engineers. Using prestressed concrete panels for the sides and roof of the building, construction was easy. After pouring the foundation, cranes would lift all the panels into place. *Voilà!,* you had the shell of your building ready to go. In March, Dad got a new loan from the First National Bank. He contracted with an out-of-state prestressed concrete specialist to do the work. I know all this because Dad told me this story a hundred times and he always said that, "Everything was in place for a quick transition—until the Union came to visit."

— Mr. Aaronson —

It was the Friday of the Memorial Day weekend, one of our busiest days of the year, when two huge Lincoln Continentals parked near the back door of the store. Dad was helping out during the lunch hour when Charlotte told him he had a visitor.

"You Lu Syckes?" said a guy in a dark three-piece suit sporting impenetrable sunglasses and looking like he'd walked off the set of a Hollywood gangster movie.

"Yes, how can I help you?" Dad said, staring out the screen door at two of the biggest production cars ever made in the United States.

"Mr. Aaronson wants to talk to you," said the suited ape as he opened the screen door and signaled for Dad to come out. Dad walked over to the first Lincoln as the back window slid down and cigarette smoke happily escaped.

"Mr. Syckes, we understand you are planning on building a new store here in a few weeks. Is that right?" said a voice from inside the Lincoln, as a stubby hand pushed out with a business card stuck between two fingers.

"Yes," Dad answered, taking the card.

"And you plan to have this building built using pre-stressed concrete?" the voice continued.

"Yes."

"And the contractor you have chosen is a non-union one from out of state?" asked the business card's owner.

"Well, I don't know about its union affiliation, but I'm using a contractor recommended by the Tastee Freez corporate front office. Why?" Dad asked as he read the business card and realized he was talking to the President of the International Union of Bricklayers and Allied Craftworkers.

"Mr. Syckes, this is a free country, and you are welcome to choose whomever you'd like to build your new building, but I think it is important for you to know how your actions will impact local contractors. I'm talking about your neighbors who make their living building stores for businessmen like you. Don't you want to support them in their labors so they will, in turn, support you?" said the voice in a most pleasant tone.

"Why yes, and I've used local labor for all of my improvements through the years, but I'm going with what my franchise corporate office recommends," Dad said, standing his ground.

"I understand, but those Chicago boys don't give a damn about my local union members. I'm here to persuade you to reconsider your decision," the voice said with a bit more menace.

"But I've signed the contracts, and the work will start next week. I can't back out now," Dad stated.

"We will help you with that," the voice said, as the door to the black behemoth opened.

A short, stocky man swung his right leg out of the car. Standing up and brushing ash from his coat, President Aaronson closed the door and put his arm on Dad's shoulder.

"Now, Mr. Syckes, you're a smart man. You know there are lots of permits required for a construction project such as yours to go smoothly. The state zoning boys need to be sure you have done everything up to code, and you don't want them to find problems, now do you?" the Union boss said.

Taking a long drag on his multi-filter low-tar cigarette, Mr. Aaronson coughed, looked at it like it bit him, then threw it on the ground. "Christ, these new cigarettes are like smoking a tampon. Frankie, give me a Camel."

Before the last word was out of his mouth, an arm the size of a leg holding a cigarette thrust past Dad. "Mr. Syckes, I want you to think about this, and if you change your mind, call me. I'll have my boys line up all the help you need to get your building built by the finest union laborers the state of Maryland has to offer. Okay?"

Aaronson didn't wait for Dad's answer as he got back into his Lincoln and signaled his errand boy to get in his. The cars backed away from the building as Dad stood, stunned, trying to figure out what just happened.

"I've got to call Bill Wilson," he said.

William L. Wilson was Dad's attorney and long-time friend. He had assisted Dad in all his legal matters since getting his JD after the war. Dad made the call, "Bill, this is Lu. A union leader is pressuring me to cancel my contract on the new store and use their labor. Isn't that extortion?"

"It depends," said Bill Wilson, applying the phrase all lawyers learn on the first day of law school. "Did he threaten you with violence if you didn't do what he said?"

"No, but he implied that I might have trouble with permits if I use non-union labor," answered Dad.

"What union?" Bill asked.

"The International Union of Bricklayers and Allied Craftworkers."

"Was it one of the local reps?"

"No, it was someone named Aaronson, and his card says he's the president of the Union."

"Oh," Bill said, then after several silent moments, "Lu, you need to give me until tomorrow to find out what we are dealing with. Give me the information on his card."

Bill Wilson called Dad the next day and asked him to meet him for lunch. Dad entered the lobby of the Algonquin Hotel and crossed in front of the desk where, a few weeks later, a night auditor would report three suspicious boys out for a walk at 3 a.m. Dad saw Bill Wilson sitting at a table near the entrance of the hotel's restaurant.

"Lu, over here," called Bill as he stood and shook Dad's hand. "Sit down; I ordered you a vodka and tonic."

Dad didn't like the sound of that. He rarely had a drink before four. "What did you find out?"

Dad's old friend paused and took a deep breath before he answered. "Lu, it's not good news. I called a friend of mine who's done legal work for the bricklayers, and they're a tough group. They have a history of picketing non-union construction sites and filing legal petitions with the court to slow down work, but that's not what worries me."

"I'm worried about the new parking lot curb cuts you need. State Permit Services is a good organization and will likely approve your curb cuts, but then they hand that job over to a union-controlled contractor to do the work."

"That means the entry and exit ways your new parking lot requires will be subject to the scheduling whims of a union, and unions stick together. They might not get around to your work for a year, what with all they're doing to extend the interstate. Lu, you've got to think about canceling your current construction contract and going with a union contractor. I'm sorry, but that's my recommendation."

Dad was halfway through his vodka and tonic when Bill finished. He stared at his drink for a long while.

"I've already called your contractor, and they will let you out of their construction contract if you pay fifty percent of their fee. If you allow me, I'll contact Aaronson and see what help he can provide us with lining up replacement contractors. Do you want me to do that, Lu?" Bill finished and took a long sip of his rum and Coke.

As I mentioned earlier, Dad was smart, and he also wasn't a quitter, and I'm sure his gut was telling him to fight these guys. But at heart, he was a realist and knew he had to deal with the facts as they were.

"Yes Bill, please see what you can do." Dad sighed. "Waitress, another vodka and tonic, please."

— Was It Worth It? —

In the end, the cost of the new Tastee Freez increased by twenty percent and gone was the design provided by the corporate front office. Out were the modern wavy roof and pre-stressed sides, in were concrete block, brick veneer, and a metal truss roof. We kept the large glass windows, but the building took twice as long to build.

The higher cost required additional financing from the bank, which meant more collateral. The Tastee Freez property and business potential was enough for the original loan but not the new price, so Dad mortgaged the family home again. Just like 1957, he was all in—everything was on the table.

The delay in the start of construction pushed the transition to the new building into December. This turned out to be for the better, as it was the slowest month of the year for sales. The opening of the new Tastee Freez went off without a hitch on December 15th with Dad, Mom, and all the employees on hand for a ribbon-cutting; also in attendance were representatives from the Tastee Freez Corporation and local distributors.

The New Uncle Lu's (Syckes Family Photo)

About ten minutes before the ceremony, two black Lincoln Continentals pulled through the new curb cuts on National Highway and parked at the far end of the lot on the shiny new blacktop. Out of one of them poured an expensive sharkskin suit housing more Weeble than man wearing Ray-Ban sunglasses despite the overcast skies. Mr. Aaronson didn't join the dignitaries; he stood in the crowd with the employees.

At the end of the ribbon-cutting, he made his way over to Dad, took his cigarette out of his mouth and said, "Thank you, Mr. Syckes. You won't regret supporting the Union." With that, he was back in his armored car and gone.

Three months later, Dad stopped by the store at lunch hour to drop off a replacement rotor blade for the ice cream machine when Arvada called him over to the sundae counter, which had a grand view of the dining area.

"Uncle Lu, look over there. Do you see that group of guys in overalls and work boots? They've been here for lunch every day this week, and they are tipping the staff!"

"Tipping?" Dad asked. "This is fast food. Nobody tips at a fast food restaurant."

"I know." Arvada said. "And that's not all. The tall one said to give this to the owner."

Arvada handed Dad a business card. It had a colorful logo of a trowel, hammer, and mortarboard. Printed in boldface font, it read *International Union of Bricklayers and Allied Craftworkers Local 59.*

Written on the back was "Thanks."

— Bye, Bye, Patty, Hello Jimmy —

Christmas came and went, and so did Patty. After the Victory Dance, our time together declined, and over the holidays, we barely saw each other. It was all my fault. I'd killed whatever affection was there, and now I was on my own. I wasn't that upset because my attitude was changing. I didn't think of myself as a kid anymore as I did when I was throwing Frisbees with Tim and Mike. I was a young adult, and young adults need real girlfriends.

The new year started, and things were going well at the new store. The local community came out in force to see what the new Uncle Lu's was like, and traffic off the interstate picked up. More business meant more employees, and one Friday night, I reported to work to find Jimmy Eaton in the back room trying on his new Tastee Freez smock. The smocks were one of many changes that came with the new store.

The Tastee Freez Corporation decided in the late '60s to take McDonald's head on. Until then, all they cared about was the ice cream products. As long as you were selling quality ice cream, you could sell whatever else you wanted, but the new leadership at the corporate offices in Chicago wanted to play with the big boys, so they changed the franchise licensing agreement to require all stores to standardize all products. Out were any nonstandard products, and we had many favorites. For example, McDonald's introduced a double-decker hamburger to the world in 1967 and called it the Big Mac.

Do you remember how they sold it?

"Two all-beef patties, special sauce, lettuce, cheese, pickles, onions, on a sesame seed bun."

Well, we had been making and selling a double-decker like it for ten years called the Lu Burger, and it had its own special sauce—mayonnaise. The Lu Burger had to go, and in its place, was the Big-T Burger with a different special sauce—Thousand Island dressing.

Also, out the door were the homemade soups Arvada made and were favorites of the working men who made up much of our weekday lunch crowd. Milkshakes made the old-fashioned way also ended. We used to put milk, ice cream, and flavoring into a metal cup, mix it on a multi-mixer's spindle, then pour it into a large Tastee Freez cup. Its replacement was a frozen premade milkshake mix that came out of a special milkshake machine ready to go right into the paper cup. I never found a milkshake made this way to be satisfying. The old way, you were enjoying an amalgam of three different things blended imperfectly. You'd find lumps of vanilla ice cream floating in your flavored milk or patches of pure chocolate swimming around. The new way was perfectly perfect and had the consistency and appeal of cold, unset concrete.

The most significant change for male employees was the new, official Tastee Freez men's uniform. If you remember, I told you that my uniform before was a white shirt and apron topped with a Tastee Freez hat. The hats were still there, but we said goodbye to our aprons. We now had to wear bright red sleeveless smocks that went over our heads like a sandwich-board sign from the 1930s.

Before I continue, I want you to know when the corporate front office made these decisions; there were close to 2000 Tastee Freezes in the United States. Today, there are fewer than 200.

McDonald's kicked our ass.

Jimmy had on one of the new red smocks when I walked in the door, and I could tell by his face he thought it was about as fashion forward as a corset.

"Don't say a word," Jimmy hissed. "Do I have to wear this thing where people will see me?"

"What the hell are you doing here?" I asked.

"It's simple. My Dad cut off my allowance, and if I want to drive the car, I have to pay for my gas, so I need a job, and I heard this was the easiest place to work in town."

"It is. Just stay out of Flora's way. She likes to jiggle your junk," I said while grabbing my crotch like Michael Jackson in his "Beat It" video.

Please forgive this reference out of sync with the timeframe of the story. Michael Jackson didn't grab his crotch until 1986, but we should have seen it coming because, in 1972, he was singing a love song to a rat.

"If anyone touches my package, I'm screaming rape," said Jimmy in a most determined way.

"Okay, calm down big boy. If you're going to survive around here you need to know the rules," I said.

I then gave Jimmy the short version of Uncle Lu's 101. It wasn't long before Jimmy and I were fast friends and doing about everything together.

— Drama —

January slid into February, and I started looking for that real girlfriend. My class after lunch was Drama with JoAnn Homburg and my most vivid memory of it is that once a week, Sam Nutter would come to the door a few minutes after class began and tell JoAnn my father wanted to talk to me about band stuff. She'd say okay, and Sam and I would spend the next hour cruising Cumberland.

Sam was my part-time friend, and he became my "young adult" mentor. He slid in and out of my life on his own schedule. Purely by coincidence, that schedule corresponded with when I had access to my dad's Barracuda. Sam wasn't allowed to use his dad's car after the police impounded it one night. You see, Sam left it parked in the center of the Blue Bridge crossing the Potomac River. The way I heard it, after a six-pack of Old German Beer, Sam decided to go for a swim, and as stupid as that is in and of itself, he thought it would be fun to dive in off the bridge. The police were not impressed, so they arranged for Sam to have alternative transport.

I only mention Drama class here because the word got out I had broken up with Patty, and after class one day, JoAnn said to me, "Shelby, I heard you and your little friend aren't seeing each other anymore."

Little friend? What does she think I date, gerbils?

"Yes, ma'am, we sort of lost interest in each other," I answered.

"Well, that's too bad. Have you been dating anyone else?" JoAnn continued.

"No, ma'am, I haven't met the right girl yet." I squirmed, looking for the earliest opportunity to escape.

"Okay, well, keep me informed of how things are going. Having a girlfriend in high school is important," she finished as I backed out of the room.

The next day in the lunchroom, I was sitting with Jimmy and Garrett trying to decide what to eat first—my cold fish stick or what looked like field corn encased in margarine when Joyce Carman plopped down beside me with a big smile on her face. You remember Joyce; she was the Queen of the cool kids who invited me to the cool side of the pool. "I want you to meet a friend of mine," Joyce said.

"Hi, Joyce, this is Jimmy and Garrett. They're my—" I tried to say before she interrupted me.

"Meet me after practice today inside the front entrance of the gym," she ordered while glancing at my friends and squinching her nose like a foul odor was in front of her. Before I could reply, she was up and gone.

"Taking orders from Arrowettes now, are you?" Jimmy purred. "Do you even have a dick anymore, or does that high-kicking queen keep it in a box for you?"

"Go pound sand, Eaton. At least I have a hope of someone other than my sister touching my dick," I shot back.

"Oh, you practiced that one, didn't you, Drama Boy. Bravo!" Jimmy said as he applauded.

— Cindy —

I slipped out of band early and crossed through the gym and went down the steps to the front lobby. It was empty except for Twiggy. I guess his real name was Mr. Twigg, but Twiggy was what we called our favorite ALCO janitor. He was at least sixty-years old, balding, and was always smiling. I waved to him as he used his large wheeled garbage can with brooms and mops sticking out of it to push open the restroom door. I sat on the steps and looked at the clock; it was 3:25.

Well, I'll give Joyce ten minutes tops.

At 3:30, the last bell of the day sounded, and I heard door after classroom door open and bang against the cool green walls of the gym's lower hallway. Next came happy voices all jumbled together in celebration of the end of the school day. Soon kids were flooding through the lobby and flowing out the front doors. A long line of yellow school buses waited for them on the street to take them home.

"Shelby, I want you to meet Cindy. Cindy, this is Shelby," I heard Joyce's booming voice announce from behind me.

Standing and turning around, I looked up at Joyce and a cute, blonde girl with her hair cut mid-length. I heard banging as Twiggy maneuvered his garbage can out of the bathroom.

"Cindy is looking for a boyfriend, and I know you're unattached, so why don't you take her out on a date?" Joyce announced as if she were reading a menu aloud.

I didn't know how to respond. Cindy was smiling and looking down at me from about four steps up, so although she looked great, I could not tell if she was taller than me or not.

Remember, that's important.

"Hi," I said as they both moved down three steps.

"Hi, back at you," said Cindy with a devious look on her face.

She was clutching her books with both arms across her chest, and there was a long pause before I heard, "Ask her out, dummy," from below me. "Ask her out," Twiggy said.

I turned to see him leaning on his broom handle, smiling up at us and shaking his head.

"Sure, ahh, Cindy, would you like to go to the movies on Saturday? I don't know what's playing, but I'm sure there is something we can find at either the Strand or Center theaters. I can look in the paper when I get home and call you if you need to check with your parents first," I babbled.

"He talks a lot, doesn't he?" Cindy said to Joyce.

"You're on your own. I've done what JoAnn told me to do," Joyce said as she turned and went back up the steps.

Cindy opened the cover of the top book in her stack and took out a piece of paper torn from a three-ring binder. "Here's my phone number. Call me tomorrow when you know what movie you'd like to see."

She smiled, and I saw she had beautiful straight teeth and dimples. Taking the last step down to my level, she handed me the slip of paper and my stomach tightened like a fist. I was looking straight into her pretty blue eyes. I glanced down, hoping to see shoes with heels on them but found she had on Mary Jane flats. I was wearing my Dingo boots that added an extra half inch to my height.

She kept on going as I blurted out, "Great, I'll call you tomorrow," and she was out the door and gone.

Twiggy was still there but sweeping. He looked up at me and said, "Lucky boy."

Clint Eastwood's *Dirty Harry* was playing at the Strand, so I called Cindy, and after stumbling through an unneeded introduction, I asked if she'd like to see it. She said, "Sure." Apparently, not all parents of freshman girls are as strict as Patty's, because Cindy's parents weren't even involved in the process. She could date anyone she wanted as long as they knew where she was going and when she'd be home. Dad agreed I could take the big Buick on the date, so I cleaned it up Saturday afternoon. I decided to get to her house early so we could stop at the Tastee Freez for an ice cream cone beforehand. I pulled up in front of Cindy's house and walked around it towards her front door. Cindy was already out and bounding up the steps to the car.

"Oh my God, you own a Cadillac!" she said as if she was witnessing the Second Coming. "It's so big," she gushed as she walked around the car.

"Thanks, Dad and Mom really like it. She rides like a dream. But, I'm afraid it's not a Cadillac."

"It's not?" Cindy said, stopping her tour and sounding shocked.

"No, it's a Buick, but they are both made by GM, and Buick is almost as luxurious," I tried compensating.

"Oh, I've never been in a Cadillac before, and it would have been really cool," she said with great sadness while opening the passenger side door by herself. I felt like a helium balloon with a pinhole in its side.

The date was a disaster.

At the Tastee Freez, someone unskilled in the art of dip-top cones made two of them for us, and they were a sticky mess. Sitting in the car, I tried to wipe my hands on a napkin and ended up dropping my cone in my lap, right onto my white jeans. I spent the next ten minutes in the men's room trying to remove a stain that was in a very awkward location. When I returned to the car, Cindy looked at the wet spot on my pants and blushed.

We drove to the theater in silence. There wasn't much of a line, but when it was our turn at the ticket counter, the manager peered out through the hole cut into the glass and said, "This movie is R-rated. I need to see your I.D. cards. You have to be at least 17 to get in without your parents."

"Oh, my parents just went in, didn't you see them? We were parking the car," I lied.

"I.D. or no tickets," the manager said with finality, and I backed away from the booth. Cindy was staring at me in disbelief. I was thinking about running away when I got an idea.

"Wait here," I said, and went to the phone booth near the rear exit of the theater. I called home. When finished, I walked back to Cindy and said, "I think I've solved the problem, but it will take a minute or two. Let's step inside the first set of doors; it's freezing out here."

"Don't you have a fake I.D?" Cindy asked.

"Not yet." With that, I had to endure ten minutes more of silence until Dad pulled up to the curb right in front of the Strand's ticket booth.

He went up to the window and said, "Give me three tickets, please."

"That's $3.75. Enjoy the movie." The manager laughed.

Dad handed me two tickets, and we went in. The usher tore them in half and returned the stubs.

Dad looked at us, said, "Have fun," and returned to the Barracuda. Cindy walked into the theater without me, shaking her head. The movie had started, and although we enjoyed *Dirty Harry,* there was no warmth between us. It felt like I was watching it with one of my sisters and when it was over I took Cindy straight home. Walking her to the front door, I said, "Thanks for a fun night."

"Well, it was something I won't forget," she said as she leaned forward and kissed me on the cheek.

Lost for words, I said, "See you at school," and turned and went back to my not-quite-a-Cadillac. As I drove home, I thought of the famous line from the movie. You know the one when Clint Eastwood is pointing his .45 Magnum pistol into the face of the bad guy and says, "Do you feel lucky? Well, do ya, punk?"

I felt lucky about having the greatest dad in the world, but my luck with Cindy was all bad. It wasn't her fault. We weren't a good match. I didn't feel bad, just stupid, and I'm sure our height difference would have wrecked the thing anyway. I kept looking, and a new girlfriend possibility popped up in an unexpected place.

— Elena —

I was at Garrett's house after school a few days after my disastrous date with Cindy, and I asked him if he was going on the annual school ski trip to Seven Springs Resort in Pennsylvania.

"Hell, no, why would I want to throw myself down a perfectly good mountain?" Garrett barked.

"Okay, okay," I said. "Take it easy; I'm looking for someone to sit with on the two-hour bus trip up and back."

"Elena is going," Garrett said.

"Your sister Elena?" I asked, having forgotten she even existed.

"You know she's a freshman, don't you? And she is in the flag squad in the band. Have you heard of the band, Drum Boy?" Garrett jabbed.

Wow, how could this drum major have missed that?

I didn't interface with the flag squad much, and the ones who didn't play musical instruments like Elena weren't in the band during the spring semester. Of course, I knew Garrett had a sister named Elena, but unless they are Miss Frostburg State, you don't pay much attention to your friends' sisters.

"Elena!" Garrett yelled at the top of his lungs while continuing to lie on his bed.

"What?" replied a soft voice from the bottom of the stairwell outside of his room.

"Are you still going on the ski trip?" Garrett continued to bellow.

"You don't have to yell," said Elena, now standing in the doorway of Garrett's room. "And yes, I'm going. Why?"

"Shelby's going too, and he was looking for someone to ride with him on the bus," Garrett stated.

Well, this couldn't be more awkward. I don't really know her, but I'm supposed to know her because she's in the band and my good friend's sister.

Garrett and I had been friends since seventh grade at Braddock Junior High School. He lived about two blocks from the school, so as he and I became friends, I would often hang out at his house until Mom got off from work and could pick me up. Elena was another member of the freshman class—my go-to class for dates—and when I looked at her standing in Garrett's doorway, I saw for the first time she was a cute girl. She seemed more mature than most ninth graders, with a full figure and big, sensuous eyes. Oh, and she was about five-foot-three, the perfect height.

"Sure, we can ride together. I've never been to Seven Springs, have you?" she asked.

"Yes, several times, but I'm no great skier."

"Okay, I'll see you Saturday," she said as she squinted a bit behind her round John Lennon glasses and smiled.

"Beat it now," barked Garrett, and she disappeared back down the steps.

I took extra care dressing for the ski trip, making sure I didn't look like the Pillsbury Doughboy. When I got to school, Elena was already on the bus, so I worked my way down the aisle until I found her.

"Hi," I said, "you look great." And she did. She wore a killer pink ski outfit that fit her like a kid glove. She even had a matching hat. "Wow, you look professional."

"That's the point; it's better to look good than be good," she said as she smiled, showing a row of flawless white teeth. I was outclassed but loved her Fernando Lamas attitude, so I settled in for the ride to Seven Springs.

What a surprise. Elena wasn't like the other girls I had dated. I don't know why. Maybe it was because we really weren't out on a date, but we talked, and I found we had a great deal in common, or at least she made me feel like we did. We discussed Turkey Day and the band and rock and roll. She knew all about the latest rock groups, and we discussed the pros and cons of Yes vs. Emerson, Lake, and Palmer. The two-hour drive flew by.

The rest of the day was even more fun, as we spent it riding the ski lifts and exploring all the mountain trails. We started on the bunny slope to make sure we remembered how to ski, but by the end of the day, we were fearless. We even ventured down one of the black diamond runs, taking turns falling, and I enjoyed helping her up because I got to nuzzle her a bit and smell her subtle sweet perfume.

It was a great day, and all the way home on the dark bus, I had my arm around her, but there was no kissing. It didn't seem right. I was smitten but also worried. I did not want to mess up a good friendship with Garrett by dating his sister and having things go south. I didn't know what to do, so I did nothing. I stayed away from Garrett's house, and I avoided Elena at school. I'm sure she noticed. In a day or two, I decided not to date Elena, but I had a feeling she was going to come back into my life.

— Janice —

We are all the hero of our own story, but in this next section, I am the villain.

My Frisbee buddy, Mike Manning, had fallen for a cute flute player named Noreen in the fall, and they were about inseparable as the new year got started. Tim had yet to find a steady girlfriend, and I was still single.

What happened next came very close to destroying our friendship, for Tim and I became attracted to the same girl at the same time, and that girl was Noreen's younger sister, Janice. How I handled this situation is not something I am proud of, so let me make this perfectly clear: I was a complete and total ass, and the fact that Tim and I are friends today is a testament to his character, not mine.

Noreen was in the band, and Janice was one of the few talented girls who made it into Arrowettes in her freshman year. Along with her dance team skills, Janice was also beautiful. I'd only seen her in the halls at school, but when I attended Tim's sixteenth birthday party, I got to know her and decided she'd be my next girlfriend. Why I didn't apply the same logic to Janice that I had to Elena is unfathomable to me now, but I didn't. I can only chalk it up to pure competitive greed.

All of Tim's friends were at the party, and I guess through Mike's relationship with Noreen, Janice was there as well. Who knows, maybe Mike and Noreen were trying to fix Tim up with Janice, or Tim let them know he was interested. Either way, it was clear that Tim was on the make for her, and I decided to thwart him.

I showed up late, by myself, and quickly found Mike and Noreen. They introduced me to Janice. It was a nice party, but because Tim was the oldest member of a seven-child family, all of his younger siblings were there. In addition, his mom had not yet noticed that Tim was no longer ten-years-old, so the birthday party felt more like a grade school gathering than a cool teenager thing, and I used this to my advantage.

My extrovert personality hides insecurities I protect with a stiletto wit. It shows itself when I am vulnerable or want something badly. I wanted Janice as my girlfriend, and that night I used my blade against Tim to make Janice think I was the better choice. To my regret, it worked.

Tim was a good host and paid attention to all his guests while also participating in his mom's activities which, unfortunately, included children's games. This made it impossible for him to be with Janice much, so seeing my opening, I stayed close and fawned all over her while making snide comments about Tim. When I was sure she was responding to my attention, I left the party, feigning I was too adult for this childishness. The next night I was on the phone to Janice asking her out, and she accepted.

Score one for the asshole.

Our first date was sledding with old friends. There had been a good snow a few days before, and we all went to the Cumberland Country Club to sled down the steep hills of the golf course. Janice must have enjoyed herself because from that point on, we were an item, and that item lasted for the next six months.

— See Anything You Like? —

Earlier on the day of that first date, Dad had asked me to close up the store for him. There was no way I would miss my opportunity with Janice, but I also could not duck Dad, so I said yes intending to do it on my own timeline, not his, meaning long after closing. Dad often had the staff lock up the store without him balancing the books. They knew to take all the cash out of the register and hide it in the walk-in refrigerator. Dad would then show up later and do all the paperwork and deposit the money. I figured if he could do it, so could I; at least, that was my plan.

It was about eleven o'clock when I left Janice's, and as I turned in to the Tastee Freez parking lot, I saw an eighteen-wheel tractor-trailer truck parked in front of the building. All the lights were off in the truck, and I could see only the glow of the jukebox inside the store. I parked on the far side and went around to the back door. As I got closer to the door, I heard the unmistakable sounds of two impassioned adults engaged in a hide-the-sausage party. Peeking around the corner, I saw Flora pinned up against the wall, panties down and skirt up, with a trucker pumping her like a flat tire. Remember Flora? She was my forty-something Tastee Freez "show it all". She saw me, winked, and then flashed that damn smile. I ran back to the car—determined not to come back until morning. I should point out that Flora was married and not to a trucker.

I started seeing Janice regularly, and she was a real sweetheart. She was everything Patty had been and more, and the more part was her parents let her date. I finally had what I thought I wanted: a girlfriend I could take out on dates and maybe get to third base with, but in reality, my situation hadn't changed. Despite thinking I was now a young adult, Janice was only fourteen, and there was no way the relationship was going any further physically. We went to school dances and roller skated, and of course, we saw lots of movies, but our physical relationship never advanced beyond heavy petting and lots of messy kissing.

Let me pause for a second and ruminate on the paradox of a sixteen-year-old boy's desires. Boiling it down to its essence, you want girls to like you, and you also want to have sex with them. Your inner child wants to be loved while your hormonal hunger wants satisfaction. Worst of all, you are smart enough to

know you really shouldn't succeed, so, you find yourself on an unendir
totter that slams you from one emotional extreme to the other. You w͏
into your girl's pants, but you know if you do, you will get in trouble and lose
your girl, which means you won't get into her pants.

Given this reality, I asked Sam for advice on how to move things forward with
Janice.

"Get her drunk at a party," my mentor advised.

Chapter 13 - Mama Told Me Not to Come

— An Opportunity & Ridgeley —

Dennis Swain was one of the bands sousaphone players and every March his parents went out of town for a week, so on the Saturday of that week, Dennis had a big party at his house. It was one of those legendary events that you dare not miss, and it was also a party where booze was okay. Therefore, it represented an opportunity to expose Janice to alcohol and see what happens.

I'd been running around a lot with Sam, and he had been pushing me to drink beer with him, but I could not stomach the stuff, and I figured Janice couldn't either. I wanted to have something to drink for the party, so I went looking for a suitable substitute. Jimmy told me about Boone's Farm Apple wine, so when Sam asked me if I'd drive him to Dennis's party, I said yes, but first he had to get me a bottle of Boone's Farm.

"Boone's Farm? Jesus H. Christ, Shelby, that stuff is sugar-coated shit," he said.

"Sam, do you want a ride?" I asked dryly.

"Yes, but don't you have a fake I.D. yet?"

"You're not the first one to ask me that; but no, I don't," I answered with shame.

"Get one. We can go to Ridgeley after school Friday."

As soon as we finished band on Friday, Sam and I jumped into my car, and he drove us to Ridgeley, West Virginia. Ridgeley is a smudge mark of a town sitting across the Potomac River from Cumberland. It's home to maybe 500 people—most of them without teeth. Its principal industry is awarding speeding tickets and selling beer to Maryland residents under the age of 21. You had to be 21 to buy beer and wine in Maryland, but in West Virginia, you only had to be 18, and given the folks in Ridgeley weren't very good with numbers, getting a six-pack there was easy.

The joke went like this:

"How old do you have to be to buy a beer in Ridgeley?"

"Old enough to get the money onto the bar."

Sam demanded to drive whenever we were together and as stupid as it sounds; I let him. I heard gravel shoot up behind the Barracuda as Sam fishtailed onto the street in front of the school. Careening between parked cars on his left and school buses filling with students on his right, Sam blew the horn as we whizzed through a stop sign.

"Don't worry," he said. "I'll stop twice at the next one."

He didn't.

Speeding past the side of the Algonquin Hotel, Sam just missed t-boning a car coming down the adjoining street. I glanced down at the filthy dirty seatbelt that had lain unused beside the Barracuda's bucket seat since we brought it home in 1968 and wondered if I should put it on.

No, Sam will think I'm weak.

Instead, I gripped the armrest a bit firmer as we flew across the Blue Bridge into Ridgeley. Thrown forward by Sam's deceleration to 25 mph, we were in the world of Ridgeley radar. Sam reached into his coat pocket to retrieve a pack of Marlboros and shook one free.

Pushing in the electric lighter on the dash, he said, "He'll be right up here past the viaduct. I guarantee it."

The lighter popped out, and Sam put the red-hot spiral coils up to the end of his smoke and took a long drag.

"There he is," Sam announced, as we slid under the tracks of B&O's southbound line. Sure enough, sitting on the other side of the viaduct was Ridgeley's one and only police car with a radar gun attached to the driver's side door.

Sam smiled and waved as he mumbled, "Eat shit and die, pig."

We had nothing to worry about because the highly trained Ridgeley police officer behind the wheel was sound asleep with his hat pulled down over his face.

"We should stop and let the air out of his tires." Sam chuckled.

"Hell, no. Let's get our booze and get out of here," I said.

Moseying through downtown Ridgeley, we stayed below 25 mph until we saw the city limits sign. Sam dropped the Barracuda's automatic down into second and hit the gas again. I'd never put the car in that gear before, not knowing what the number two stood for. We jumped back to 60 mph as we merged onto West Virginia Route 28 South, a road that looked as if it had been designed by an anorexic snake. It was nothing but two skinny twisting lanes of blacktop with an ancient wire guardrail on the left and a solid shale wall on the right. There were no breakdown lanes on either side. You were either on the road, in the Potomac, or part of a mountain. It was then I heard Sam say something frightening.

"Watch this, man," he announced as he put both hands on the steering wheel for the first time and floored it. The car lurched forward, but instead of following the winding curves of Route 28, he aimed the Barracuda straight down the middle of the road. As the double-yellow, do not pass lines weaved under the front tires, I prayed there was no northbound traffic. We hit a rise in the road and caught a little air as all four of the Barracuda's wheels left the pavement. I swear I heard the car groan as the chassis banged down on the overtaxed shock absorbers. Sam had his cigarette cocked up a bit on the right side of his mouth, looking like FDR, and I knew he was in heaven. I hoped I wouldn't find myself at the pearly gates as well. The Barracuda's tires skidded to a stop in gravel as we found ourselves in front of Snyder's Market ten miles south of Ridgeley.

"Sam, why did you come all the way out here? There were a couple of places back there that sell beer," I asked.

"Pop Snyder's so blind, a nun could buy rubbers, and he wouldn't notice. I've been buying beer here since I was fourteen, and he's never carded me once, but you better stay here." Sam said. "I know you're sixteen, but you don't look a day over twelve, and without a fake I.D., you're nothing but trouble."

He was out the door and into Snyder's before I could argue, so I sat there and waited, but after ten minutes I got worried. I walked to the door and peeked in through the glass panes. Sam was nowhere in sight, and the cash register was abandoned. As I opened the door, the sad sound of Tammy Wynette's "Stand by Your Man" sang to me from an old tabletop radio behind the counter, but there was no one in the store.

Snyder's was a sad, single-story, concrete brick rectangle with a galvanized metal roof that might have been a gas station in its youth but now served as a general store. There were shelves dedicated to beef jerky and pork rinds, while others had cleaning supplies and fishing tackle. In the back, was a wall of glass door refrigerators filled with all beers suitable for consumption in this part of the world, but I saw no Boone's Farm wine. I turned to head down the aisle by an old, red, floor style, *Coca-Cola* refrigerator with a cardboard sign on it saying, "live bait," when I heard a woman giggle from the back room near me say, "No, we can't do that here, Sam. Pop will be back any minute."

"Oh, come on, baby. I came all the way out here to squeeze those lovely tomatoes of yours," Sam crooned.

As I turned to where the voices were coming from, the front door opened, and in walked a white-haired bespectacled man with a wooden crate filled with potatoes.

"Suellen!" he yelled. "You've got a customer out here. Didn't I tell you not to leave the register unattended?"

"Pop, I'm back here trying to find our extra supply of Boone's Farm. The Frigidaire is all out, and I thought you told me there was extra back here," said a twenty-something woman as she slid between the two old curtains that divided the front of the store from the back.

"Mr. Sam here needs two bottles," she said while buttoning the top two buttons of her candy striper hospital volunteer outfit.

"This kid isn't old enough to buy Windex let alone wine, honey, and I've got it locked up in the shed out back anyway," Pop said as he put the box down and spat tobacco juice into a coffee can on the floor.

"Not him, Pop. You know Sam," she said as Sam followed her into the front room. I grabbed a beef jerky and moved to the cash register as Pop Snyder and Sam talked Pittsburg Steelers football. Suellen took my 15 cents and smiled at me with a grin an orthodontist could spend a year on. Not saying a word, I went back to the car and waited. When Sam came out, he had a case of Old German and two bottles of Boone's Farm Apple wine.

He put our treasures into the back seat, and as he dropped into the front, he said: "You owe me $1.89."

"Right," I said. "Let's review the bidding. You came all the way out here only because they don't card you? Ha!"

"Listen, Suellen can suck a golf ball through a garden hose. She gave me intensive care in a broom closet at Memorial Hospital a couple of weeks ago. I'm telling you, that girl's a walking Electrolux," Sam boasted.

I laughed, not fully understanding what Sam was talking about, but what I knew was I could learn a lot from him. On the way back to Cumberland, I asked him how to get a fake I.D.

"You got your driver's license last year. Did you save your sixty-day card?" Sam asked.

"Yeah, I've got it, but it expired in October," I said.

"Use a razor blade to shave the number you need off the back somewhere and then glue it over the expiration date. Do the same for your birth year and presto, you've got a fake I.D.," said Doctor Sam, the man, with a Ph.D. in I.D. forgery.

As Ridgeley faded from my rearview mirror, I thought, *I'm all set. I have motive (Janice), opportunity (Dennis's party), and now the means (Boone's Farm wine). There is no stopping me.*

— Dennis's Party —

Sam, Janice, and I arrived at the party at about 8:30 Saturday evening, and there were already more cars parked outside than we had at Uncle Lu's on a good night. Unlike the store's nice, flat parking lot, Dennis lived on one of the steepest streets in Cumberland. It was at the base of Haystack Mountain and had a grade of about 20%. The houses clung to the hillside looking like wedges of cheese stacked on a grand piano's tilted top. On either side of the road, were deep drainage ditches to accommodate the torrents of water that flowed off the mountain every spring, so parking was a feat worthy of any mountain goat.

Cars were strewn this way and that with either their front ends or tails sticking up out of the ditches at odd angles, looking like a field of icebergs adrift in the North Atlantic searching for another Titanic. I didn't want any part of it, so I dropped Sam off halfway up the hill and went back down to park on flatter earth. I had one of my bottles of Boone's Farm in a brown paper bag as Janice and I climbed back up the mountain to Dennis's. As we got closer, we could hear Santana's "Evil Ways" wafting out of every window, and there were kids standing around the front door with clouds of smoke rising over their heads.

"Cool," I said to no one as I realized I was going to my first real adult party.

Janice gripped my hand tightly and looked at me with a thin smile, "Don't let go of me. Promise."

"Absolutely, I'll keep you close, babe," I said.

We made it up the front stairs, weaving in and out of clumps of kids talking, laughing, and smoking. The door was open, but there was no room to enter. It was like under the bleachers at Greenway Stadium before the game. We stood there waiting for a gap to open so we could push our way in. I saw Dennis's trademark strawberry-blond hair glide over the top of the crowd, and I yelled, "Yo, sousaphone boy, help us out here!"

The wall of blue jeans parted as Dennis pushed his way to the door. "Come on in, you guys, there's more room in the kitchen," Dennis said as he grabbed Janice's hand and pulled her into the mosh. I hung on to her other hand and followed them in. There may have been lights on, but I couldn't tell with my face pressed against the backs or sides of my fellow ALCO brethren. It wasn't long before I broke free into a less crowded area that was bathed in a bright light that only an old-style, spiral fluorescent bulb could make.

"Thanks for coming. It's a great party. I have to go down to the basement for more ice. I'll see you later," Dennis said as he dove back into the stream of youth that was crowding his foyer.

I took a swig of my bottle of Boone's Farm in a most manly fashion and almost spit it across the room. It tasted like liquid cotton candy mixed with kerosene.

Janice, seeing the look on my face, laughed and waved off any attempt to share a drink with her. I tilted the bottle in her direction while nodding my head and her laughter stopped.

Okay, there goes my "get Janice drunk plan" she clearly isn't going to drink anything.

I belched a bit as I forced the cloying syrup down my throat.

"Smooth," I purred as I tipped the bottle back again, hoping it wouldn't be as bad the second time. It wasn't, and I'd drunk a third of the bottle before I knew it.

Everyone was there, and it was fun surfing through the crowd chatting with friends while pushed up against them. The music was loud and continuous, but the human flesh did an excellent job of muffling the tenor tones, so you felt it more than heard it. I was feeling the wine kick in when Janice tugged on my sleeve and reminded me she needed to be home by eleven.

"Sure, babe, let's go," I said, and we wormed our way to the back door.

I screwed the top back onto my Boone's Farm and tucked it under my arm. Halfway down the steep street, five guys were trying to push a Corvair out of a ditch far enough for the rear wheels to get traction. I was glad I'd passed on parking close to the house. I stayed under the speed limit all the way to Janice's because I'd had a few drinks, and there was a bottle-and-a-half of Boone's Farm in the car.

Arriving at her door, she gave me a kiss, and with a little wine on my breath, I said, "Goodnight, beautiful."

"Are you going back to the party?" she asked.

"I doubt it. I've had enough of pressing-the-flesh for the night unless you'd like to do a little more, just the two of us," I leered.

"Call me tomorrow," she said as she unlocked her front door.

The truth was, I had every intention of going straight back to Dennis's house. I had even arranged to spend the night, so I wouldn't have to drive home after finishing my wine. As I turned onto Dennis's steep street, I was disappointed to see that many of the cars had gone. I looked at my watch and saw it was 11:50.

Had I missed the best part of the party?

Grabbing my remaining wine, I went in the front door to find the mood of the party had shifted from mix-and-mingle to make-out-and-more. All the lights were lower, and instead of Santana, the stereo was playing Al Green's "Let's Stay Together." There was something else that was different about the place I couldn't put my finger on at first. Along with the familiar smell of cigarettes and stale beer, there was another smoky smell that made my nose turn up. I took a big sniff and was sure someone was burning dirty rags somewhere.

Whoa, was that what pot smelled like?

Most people had either paired up and were necking or vegging out on the floor listening to the music.

"Shelby!" I heard someone call from behind me. "Up here."

It was dark, and I didn't see it was Sam calling me until I was at the bottom of the stairs that led up to the bedrooms. I walked up to him, and he said, "You're gonna love this. Keep quiet and stay right here. I've gotta tell some others," Sam whispered as he jumped down the stairs.

He was back quickly with a guy named Skip, and five others and led us to the bedroom door at the end of the hall.

"I saw two guys and a girl go in here as I was coming out of the crapper, and they had something special planned because the one guy was all over the girl," Sam said as he leaned his ear up to the bedroom's door.

"Oh yeah, we've got serious he-ing and she-ing going on in there," Sam cracked as we crowded in to listen.

"Wow, we gotta tell everyone about this," Skip said before the others shushed him into silence.

He disappeared down the stairs, and I was leaning in to have another listen when Sam opened the door and flipped the light switch on.

"Oh, my God," I heard myself say out loud. "Oh, my God!"

There were hoots and gasps as we all drank in the unbelievable sight that lay before us on a twin bed across from the door. My strip poker sweetheart, Joleen Johnson, was face up and naked. On top of her and also naked was an unknown guy, doing his best to complete what he'd started. Skip was back, and with half the party following him, we were all pushed forward into the room as Joleen shrieked, and the guy yelled, "Get out! Get the fuck out!"

Sam cheered, "Go, boy, go," as he started clapping rhythmically chanting, "Go, go, go!"

More people entered the tiny room, pushing me back away from the bed against a desk. That's when our host, Dennis, forced his way in and started giving orders.

"Okay, everyone out. There's nothing to see here. Everyone out. Let's give them a little privacy," Dennis said like a cop moving gawkers away from a car crash.

"Nothing to see?" I murmured, knowing I had a big grin on my face.

I had my bottle with me, so I took a swig and drank in the sight of Joleen and her friend trying to get up from the bed without letting us see any of their private parts. They failed.

"Hey, can I have a drink of that?" I heard a familiar voice say from my right. I turned, and there was Dill Denton, pushing his big black glasses up off his nose.

He was sitting in the desk's chair and had a shit-eating grin on his face like the Joker in Batman.

"Sure, Dill," I said, handing him the bottle. He reached out with his right hand, and I saw he had a deck of playing cards in his left.

He took a healthy drink, and handing the bottle back said, "You should have played the game, Shelby. You should have played the game."

I finished that bottle and started on the next one. I don't remember anything after that.

— Get Up! —

"Phone," I distantly heard as I felt a shoe tap my leg. "Get up. Your mother's on the phone."

Is that Dennis? What's he doing in my bedroom? I thought as I opened my eyes to nothing but beige corduroy. Lifting my head, I felt a sharp pain as if someone had ripped a six-inch Band-Aid from the right side of my face.

"Ouch!," I wailed.

There was another kick as I heard, "Get up and answer the phone! Your mother is hopping mad."

I was facing the side of the living room's couch, and under the right side of my head was a six-pack of beer.

"Sam, put that under your head to keep you from drowning in your own puke," Dennis said. "Oh, and after you get off the phone, clean that up."

I felt the clear and painful circular indentations left from the six-pack.

"Dude, you look like the Olympic rings," Dennis laughed.

"Where's your phone?" I croaked.

"Kitchen," he said, grabbing my arm and helping me right myself. As my head reached its maximum height, I knew the pain in my face was the least of my problems. My arms and legs tingled, and my head felt as if there were seventeen hamsters in there trying to gnaw their way out. Dennis steadied me.

"She's seriously angry, dude. You better get on the phone fast."

"What time is it?" I asked.

"Seven," said Dennis as I limped to the kitchen. My mouth was drier than a snake's ass in the Sahara, and I practiced saying hello a few times before I picked up the phone from the kitchen counter.

"Hello."

"Get your ass home now. You have acolyte duty at church at 8 a.m., and you are not going to miss it," said the angry voice of my loving mother.

"But, Mom, I'm sick," I whispered.

"I'm sure you are, and I don't give a damn. Get home now, or I'm coming over there to drag you out."

The sound of Mom slamming the receiver down reverberated in my ear like a cymbal crash. I stood there and shuddered for a few seconds.

"Here's a bucket and rag. Clean up your puke before you go, or you're never coming to another one of my parties," I heard Dennis say through a sonic fog that separated me from reality.

So, this is a hangover.

I took the bucket from Dennis and moved to the sink for water. The carpet wasn't stained, and my nocturnal regurgitations came up with little problem, but my stomach twisted and turned with each swipe of the cloth.

Am I going to live through this?

Stumbling out the door, the crisp March air felt good for a second before the torturous turning in my stomach returned. The hamsters in my head had escaped but were back with hammers and were busy driving nails into my skull as I started up the car and drove home. Glancing in the rearview mirror, I saw three perfectly round red indentations on the right side of my face, with one of them circling my eye like the Little Rascals' dog, Petey.

Oh, my God! How am I going to explain this to Finley?

— Finley —

Finley Cooper became rector of Emmanuel Episcopal Church in January of 1969, and to say the least; he stirred things up. America was changing, and Finley wanted to bring a little of that change to the church. The minister he replaced was Reverend Ray Richardson who presided over decades of dullness but was good at his job. Everybody loved Ray.

I thought the Reverend was God himself when I was a kid, and he loved telling the story of how one Sunday I said so in church. I was about three, and it was the point in the service where the minister reads the Gloria Patri. If you don't recognize the name, you'll recognize the words; it goes like this:

"Glory be to the Father, and to the Son, and to the Holy Ghost.

As it was in the beginning, is now, and ever shall be: world without end, Amen."

When he said, "Shall be," I asked in a most noticeable voice, "Mommy, why did God say my name?" The congregation muffled guffaws, and Ray Richardson damn near did a spit-take.

As soon as Finley took over, he started changing things. First, he added a youth service with, long-haired boys and girls in short skirts singing Bob Dylan songs. Then, he tried to move the altar down from behind the brass gated no man's land of the chancel right into the middle of the church, sort of a theatre-in-the-round kind of thing. Both ideas died quick deaths. Finally, Finley chose a more focused attack. In the fall of his first year, he organized the church's youth groups to open a coffeehouse in the basement that would only be for them and their friends. It was called Noah after the Ark builder; and bingo, Finley had a winner. Not only did the kids love it, but the coffeehouse made money, and anything that makes money in the Episcopal church is a good thing, by God.

— Communion —

Driving home I thought, What's Finley going to think when his acolyte shows up looking like a Ballantine beer ad?

I dashed into the house, changed my clothes, and ran back to the door. Mom was there and handed me two aspirin and a glass of orange juice, saying, "This always helps me on Sunday mornings."

It was 7:55 when I pulled into the church parking lot. I found Finley in the sacristy, the room on the ground floor of the steeple where he prepared for the service. It had closets and cupboards containing things like altar decorations, and communion items. There was a small sink in the corner next to a large rope hanging down from a hole in the ceiling. The rope was attached to the church bell, three stories above us. Tucked under Finley's desk was a small safe that stored the Harvey's Bristol Cream Sherry and wafers used as Eucharist.

Episcopalians don't fool around when it comes to communion; it's Harvey's Bristol Cream or nothing.

Finley saw me and said, "Shelby, we have very little time. I need you to change and get me the communion silver from the altar."

"Yes, sir," I mumbled as I put on my two-piece acolyte's frock.

Scooting out the side door that connected the sacristy to the chancel, I felt a sharp pain in my eyes as I was blinded by the brilliance of the Holy of Holies altar area.

Separated from the rest of the church, the altar sits at the top of the cross-shaped floor plan of the building. Gleaming from ten ceiling spotlights, the floors and walls are covered in white marble and embellished at every angle with polished brass and colored tapestries. It is an area of the church that few members of the congregation ever enter. They are only allowed to come up to the gated fence to receive communion on their knees.

God wants you close, but not that close.

Using a large silver tray, I gathered up all the chalices, decanters, and platters necessary to serve fish wafers and sherry to thirty people and took them back to Finley. Setting them on the table, I felt Finley's hand on my chin as he lifted my face up to his.

"You look like you slept with a giant squid last night."

"I know, I was watching TV and fell asleep on the plastic rings that hold Coke cans together," I explained.

"Right," smiled Finley. "I guess that explains your pale green complexion as well."

Finley handed the silver tray full of sacramental vessels back to me to carry to the altar, and I got my first whiff of the Harvey's Bristol Cream.

Feet don't fail me now, I prayed as I felt my knees go wobbly and my stomach flip.

Get me through the next thirty minutes, God, and I'll never drink Boone's Farm again.

I set the tray down on the right side of the altar and moved the items to a side table then went back to Finley for a candle lighter. He had one ready for me, and I lit all the candles on the altar. Then, I went back to Finley and waited.

The eight o'clock communion service at Emmanuel is a short one with no music or sermon. Now and then, I'd have to get up and move a silver chalice or pitcher or serving plate for Finley as he prepared, then provided, the Holy Eucharist. But, that was it. Hell, I might make it.

Before Finley entered the chancel, he pulled the rope by the sink in the sacristy to ring the big bell three times, and the twenty-five or so congregants rose from their seats. It was show time. I followed him in and sat on a small chair against the right wall near the altar.

Everything went well. Finley droned through the service in his sing-song, made-for-Episcopal-minister voice, and I was feeling a bit better as Mom's aspirins started doing their job. At communion time, I jumped up and swapped plates and goblets with Finley as he blessed the bread and wine. Then, he called the congregation forward to receive their very own wafer and sip of joy juice. I thought I was going to make it when I saw Finley signaling me to come over to the altar. It was my turn to receive communion.

Gasp!

I inhaled and tightened my throat to stop any stomach acid from climbing up my esophagus as I knelt at the side of the altar. I accepted my wafer and placed it in my mouth. Finley turned and picked up the chalice full of that syrupy sweet sherry, and I swear he had an evil look on his face as he tilted it up to my lips. I braced myself, keeping my mouth tightly shut, but Finley had started a wave of Harvey's Bristol Cream rolling in my direction, and when it reached my face it crested over my upper lip and entered my nose.

My reaction was involuntary. Beads of sweat popped out on my forehead, and my eyes bugged out like they'd been pushed from behind with pool cues. I felt a pressurized rumbling in my gut that would not stop until it skyrocketed out of my mouth. I knew I had only seconds before I erupted like a volcano. I stood still for a moment deciding which way to run. Then, I charged for the sacristy. Pulling up my acolyte dress, I hurtled the ornate brass gate and dashed through the small door. There was my salvation—the sink in the corner of the room. It was only steps away, and I thought for a moment I would make it as a primordial force thrust up my plumbing. It was then the toe of my shoe caught on the carpet, and I found myself airborne. Grabbing at anything to stop my fall, my hands found the church bell's rope, and I pulled it down with me. I hit the floor as my mouth exploded with a sour, orangey-apple-sauce, not of this world.

Do not ask for whom the bell tolls, it tolls for me.

As my dry heaves subsided, and my vision cleared, I saw Finley, Bill Wilson—Dad's lawyer—and several other people staring down at me on the sacristy's floor. An older woman knelt beside me and was wiping my face with a cool cloth, and I heard someone ask, "Is he going to be all right?"

"I'm sure he'll be fine," Finley answered. "He had a rough night out with friends."

Bill Wilson spouted a deep laugh, then said, "Well, you know whenever four Episcopalians get together; you always find a fifth."

They all laughed as I tried to evaporate.

Chapter 14 - Gimme Dat Ding

— I Can Learn a Lot from Sam —

"Let's see, that's 95 cents for the six-pack and 10 cents for the Slim Jim plus 4 percent for the State House—that makes $1.09. You got an I.D.?" Mr. Malone asked, looking at me over his reading glasses.

"Sure," I replied, already pulling my new-and-improved sixty-day card out of my wallet. I had carefully placed it in the transparent plastic window section set aside for drivers licenses so it would look extra official. I marveled at its beauty as I passed it to him. Not only had I perfectly placed the number I shaved off the back over the last digit of my birth year making me 18, but I also extended the expiration date until I turned 20.

Brilliant!

Malone glanced at it as if he was checking his watch and handed it back, and I passed him a dollar and a dime. "Thanks," I said as I picked up the bag and penny he'd placed on the counter.

As the screen door slammed shut, I heard Mr. Malone say, "By the way, that was a good one, and I should know. I see at least two of them a day."

I felt my neck jerk around like I'd caught it on a hook. Then, I darted for the car and was out of West Virginia before you could spit. Reaching down under the dash, I pushed an 8-track tape into my recently installed Muntz player and waited for the clicking noise signaling it had jumped to the next track. Three Dog Night's song "Liar" belted out of the new rear-mounted speakers as I pointed the nose of the car towards Sam's.

I'd done it. I bought beer on my own with my own money. Sell my clothes; I'm going to heaven!

As I pulled up to his house, Sam was in the driveway washing his dad's Oldsmobile Delta 88 that he couldn't drive.

"Touchdown!" I yelled out the window as Sam turned the hose off.

"You got it?" he asked.

"Yeah, I got it. No problem," I beamed.

"How much did you get?"

"A six-pack," I answered.

My Fake I.D. (Syckes Family Photos)

"Is that all? What am I going to drink? We'll go through that in an hour," he snarled.

"Give me a break; I'm new at both buying and drinking beer, and I'm not sure I'll be able to drink more than two of them anyway," I whined.

"Listen," Sam said seriously. "I'm not going to hang out with you if you don't drink like a man. Men drink beer and lots of it—never that Boone's Farm crap. Did you tell your parents you were spending the night?"

"Yes," I said meekly.

"Good, let me go tell my old man I'm staying at your place, then we're heading back to Ridgeley. Oh, and get that "dog-music" off your stereo. We're listening to man-music tonight," ordered my mentor.

It was 8 o'clock when we left Sam's, and we went straight to the White Coffee Pot restaurant in LaVale before getting more beer. Sam knew a waitress there who gave us two dinners for the price of one. I was glad to hear it, wanting something in my stomach before I was forced to drink more beer than I ever had before.

"Why are you in such a piss-poor mood, Sam?" I asked, hoping to find out why he was giving me so much shit.

"I got fired from Gehauf's yesterday," he moaned.

"Fired! Why? You only started there in December, didn't you?"

"Yeah, but it seems Dave the manager doesn't like it when he finds the busboy making out with the cashier in the closet. You'd think they'd tell you about rules like that in advance." Sam laughed. "Hey, doll, how about you give me a little more coffee?" he said, redirecting his attention to his waitress friend. As she leaned over to fill his diner-style white coffee mug, Sam slid his hand up the side of her stockinged thigh.

I can learn a lot from Sam.

We finished our dinners and drove to Pop Snyder's. Sam was in and out in a flash with two more six-packs and a big bag of potato chips. As we drove back to Maryland, I asked, "What now?"

Sam leaned down and turned up the volume on Alice Cooper crooning, "School's out for summer, school's out forever, school's been blown to pieces," and reached into the paper bag to pull a can of beer loose from the others. "Now we drink. Since you're just starting, let's go back to where you and I got started. Braddock. Let's go over to Braddock Junior High School and suck down these brews."

Sam and I had met there in the band room in September of 1967. Sam was starting the eighth grade and was the unbeatable first chair of the trumpet section. At only thirteen, he was already challenging the better players from the local high schools at music competitions.

Arriving at Braddock, Sam drove the Barracuda up over the parking lot curb and out onto a narrow lawn that ran behind the school and separated it from a steep embankment on the left. There he stopped a few feet from the school's wall. He pushed open his door with his foot, killed the engine and opened another beer.

"It's your turn now," he demanded. "Pop a top and get going."

"Okay, give me those chips; I need salt to kill the taste," I begged.

We spent the next two hours sitting in the car listening to tapes and enjoying our beer. I took my time; I did not want another morning like I had at church a few weeks ago.

By eleven, Sam had killed a six-pack, and I was nursing my third can.

"Time to go," he announced, looking at his watch. "The Purple Heart should be heating up about now."

"The Purple Heart?" I said with fear quivering in my voice. "What are you talking about?"

"As it gets closer to closing time, the bars stop checking I.D.s. They're always looking for extra cash, and the police are usually asleep in their cars by then," Sam tutored.

He threw all the empties out the door, then started the car and proceeded to drive forward on the lawn, not backing out onto the parking lot.

"Where in the hell are you going?" I gasped as Sam sped up.

"Fasten your safety belt, boy, this is an E-ticket ride," Sam gleamed and launched the Barracuda part-way up the embankment on our left to clear the corner of the building jutting out in front of us. I felt like the air bubble in a carpenter's level set on the side of a pyramid as I watched the horizon of the city tilt 45 degrees to the right.

"Jesus!" I blurted as my view leveled off, but then we spun counterclockwise. Sam had pulled the steering wheel hard left once back on flat ground, and the back end of the car was arching in circles over the damp grass of the sports field.

Donuts without snow.

Finishing a 360, it was back up the side of another hill to clear the final corner of the school building. Then the real fun began. In front of us was a steeply sloped grassy hill that led down to the one-way street in front of the school.

"Whoa!" I exhaled as the nose of the car tipped down the hill.

I braced my hands above me to avoid bouncing off the ceiling as the city lights disappeared. Darkness filled the windshield. Jumping the curb onto the street, Sam turned south on the northbound one-way. He had his beer up to his mouth and was enjoying the last drops as headlights appeared coming straight for us. Expecting him to slow and pull to the side, I cringed as Sam hit the gas and tossed his empty can out the window. He executed a perfect Bat-turn at the next intersection barely avoiding a head-on collision. The frequency of the approaching car's horn Doppler-shifted down as it passed the street we'd escaped on to milliseconds before. I couldn't see anything now because I'd slid off the seat into the wheel well hoping my body would stay in the car upon impact. Sam had that FDR look going again, and I knew I could do nothing but hold on till we got to the Purple Heart or the coroners.

— The Purple Heart —

The Purple Heart was a bar on the Dingle Circle right next to Smitty's ESSO station, and it was a fixture for Westside middle-age males. Every Friday and Saturday night, members of The Greatest Generation, or as we knew it back then, the G.I. Generation, packed the place to play pool and shuffleboard while consuming mass quantities of alcohol. It was a back-slapping, remember-the-good-old-days watering hole for all those guys who spent their childhoods trying to survive the Great Depression only to find themselves on the front lines of a World War. They had good reason to drink. Why Sam thought a couple of teenage boys would fit in was beyond me, but mine was not to reason why. Sam led the way to the front door.

"Listen, stay behind me, and I'll order our drinks at the bar. Then, we'll go back to the shuffleboard table. Keep your head down, and don't talk to anyone," he said in a hush as he pushed open the door.

The door had a huge replica of the Purple Heart medal affixed to it that passed through to a wall of glass bricks illuminated with red, white and blue neon lights. The first thing you notice when you walk into the Purple Heart—which was like every other bar in Cumberland—is that it's dark, smoky, and noisy.

Right inside the door was a long, wooden bar. Behind it was a large mirror with row upon row of liquor bottles sitting on tiered shelves in front of it. Hanging over the upper right-hand corner of the mirror was a vintage 1950's TV with a bulging cathode ray tube. It was off tonight, so it looked like a large greenish eye staring down at us. Men and women filled the few stools along the bar. The smoke was tolerable, but the cacophony of clinking glasses, loud voices, and clashing billiard balls pierced your very being.

I did as I was told and stayed low as Sam stopped at the bar. I hoped to find someplace to hide once I reached the back of the building. There was no joy. As the room opened up, I beheld two pool tables crowded with smoky men, each holding a pool cue and looking like spear carrying African warlords awaiting battle on the Serengeti.

Along the back wall was a sixteen-foot-long shuffleboard table covered in sawdust and dotted with shimmering silver disks, each the size of a hamburger. Stacked at each end of the table were four men leaning in to observe the style of the current curler executing his next slide. There were tables filled with partiers but no unoccupied chairs in sight, so I decided the best place to hide was in the men's room.

Its entrance was to the right of the shuffleboard table, and I turned towards the fluorescent glow that emanates from all such relief facilities. Passing through the L-shaped entryway, my pupils constricted, overwhelmed by the brash lighting bouncing off the subway-tiled walls of the restroom. It was almost as bright as the church's altar area and about as well populated. There was only one other man in there, and he was facing one of the two urinals. I couldn't tell if he was leaning against the wall or trying to hold it up as he intensely focused on forcing fluid from his body. I turned and washed my hands. I had spent about all the time I could at the sink when I heard Sam's voice call. "Syckes, you in there?"

"Yes," I answered and scooted back out the entrance.

"Here, let's go over to the far side of the shuffleboard table. It's pretty dark there, and you won't stand out so much," he said while handing me another beer.

"Thanks, I think," I said.

It was then I noticed not all the people in this area of the bar were men. There was another breed that appeared to be a kind of female. I'd encountered this species before. It was *Deformis Canis Antiquis*, or as we knew the one that prowled the Tastee Freez: Flora. They were in varying stages of intoxication ranging from ready, to willing, to able. Some were intertwined with their partners; while others were engaged in acts I'd only heard about at church camp.

"Over here. There are chairs against the wall," Sam said. He pulled me by my sleeve and I followed him to sit in chairs with the ass-end view of two guys waiting for their turn at the shuffleboard table.

It was then a balding, blurry-eyed guy appeared in front of me and announced, "You're in my chair, faggot."

I looked left and then right, hoping to see someone better fitting that description, but no luck.

"Are you talking to me?" I asked, pointing my index finger at my chest. I did this nothing like Robert De Niro would do four years later in the movie *Taxi Driver*. There was no bravado in my tone. I sounded more like one of the frightened puppies in *101 Dalmatians*.

"What the hell are you anyway?" he growled.

"Leaving," I said as I rose and slid off to the right.

Before I could escape, Sam shoved the guy into the group of his now very interested friends and said, "Back off!"

"Look, boys, the little pussy has a big pussy for a friend," the shuffleboarder chortled.

Sam smiled, "Well, you know what they say. You are what you eat."

Anger rose in the bald guy's eyes. He lunged towards Sam with his right fist cocked and ready to fire. I grabbed his arm as it swung past me. Having not fully thought through this action, I found myself hanging from the elbow of a six-foot-tall angry drunk. He looked down at me in surprise. Then, with about as much effort as a horse needs to swat a fly from its ass, he sent me tumbling into one of the occupied tables. Sam used this time to pick up a metal napkin holder and was about to plant it on the guy's forehead when the overhead lights turned on, and an older man in a stained apron yelled, "All right everybody. Cool it! There will be no fighting in here."

It was the bartender, and he had a baseball bat and an arm on him that looked like he'd swung it a few times.

"You're right, you're right," said Sam as both he and his adversary backed away from the center of the ring.

Pushing myself up off the floor, I was reminded of the two universal constants: gravity hurts, and bar floors are sticky. The man whose table I almost overturned was helping me up when he said, "Shelby, is that you?"

"Oh, shit," I mumbled as I saw Al Homburg's shocked face looking down at me.

Still seated was a semi-attractive, thirty-something woman who was definitely not JoAnn, and next to her was another couple I didn't know at all.

"Hi, Mr. Homburg. I stopped by to pick up a late-night snack when I was attacked by that shaved ape over there."

"Right," Al said with a twinge of nervousness. "How about we keep this little meeting to ourselves," he continued as Sam came up from behind me and looked over my shoulder.

"Hey, Mr. Homburg, Mr. Waters, small world isn't it?" Sam said with great satisfaction. "How are Mrs. Homburg and Mrs. Waters?"

The man with Al was Dave Waters, the general manager who fired Sam from his restaurant job the day before. His date was not wearing a wedding ring.

"Fine, fine. We'll see you boys another time," Al said as he put a dollar on the table and helped his friend put her coat on. Waters glared at Sam and backed away from us with his friend.

Sensing it was time to go, I pulled Sam out the back door as he laughed out loud. "Did you see that? Caught in the act! We caught them both in the act."

The bartender closed the door behind us, and we went back to the Barracuda. We'd had enough of the Cumberland bar scene for one night. It was time for us to return to what we did best: vandalism.

— Gehauf's —

As Sam drove, he said, "I can't believe I got fired by that shit for doing exactly the same thing he's doing."

"Screw him. He's not worth getting pissed about," I added, hoping to calm Sam's building tension.

"That's what I'm going to do. Screw him," he said as he accelerated and pushed in the Black Sabbath's *Master of Reality* tape. Ozzy Osbourne's whiny voice screamed out, "Would you like to see the pope on the end of a rope? Do you think he's a fool?" as we drove west.

Sam pulled into the parking lot of Sears Town and got out of the car. He paced back and forth for about a minute, then came over to my side and leaned into my open window.

"Here's what I want you to do. Drive me over to Gehauf's, and pull in behind the main building. I'll get out, and while I'm gone, turn the car around and be ready to go when I get back. Don't turn the engine off," Sam detailed like a battlefield commander giving last-minute orders before the attack. His eyes were on fire, and I knew I'd been drafted and had no choice.

Pulling out of Sears Town, I drove past Gehauf's so Sam could make sure no one was around.

"Kill the headlights," Sam ordered, as I turned in behind the building.

The back end of the Barracuda was soon hidden, and Sam jumped out and ran around the corner. I busied myself executing a quiet, three-point turn, hoping to avoid backing into anything noisy. Then I watched through my rearview mirror and waited for Sam. With my senses on high, I heard crickets chirping and an occasional croak of a frog, but there was no sign of him. The Barracuda didn't have a clock, so time stretched out. Suddenly, I heard a rustle, and I saw Sam. He was moving with a strange, hunkered-down gait as if shouldering a heavy burden. As he got closer, I could see he had a large item shaped like a duffle bag slung under each arm.

I reached over and popped open his door, and he yelled, "Push the seat forward so I can get these in the back!" I flopped the front seat forward, and Sam threw first one and then another heavy clear plastic bag full of what looked like red clay on to the rear seat. I felt the car sink on its shocks as they hit the cushions behind me.

As Sam's butt hit the seat, he grabbed the gear shift with his left hand, moving it into drive and yelled, "Move Out!"

Pushing on the gas pedal a little, we rolled forward, and Sam yelled again, "Move, man. Move!"

I did as ordered and pushed the pedal to the floor, as the right rear wheel caught the curb. We hopped east onto the main road and sped forward into the darkness.

"Can I turn on the headlights, please?" I begged.

"Sure," Sam said. "Get on The Bridge for Cumberland."

"What's in those bags?" I asked, not really sure I wanted to know. Sam was looking out the windshield and breathing heavily as he reached into his shirt pocket and retrieved his ever-present pack of Marlboros.

"Hamburger." He laughed. "There are thirty pounds of hamburger in each of those beautiful big bags."

Lighting his cigarette with the dashboard lighter, he inhaled enough smoke to cure a side of bacon. Then, he leaned his head back over the top of the seat and hung his arm out the car's window.

"Do we have any more beer?" Sam asked.

I twisted my head as much as I dared while hurtling down the highway and saw that Sam was telling the truth. There, sitting upright in the backseat, like two small children, were sixty pounds of ground chuck. Sam had found the last six-pack and was sucking the foam off the top of the can he'd opened when I asked with honest interest and much respect, "How in the hell did you steal sixty pounds of hamburger from Gehauf's?"

Smoke poured out of his nose and lips as he exhaled slowly. "They have an outdoor walk-in refrigerator with a combination lock on it. Two days ago, I helped them unload a truck full of those bags, and I figured they hadn't changed the combo yet. So, we now have more cow than Kansas," Sam bragged as he drained the beer can and crushed it in his right hand.

"What are we going to do with sixty pounds of hamburger?" I asked.

"I don't fucking know," laughed Sam.

"But what I do know is Dave Waters is gonna have to explain to Mr. Gehauf where those sixty pounds of moo-meat went. Head downtown. We'll finish this beer, then decide what we're going to do with it."

Steering the course set by the ship's captain, I glided down the road, hoping those plastic bags didn't leak.

How would I explain blood all over the back seats?

"I can sell it to another restaurant," Sam announced, as he threw his latest empty out the window.

"Listen, no restaurant owner in his right mind will buy sixty suspicious pounds of hamburger from a high school kid, and you've only got about twelve hours before that cold meat turns into fly-covered carrion. You accomplished your mission: you've hurt Waters. Now we need to get rid of it, but we can be creative in doing that," I said, sounding far wiser than I was.

"Okay, you're right, but I stuck it to the man tonight, didn't I?" Sam asked not expecting an answer given he was already basking in the glory of his victory over the Restaurant Industrial Complex.

"Any ideas?" I asked.

"We could smear it all over the front door of Fort Hill. It would smell pretty ripe by Monday," Sam suggested.

I visualized us standing in front of Fort Hill using our hands to paint the doors with hamburger. "No, that will take too long. We need to dump this stuff fast, maybe off a building somewhere."

There was a pause, and then Sam said, "Yeah, let's dump it off that bridge right in front of your church."

Remembering the last time I was standing on that bridge with Mike and Tim, there was no way I was going back there carrying a ton of stolen hamburger with beer on my breath.

"The bridge idea is good, but that one's too close to the police station," I cautioned.

"Well, there are lots of bridges around here," Sam said as we approached the Fletcher Drive overpass that spans the interstate and took me to Patty's house a hundred times.

"There, let's throw it off there!" I yelled while pointing up at the roof as the car passed under Fletcher.

Sam leaned out his window and looked back at the sculpted concrete span that arched from right to left over the interstate. "Yeah, that's perfect. Let's go."

"All we have to do is stop up there and dump it down. How cool is that?" Sam chortled.

I stopped in the dark shadows of the trees that cover Fletcher Drive near the overpass.

"Okay, we need to do this quick," I ordered, somehow having taken command of the second phase of the operation. "Once I stop, we will each grab a bag and toss it over the side."

"Got it," said Sam, fueling his courage with yet another beer.

He already had his door open as I pulled forward, and feeling me hit the brakes, he jumped out and grabbed his bag. I took a few seconds longer, but I flung my door open and started to get out when I realized I hadn't put the car in park. With one foot out, the car rolled backward, and the door slammed into me. At the last second, I jumped back into my seat and pushed the brake before the car hit the curb.

"Drive much, dumbass?" Sam yelled as he lifted his thirty-pound bag over his head and hurled it into the void.

I missed seeing it hit the road, but the sound was overwhelming. It was like a herd of flatulent elephants all releasing a watery fart at once. Sam jumped back in awe. It was my turn. Lifting the bag out of the back was tricky as condensation had formed on it, and it slipped out of my grasp like a greased pig.

"Are you really that weak?" Sam jabbed.

I did not reply and hoisted the clammy bag on my shoulder. I felt the center give way a bit as I jogged to the edge. Glancing down, I saw a five-foot diameter starburst of red with shreds of plastic flapping in the breeze.

"Go for the same spot. We want as big a mound as we can make!" Sam yelled.

I tipped my treasure over the edge and watched it tumble to its death. The elephants broke wind again, and I saw red goo shoot out in all directions. It landed near Sam's. He slapped me on the back and said, "Bingo."

Huffing and puffing a bit, I looked up while still leaning on my knees with my hands and asked, "Now what?"

"Now, we go down and drive through it," Sam answered as he went back to his side of the car.

"Why?" I asked, and I got an answer I've heard from my mother a thousand times.

"Because I say so."

Driving down the interstate entrance ramp, we could see our mound of meat sticking up almost two feet at its peak. With no other cars in sight, we might be able to loop around and hit it before anyone else does. Sam looked at me with great intensity and said, "Fast, man. Hit it going fast!"

I pushed the accelerator down, and as the overpass came into view, we were doing at least 70. Our target was clearly outlined by the streetlights. I aimed the front left tire of the Barracuda right at the center of the mound. With a resounding *thud* and deafening *squish,* I felt the car skid to the right as a spray of shredded meat flew up over the hood and rained down on the windshield.

Sam gave out a loud hoot then yelled, "Let's do it again!"

I made the mistake of turning on the windshield wipers, and the meat smeared across the glass, making visibility nonexistent. I pulled over to the side of the road.

"I've got to wipe that shit off before we go again," I told Sam as I opened my door.

It was then the police car flipped on its flashing lights as it slid in behind us.

"We are so screwed," I stated without any emotion.

Sam was busy stuffing the three remaining beers under his seat as the police officer got out of his car, turned on his flashlight, and walked towards my side.

"Stay in your car, sir, and show me your license and registration," the cop ordered.

Closing my door, I leaned over and got out the registration while Sam was lighting up another smoke to kill any potential lingering beer smell. Sitting upright, I squinted at the flashlight beam as it hit the center of my face.

"Yes, sir, I've got them right here," I said, sliding my wallet out of my back pocket. I flipped it open and damn near took out my modified sixty-day card.

Shit, let's not add to our trouble.

I handed my real license to the police officer along with the registration.

He turned his light to study what I had given him and said, "What are you boys doing out this late at night?"

"We just left the Super-51 Drive-In," Sam chimed. "They had a great double feature, *Deliverance* and *Shaft*."

I interrupted and added, "Officer, there is something dead back there on the road. I couldn't avoid running over it, but I don't think we were the first to hit it."

The cop shined his flashlight back into my eyes. I stopped breathing in dread of what might come next. What the policeman said I'll remember until the day I die.

"Yes, I saw it, too. Whatever hit it really chewed it up. It looks like hamburger."

— Sam Has Needs —

The policeman let us go, telling us to head straight home although he suggested we hose down the car or it would smell pretty bad tomorrow. We thanked him, and after wiping off the windshield, we took the next exit and drove to a do-it-yourself carwash. As I was spraying the drying meat, mud, and grass from my car, Sam announced, "Take me to South Cumberland when you're done."

You'd think I'd get tired of asking, but I went ahead. "Why?"

"I have needs," Sam grinned. "The White Coffee Pot waitress gave me her address and said to stop by tonight if I had time. Well, I now have time."

I drove to South Cumberland while Sam looked for a different 8-track to play. "Here, you can listen to your girlie-man music while I'm there." He shoved *Nilsson Schmilsson* into the player.

It was at the top of the track, and I switched it to the beginning of the album. I pulled to a stop across the street from the house. It was a single-story ranch home, and the only light on was coming from one of the basement's half windows. Sam didn't invite me to join him, and that was okay. I'd had enough adventure for one night. He got out with the three remaining beers and walked towards the door. Stopping he turned back and looked at me.

"Hey, kid, that was great fun tonight. You know how to have a good time. Thanks," he said, as he pulled loose a beer and tossed it to me.

I knew I'd be showered in foam if I opened it right away, so I settled into my seat to wait for Sam and instead of the beer, I drank in the sounds of Harry Nilsson.

Chapter 15 - Whole Lotta Love

— It Pays to Say Hello —

I t was the car door closing that woke me. Sam was settling into the passenger seat and closing his eyes. "What time is it?" I asked.

"Sorry, man, I didn't mean to wake you. It's about 8 o'clock, I think," Sam said.

I'd slept in the back of the Barracuda, and it was not a comfortable bed. I moved to the driver's seat realizing, *Hey, I don't have a headache, and my stomach feels fine. Beer is better than Boone's Farm. Thanks, Sam.*

He was sound asleep the whole way to his house. Pulling into his driveway, I had to push him twice to wake him up.

"You're home. Party's over, Sam."

He was firing on only about three cylinders, and as I watched him shuffle towards his house, I waited to make sure he made it. I was putting the car in drive when Sam burst back out of his front door looking like he'd won the lottery. "Stop! Stop!" He was waving a piece of paper.

"What is it?" I asked.

"All I've got to say is it pays to say hello to folks in bars. Dave Waters called this morning and wants me to come back to work starting tomorrow. Mom took the call. Here," Sam said as he handed me the piece of paper.

In a woman's hand, the note had the news Sam had already shared, but it also had the following message: "Tell Sam I'm sorry, and I know now how important it is to have an employee like him who is always on the boss's side."

"Is this for real?" I asked.

"I shit you not," Sam beamed.

"Hell, if I'd caught him in the sack with that skank, he'd have made me assistant manager."

I shook my head and grinned, wondering if Al Homburg would offer me free guitar lessons.

— Friends with Benefits —

Janice was my girlfriend, and we fell into a comfortable pattern only slightly different from the one Patty and I enjoyed. I'd walk her to class, drive her home from school, take her out to movies and dances, and of course, make out on the couch at her place, but that was it. After her brief appearance at Dennis's party, she was not interested in attending any more events where alcohol was consumed. I really liked Janice, so I went along with this hoping she'd change her mind. She didn't. I, on the other hand, was enjoying a whole new world of partying and was not ready to give it up, so I compartmentalized. Picture the scales-of-justice. I figured I could keep Janice on one side of the scale and everything else on the other, and there were girl friends over there too. Note: I separated the words girl and friend. That's because they were more "friends with benefits" than girlfriends. Janice was my one and only girlfriend, but I was afforded opportunities I could not turn down. All I had to do was keep things balanced.

Tim and I were not talking, for obvious reasons, and Walter was busy dating lots of girls, so I spent more time with Jimmy. Having a little control over the Tastee Freez work schedule, I arranged for us to work the same shifts, and I made sure we always had either Friday or Saturday night off, but even on those weekend nights when we worked, we'd often party afterward. I would buy beer before work, and keep it chilled in the walk-in refrigerator until closing. Then, we'd crank up the jukebox and enjoy our cooled brews with the rest of the staff.

Garrett would often join in the party with us at the Tastee Freez after he finished working at his parent's clothing store. One weekend, Garrett's parents went out of town, so the party moved to his place. It was a low-key affair— nothing like Dennis Swain's party, but what made it different was it included people you didn't see at other ALCO events. I'm talking about kids from Fort Hill and a few of the African-Americans from Allegany. I knew one of them, Benjamin Evans, who had been in the choir with me. I was happy to count him as a friend. Now, don't think I'm proposing I was a great egalitarian or forward thinker. I wasn't, but Benjamin was a good guy, and we got along well, so he was a welcome addition to what was shaping up to be a fun night. The big surprise for me was that Elena was there with a few of her girlfriends, and we reconnected but in a roundabout way. As was the standard practice, I told my parents I was staying overnight at Garrett's.

I need to pause again from the story to comment on the level of parental oversight I was receiving at the time. I don't know if it was that my parents were very busy people, burned out after diligently monitoring the development of my two older sisters, or just tuned out, but I pretty much had a free hand as a teenager. I think the events I've described so far back that up, but my parents' due diligence was even slacker late in my junior year. I had access to the Barracuda whenever I wanted, I didn't have to check in with them every night, and they didn't seem very interested in what I was doing when not at home.

On top of that, I got an allowance of five bucks a week, free fast food at the Tastee Freez, and I could go into a dozen different stores in Cumberland and buy stuff without paying for it. I'm not talking about using a credit card. I had access to an old style of credit that is long gone in American business. I could walk into a store, pick up something I wanted, and sign for it at the checkout counter. At the end of each month, a bill was sent to my parents. In summary, I was spoiled rotten.

Garrett's party was mellow and mild with everyone sipping drinks, mingling, and listening to the latest rock and roll. Garrett hooked his cassette player up to his dad's hi-fi and blasted the sounds throughout the house.

About two hours into the party, I noticed Elena was on the other side of the room paired up with someone on her mom's chaise lounge. I'd been talking to a cute Fort Hill girl, but I wasn't getting anywhere. I got up to get another beer and made sure I walked by Elena on my way.

Whoa! That's Benjamin she's necking with.

I've got to say, interracial dating was on the far end of acceptable then, but I didn't care what color he was; I was just disappointed I wasn't him. I stayed in the kitchen and sipped my beer for a while, then I went back to the comforts of the living room. Elena and Benjamin were gone.

Don't tell me they are shacking up!

They weren't, because before I got back to the couch, Elena hugged me from behind.

"Been skiing lately?" she asked with a twinge of sharpness.

"Hey, Elena," I said as I twisted around so I could see her.

She did not let go. She looked up at me and planted a kiss on my lips.

Okay, that wasn't what I was expecting.

"Wow, that was nice, thanks. Hey, what were you doing with Benjamin?" I asked.

"Getting your attention, and it worked," she answered.

I leaned in for another kiss, but she broke away from me and melted into the crowd.

Okay, it's clear she is letting me know what I gave up when I didn't follow up after our ski trip.

Feeling stupid and sorry for myself, I decided to have my pity-party alone with my beer. I went upstairs to the guest bedroom Garrett said I could use. Kicking off my shoes, I laid on the bed and dozed off. I don't know if it was five or thirty minutes later, but I woke up to find Elena lying on the bed beside me. For the record, she was fully dressed.

She snuggled up to me, and that's how we spent the night. We talked as we had on the bus and made out until we fell asleep. The next morning, I woke to find myself alone. I'm not sure what it was all about, but it was great fun, and I could now say I slept with a girl and not be lying as long as there were no further questions.

— Linda & Debbie —

About the same time Jimmy was hired at the Tastee Freez, Dad brought on two girls named Linda and Debbie. Linda was a senior at ALCO, and Debbie had recently graduated from Bishop Walsh High School, and they both liked to party. Unfortunately, they were not what you could call pretty.

Working at the New Uncle Lu's (Syckes Family Photos)

Linda had the bad luck of looking more like her father than her mother, and her father looked like Edward G. Robinson. Her dark eyebrows reached out for each other, and her jowls were more hound dog than high fashion. Despite carrying ten more pounds than she should, she had a nice figure. She wasn't my type, but I found out soon after she started working, she had her eye on me.

It became clear one night when she said, "I'll get Debbie to buy you beer if you party with us after work."

Now, how could I turn down such a concise and courteous invitation?

Debbie, on the other hand, was a big, happy, fun ball, all round and ready to bounce, but more importantly, she had a fake I.D. that made her twenty-one-years-old and able to buy real beer or anything else at Maryland liquor stores. Our initial forays were harmless. Debbie would procure the libations—beer for the boys and sloe gin for the girls. After closing, the four of us would go parking and enjoy our drinks and listen to music. Linda always insisted that she and I be in the back seat, and we snuggled but nothing else. I was there for the beer, not the babe, but things changed when Debbie got custody of a trailer parked near Deep Creek Lake. It belonged to a friend of a friend who asked Debbie to take care of it while she was away. As when parents leave town, that meant party time, so on a night we all had off from work; we met up at the trailer.

Let me take a moment to describe said trailer. It was stuffed into an overcrowded park and was more trash than trailer. There were no wheels, no hitch, and plywood replaced a significant portion of the original metal siding, and the wood was warping into a modern art sculpture, but the really bad news was the outside was better than the inside. It was like walking into a dirty sock with windows, and they were dirty too. The floor was dark, the walls were darker, and the furniture was darker still. I figured it was better to not see what we were sitting on.

There were only two rooms connected by a narrow hallway that had a bathroom attached if you are willing to accept that a shower/toilet/sink combination made of linoleum tiles and rusty metal was a bathroom. It was dirtier than everything else. Halfway down the hallway to the bedroom, you could feel a breeze blowing in through a poorly patched hole in the floor. I was not worried about messing the place up.

We started in on our drinks and snacks and were about halfway through *Fragile*, the new album by Yes when Debbie got up and started dancing. This was fun in and of itself and had many of the same characteristics of the hippo dance in Disney's *Fantasia,* but it got extra fun when she started stripping. Her shoes went off, then her hose, and then the skirt dropped to the floor. Finally, her top flew off behind her. Debbie had on a tight-fitting bra, and I was worried if it gave way, someone could lose an eye, but I was enjoying the show, so I was willing to risk it.

Linda did not join in. She was sitting with me on the couch, massaging my back. We had never kissed before, and that was okay with me, but she nibbled my neck, and I knew things could escalate quickly. I'm not one who likes to share, so I wasn't interested in fooling around on the same couch Jimmy was sitting on while Debbie tested the structural integrity of the trailer's floor. I stood and said, "Let's go back to the bedroom."

This surprised Linda a bit. She didn't jump up right away and drag me back there. But after I got another beer and made her a fresh Sloe Gin Fizz, she followed me into the dark.

The bedroom only had room for a double bed and a nightstand with a light, so I turned it on and flopped down. It was Linda's turn to strip, and she got right to it but without Debbie's *Fantasia* fanfare. Linda methodically took off her top, skirt, knee-high socks, and then everything else. I was dumbfounded. For the first time in my life, I was staring at a real, live, totally nude woman. Like I said before, Linda was a bit on the big side, but she had the general proportions right. I'll use the lyrics from the Broadway musical *South Pacific* song "Honey Bun" to describe her; "She was broad where a broad should be broad."

I stood and seeing things I'd never seen before, I put my hands on her breasts and caressed them.

"We're not going to do it," she announced in a most authoritarian voice.

I let go of her and sat on the bed. "Okay, what are we going to do?" I asked.

"Let's just enjoy each other," she said in a mellower tone as she pulled me back up and started unbuttoning my shirt.

Before I could blink, we were both stark naked and laying on the bed kissing. The part of me that reacts to stimulus like this was ready to go, but he was as confused as I was about what to do next. We sort of explored each other's bodies. I was first and went over her from top to bottom studying everything I stumbled upon; then she did the same to me. To this day, I am furious at the Allegany County Board of Education's Sexual Education curriculum development office for not providing me with the whys and wherefores of oral sex.

If I'd known then what I know now, we'd both have had a much better time, but I didn't, and Linda didn't either. We both got frustrated quickly and gave up. I put my clothes back on, grabbed my beer and opened the door. Walking down the hallway, I saw an odd sight. Debbie was still dancing, but now she was topless. Jimmy was where he had been when I left—fully dressed and sitting on the end of the couch drinking his beer. Seeing me, Debbie gave up and got back into her clothes, and Linda came out of the bedroom dressed about a minute later.

The whole party sort of collapsed. I looked at Jimmy, and he nodded towards the door. It was go time. I packed up what beer was left and said good night, and neither girl paid any attention to our departure.

On the way home, I asked Jimmy why he and Debbie did nothing, and he answered me by saying "I don't do that."

I figured he wasn't into Debbie. That was the last of our Tastee Freez staff strip parties. Linda and I kept our distance from each other from then on. I guess we both got what we wanted. I know I learned a lot.

Thanks, Linda.

I didn't spend *all* of my time partying. I still had school, but with marching band season over, it wasn't as much fun as before—that all changed when the senior's decided to put on a play.

— JoAnn vs. Lindalee —

The conflict was inevitable. From the day she arrived, everyone knew JoAnn Homburg would not be happy. For seven years, she'd been the regal ruling queen of kingdom Allegheny, but in the fall of 1971, a beautiful new princess arrived to lay claim to the throne. Worst of all, she moved into JoAnn's part of the castle.

Lindalee Jensen was twenty-three-years-old when she became ALCO's director of choral music and occupied the classroom below JoAnn's. She was pretty, perky, and personable and a former star twirler at Frostburg State Teachers College. All of five feet tall, she was slim and shapely with long, brown hair that perfectly framed her cheerful face. JoAnn was showing her age as she slid past forty but was clinging to her perch depending more on bold fashions than good looks. It was a losing battle. In the spring of 1972, ALCO's auditorium became the backdrop for one of the most epic catfights in the history of Cumberland.

For the previous eight years, there had been a senior class tradition of producing a play. JoAnn had directed the last three, so she was set to direct again this year. These were big productions that involved over a hundred students and more than $500 in upfront cost. When the senior class picked the musical Hello Dolly, it set in motion the unavoidable clash because Lindalee, as the choral director, would have to work with JoAnn. A successful production required cooperation and teamwork. JoAnn's solution to this was dictatorship. The previous choral director had bowed to JoAnn's will, but Lindalee was different. Dad was in charge of the orchestra, but he saw the fight coming and stayed out of the way.

I was a junior, so I did not expect to take part in the play, but that changed one day in drama class. It was early March, and we were finishing up our recitations of selected works of Shakespeare. When the bell rang ending class, I grabbed my books, but found JoAnn standing in front of me.

"Can you stay after class? I need your help."

"Sure," I said and sat back down. She waited until everyone had left, then sat beside me.

"Two things," she stated. "The chorus is weak, and I need a band."

I asked, "What chorus? And are we talking the entire band or the pep band?"

"No, no not the real band, I'm talking about what I need for the play, *Hello Dolly*. It calls for a band to march onto the stage in two scenes, and I'd like you to organize and lead it. Since you've got a good voice and can read music, I also want you to be in all the scenes requiring the chorus. I've only got three or four decent male voices right now, and they aren't strong enough. Can you be at rehearsal tonight?"

Like all of JoAnn's requests, I didn't have a choice, so I said yes and asked if I could get a copy of the choral parts. "Ask what's-her-name," she answered, standing and pointing at the floor. I took this to mean Lindalee.

"Does Miss Jensen know you want me to help out?" I asked.

"It doesn't matter." Ending the conversation, she got up and moved to her desk. I was dismissed.

After band, I walked over to Lindalee's classroom and knocked on the door.

"Come on in," she said without looking up.

"Miss Jensen, do you have a minute?" I asked.

"You're Mr. Syckes's son, the drum major, right?"

"Yes, ma'am, I'm Shelby. Mrs. Homburg asked me to join the *Hello Dolly* chorus and told me to ask you for a copy of the score so I can learn the music." I expected her to welcome me aboard and quickly find me the music, but that's not what happened.

"Can you sing?" she asked, with her head tilted to one side and back a bit.

"Sure, I was in the choir and one of the Von Trapp children in *The Sound of Music* put on a few years ago."

"Well, Shelby, you know all the other members of the cast tried out for their parts, and it might not be fair to them if you are allowed to join without going through the same process," Lindalee scolded.

"Maybe you should talk to Mrs. Homburg because I'm not trying to join the chorus. She asked me to join."

Lindalee didn't answer but instead walked towards the door, cricking her finger, indicating I should follow. I knew where she was going, and I didn't want to go, but I wasn't sure how I could get out of it. She marched up the zigzagging staircase that led to the second floor and tapped on the only door on that level.

"JoAnn," she called. "JoAnn, it's Lindalee."

"Yes?" answered the authoritative voice that belonged to only one person.

"Shelby wants to join the play's chorus and says you okayed it," Lindalee stated.

I started to say, "No," but JoAnn was at the door and was ready to engage, so I stayed back and watched. She used the same word I had planned to, but she delivered it with a clarity and a certainty I could never have mustered.

"No, Lindalee. I want him to join the chorus because it is weak, and he can sing."

"Give him the music so he can practice, please." The word "please" shot out of her like a viper's tongue.

"He'll be at rehearsal tonight which is only three hours from now, so give it to him so he can get to work."

Lindalee had her arms crossed now and was preparing for a thorough discussion, but before she fired the first shot, she turned and said, "Shelby, please wait downstairs?"

I was already on the precipice of the stairs and coiled to escape, so by the time she finished her request I had jumped down six steps. I could hear the conversation as it escalated from the choir room. The words weren't clear, but the thrusts and parries were. Suddenly, there was silence. Then, I heard the most distinctive stamp of a small foot followed by the sound of leather heels on the stairs. I stood by the door to be out of her way. Lindalee went straight to her desk and shuffled through stacks of music.

"We'll be focusing on 'Put on Your Sunday Clothes' and 'Before the Parade Passes By' tonight. Here's the music for them. I'll get you the rest of the songs tomorrow," she huffed.

"Thank you," was all I could muster as I reached out and took the music.

— Hello Dolly —

I showed up at the auditorium fifteen minutes early hoping to get a better understanding of what JoAnn wanted me to do, and things were already stirring. It was less than a month from the first performance, and all the costumes had arrived from the rental company. The cast members were on stage, sorting through boxes. I saw Sam there with an apron similar to my Tastee Freez one and went his way. He was playing Barnaby Tucker, one of the young shop apprentices of lead character Horace Vandergelder.

"Sam, what's with the apron?" I asked.

Looking dismissively at me, he said, "This is my costume for the first act. What the hell are you doing here?"

"JoAnn drafted me into the chorus and wants me to organize a band. Do you know anything about that?"

"Yeah, two songs call for a band: 'Before the Parade Passes By' and 'The Finale,' I think. But there's no room for a real band. What does she want?"

"Beats the shit out of me," I huffed.

"Hey, I did Dolly last night." Sam boasted.

"You did what?" I asked.

"Dolly, *Hello Dolly*—dumbass. I mean Stacey the blond playing Dolly. I talked her into a little dalliance in the dressing room. There's more to her than you think. She's a screamer." Sam smirked. Stacey was a cute senior who won the lead role at the January tryouts, and everyone said she was doing a great job. I heard a person clapping slowly behind me and turned to see JoAnn walking down the left aisle with her hands above her head.

"People! Listen up," she bellowed as she clapped. "We've got a lot to do and little time to do it. Push those boxes into the wings. You can find your costumes later. It's time to rehearse. Let's have all the principals for Act 1, Scene 2 on the stage. Everyone else get out of my sight."

It was as if a bright light had been turned on a swarm of roaches as everyone scattered at once. I sat two rows behind JoAnn and waited for direction. That's when Lindalee came in. She walked down the right aisle looking like she wanted to be as far from JoAnn as possible and went straight into the orchestra pit. The orchestra wasn't at rehearsal tonight, so all the musical accompaniment was to be provided by Lindalee on the piano. The music books she was carrying were almost as big as she was, but she showed no signs of being overburdened.

"Good evening, Miss Jensen. So glad you could join us," JoAnn needled.

"We're starting with Act 1, Scene 2. We'll go over dialog first, then spend the rest of the evening blocking out 'Sunday Clothes' and 'Before the Parade.'"

There was no audible sound from Lindalee. For the next thirty minutes, Sam, along with the other cast members, did their best to deliver their lines. They read from scripts, so it went well at first, but then JoAnn gave the order "no books," and long pauses between lines were interrupted by the script girl calling out hints from the wings. JoAnn was not pleased and started browbeating the actors. She ran her rehearsals like the Army runs West Point—you're going to learn what you need to learn, even if she has to shove the script up your ass a page at a time.

"Let's have all the chorus join the principals onstage!" JoAnn yelled, apparently giving up for the day on improving the scene. "Lindalee, run them through the number. Then, we'll block out the movements."

I jumped up, as did everyone else around me, but I stayed in the back of the herd, hoping not to be seen.

"What are you doing here?" Joyce Carman snarled at me. "This is a senior class play."

"Mrs. Homburg asked me to help out with the chorus. Hey, how's she getting along with Miss Jensen?" I asked, hoping to find out how bad things were between the two of them.

"Jesus, it's like Cruella De Vil versus Minnie Mouse. JoAnn's been nitpicking Lindalee all week, and she doesn't stand a chance. I think JoAnn is going for a kill. I've seen her do this before," Joyce shared.

There was the loud sound of a C chord on the piano, and the cast fell silent as they prepared to sing. Afterward, JoAnn rose from out of the dark auditorium and started blocking out the song. While Lindalee played the music, JoAnn moved members of the cast to the spot she wanted them, then she'd step back, and looking at them ominously say, "Remember this mark."

After the song was blocked out, we ran through it again while moving to our designated positions at the appropriate point in the song. Lindalee was working her butt off pounding out the song on the piano while directing and providing singing cues to the chorus. It was rough at first, and I thought we were about there, when during the third run-through, Lindalee missed a piano entrance, and everything collapsed. A hush fell over the stage.

"Sorry. Let's take it from the second verse," Lindalee offered.

"Stop!" JoAnn's voice rang out from the dark auditorium where she had returned.

"We'll move on to 'Before the Parade Passes By' since some of us can't ..." She stopped, not finishing her thought, but everyone knew what she was implying.

Lindalee can't cut it.

JoAnn came back up on the stage and started blocking the new song, but about two minutes into it she said, "Miss Jensen, would you please come up here and bring the music so we can see where things fall in the score?"

Lindalee gathered up her ten pounds of paper and came up out of the pit. This was one of the songs that called for a band to be visible. JoAnn moved me forward and directed me to stage right.

"You and your band will be in the right wing and will march out at the appropriate point in the music. It's right after ..." she trailed off then yelled, "Lindalee! Where is that place in the score where the band enters?"

There was silence. Lindalee was on the other side of the stage, marking something in her music, and must not have heard JoAnn. "Miss Jensen!" JoAnn bellowed as a street cop would at a jaywalker. Lindalee looked up. "I need your full attention if we are going to make the progress we need to tonight."

That got Lindalee's attention. She slammed her book shut, pulling it close to her chest as she marched across the stage to JoAnn. Stopping five feet from her Lindalee said in what was an amazingly civil tone, "Mrs. Homburg, I'm doing the best I can, and I would appreciate it if you would give me the respect I deserve as an equal member of the production's leadership."

JoAnn's back went rigid, and I thought I was watching that old vaudeville sketch where a man finds the guy who ruined his life and kills him. You know, the one where there is this keyword like "Niagara Falls" that stirs his memory, and every time he hears the word, he goes into a rage and repeats the sequence of his enemy's murder.

JoAnn heard her word, and that word was "equal." Glaring, she moved closer, and I swear I heard a voice say, "Slowly I turned, step by step, inch by inch." The entire ensemble inhaled, and we braced ourselves for the storm.

"If you cannot handle the pace at which I want this rehearsal to be run, I can find someone else who can," JoAnn said as she appeared to grow taller.

"Oh, you can, can you? Who, exactly, do you have in mind?" Lindalee snapped.

I was right behind JoAnn and only feet from Lindalee. I could feel the heat radiating from them. The other kids had moved back and were darting glances at each other, wondering whether the reactor was going to go critical.

Surprisingly, JoAnn relaxed and turned her head left and right. She smiled and started nodding as if she been asked the $64,000 question and knew she had the right answer. Then, she took two steps in Lindalee's direction and held out her hands.

"Give *me* the score," she said slowly.

"What?" Lindalee gasped.

"Give *me* the score," JoAnn repeated more firmly.

Lindalee's head dipped, and she handed JoAnn the three-ring-bound document. Receiving it like a folded flag at a military funeral, JoAnn executed a decent about face and pushed the book out in my direction.

"Shelby, you are now the *Hello Dolly* choral director."

I felt every muscle in my body tense, and I'm sure I had a stricken look on my face as I took the book from JoAnn. It was heavy, and I thought about dropping it and running away. Then, I saw Lindalee's face. She looked hurt. There was silence as she nodded once quickly, then turned and marched off the stage. Her little footfalls filled the hall as she walked up the aisle and out the backdoor. I looked at JoAnn as she said, "That's it for tonight, everyone. We'll pick up with Act 1, Scene 3 tomorrow."

Shifting her gaze to me, she said in a completely different voice, "You stay here. We need to talk." As the stage cleared, I dropped to my knees and put the music book down in front of me.

"Can you do it?" she asked.

No way in hell, ran through my brain but my mouth spouted, "I don't know, but I know I can't play the piano."

"I'll take care of that. All I need you to do is cue the chorus entries. Can you do that?" she asked with more urgency.

"Maybe," I said. "But I've got to look over this score."

"Good, we'll go over 'Parade' tomorrow. Be ready."

On the way home, I wondered if JoAnn had planned the whole thing. Was I there tonight just to be handed that music? I'll never know. What I knew scared me enough anyway. How in the hell was I going to lead all those singers? Directing the vocal parts in a musical is not the same as directing a marching band. When I got home, I went to my room, dug out my dad's copy of the *Hello Dolly* soundtrack LP, and opened the score on my bed. I tried to follow the music as the songs played, but there wasn't a direct correlation between the recording and the score.

I guess I'll have to hope the singers know their parts.

It was past ten when Dad knocked on my door and asked, "How'd your first practice go?"

"Dad, I need help," was all I could muster. I told him everything.

When I was finished, he was quiet for about ten seconds, then said, "I think JoAnn may have gone too far this time."

The next day was Friday, and all I could think about during school was play practice that night. I didn't see Lindalee, but Stacey, the lead in the play, stopped me in the hall and asked, "Can you do it? This play is important to me, and I don't want it screwed up because two teachers can't get along."

"I don't know, but I'll try, and I'm hoping this is temporary," I whimpered.

"Please do your best. We are all counting on you," Stacey said with a quivering smile.

JoAnn was her normal self in drama class, but when it was over, I went up to her and asked, "Any change from last night? I mean, am I still the choral director?"

"Of course, you are. Are you ready?" she said without looking up.

I hate that question.

I was thirty minutes early for practice and laid out the score on two music stands in the orchestra pit. I kept hoping Lindalee would walk through the doors, but she didn't. James Goodfellow came down into the pit and sat at the piano with his own copy of the score. As he opened it, he said, "I've been drafted to play the piano tonight, but you still are in charge of keeping everyone together."

"Thanks, I think," I said. James was an outstanding pianist, and having him there eased my tension, but I was still on the hook to direct.

JoAnn made her entrance and rolled right into rehearsing dramatic scenes. Then, it was time to run through "Before the Parade Passes By." With everyone on stage, she had the cast move through the scene, hitting their marks while tapping out the beat of the song. She looked down at James and me and said, "Take it from the top."

James nodded, and I looked at the anxious kids on the stage saying, "I'll give you the downbeat, but I'm counting on you knowing your cues."

JoAnn frowned. As I was about to start I heard the door to the auditorium swing open. "Please, God, let it be Lindalee," I whispered.

"Amen," said James.

Everyone on stage looked up to see who was coming in. I stepped up on a chair, so I could see over the pit's railing. It was Bob Hutcheson, and he was sitting in the last row when he realized he had been seen. "Press on. I'm here to see how you're doing," he said.

Dropping off the chair, I looked at James again and said, "Give her the first note."

James put his index finger down firmly on the E above middle C. I looked at Stacey, who would be the first to sing, and counted off "One, two, one two three."

She belted out, "Before the parade passes by," and we were off to the races. My horse stumbled soon out of the gate when I forgot to cue the chorus for its entrance. Stacey stopped singing as James kept thumping the keys.

"Sorry," I said. "Let's try it from where the chorus starts."

And we did, with better results, but it was a portent of how the rest of the night would go. We'd start and stop, and I'd miss a cue, or James would flub an entrance. The chorus did its best but could not make up for our shortcomings. I felt like shit and could tell James felt the same way. As he closed his book, he looked at me and said flatly, "We're fucked."

Sometime during the ordeal, Bob Hutcheson left, and JoAnn disappeared quickly after practice without saying a word. It was Friday, so I had the weekend to continue learning the music and praying for divine intervention.

I saw Dad the next day, and he said, "We have a standoff, and unless someone bends, the play may be canceled.

Hutcheson met with Lindalee and JoAnn and asked how we could resolve the issue. Apparently, Lindalee said she would not return unless JoAnn made a formal apology in front of the cast, and we both know the likelihood of that."

Monday came, and I felt no more confident than I had on Friday. I was really worried that if they canceled the play, all the seniors would blame me, but I wasn't just in over my head; I was tied to an anchor at the bottom of the Mariana Trench. I neither had the directing nor musical skills to do what JoAnn was asking, but if I quit, I felt I'd become a pariah for sure.

School was normal until I sat next to Tama Smith in drama. "JoAnn's out sick, and we've got a substitute who doesn't know his butt from his bonnet." I looked up, and there was Flash Faherty sitting at JoAnn's desk.

"Oh, my God, don't tell me he's going to teach the class!" I gasp.

"Are you kidding? I'm surprised he got the lights on in here," Tama said.

The bell rang, and Flash was up and in front of the room with his hands on his hips, scanning the class from left to right. His whistle was in his mouth. *Tweet!* "Now listen up, Mrs. Homburg is out today, and I've been asked to sit in. I want you to open your books to page 55, and we'll take turns reading from Shakespeare's sonnets."

Looking at Jim Midgarden, the star football player who caught the winning interception at the Snow Game, Flash barked, "Midgarden!"

"Yes, Coach," answered Jim almost coming to attention in his chair.

"You start with the first quatrain, then the person to your left will read the next one, and so on and so forth." *Tweet!* The whistle sang out again, and Jim did his best on the first sonnet.

"From fairest creatures we desire increase, that thereby beauty's rose might never die," Jim stuttered.

This laugh fest went on for forty-five minutes and was accented by more whistle tweets.

On the way home, I told Dad that JoAnn was not in class. He looked surprised and said, "Really? She was at the second meeting with Bob Hutcheson and Lindalee this morning. We may have a settlement."

I did not try to get to rehearsal early. What was the point? I was going to suck anyway. There were no adults in sight. Not JoAnn, Hutchison, nor Lindalee, so the cast stood around and chatted until the side doors opened. In walked Big Bob followed by Dad, JoAnn, and Lindalee. The room fell silent, as Bob cleared his throat.

"Let's have everyone take a seat in the auditorium; I have an announcement to make. You all have put a lot of time and talent into making *Hello Dolly* a success. In addition, the school has invested substantial funds paying for the rights to perform the play and rent the costumes. It's important that we all keep our focus on that."

Finished, he looked over at Lindalee and nodded. She stepped forward and looking out at us all, said, "I'm sorry I left rehearsal early, and I want to return and make *Hello Dolly* the best musical we've ever put on—if you'll let me."

We were stunned. *Why was Lindalee apologizing?*

There was an explosion of applause, and it was clear to her we were thrilled she was back.

Bob Hutcheson put his arm around her, gave her a squeeze, and then said, "James and Shelby, are you out there? I want to thank you for filling in last Friday. It's good to know we have you as a backup."

There was polite applause, but they could have booed as far as I was concerned. I could breathe again.

I looked up on the stage, and I noticed JoAnn was not standing close to the others. Her hands were laced together at her front. Her head was down, and it almost looked as if she was praying. Something's wrong. We're not getting the whole story, and it became clear when the rehearsal got underway.

There was a change, and it was all in JoAnn. She was still in charge and still ordering the actors around like they were her personal property, but the edge was off. Her swagger was gone, and she treated Lindalee like a princess, deferring to her, saying "please" and "thank you" more than I'd ever heard her before. Bob Hutcheson stayed for the entire rehearsal, and when I had time to talk to Dad at the break, I asked him how it had all gone down.

"We had a standoff right up until this morning," Dad said. Bob made it clear he would not put our investment at risk, and he asked JoAnn if she would apologize to Lindalee. The answer was no. He asked again, and she stood firm. He then asked Lindalee if she could do anything to break the logjam. After thinking about it, she said she could apologize to the students but not JoAnn. That was enough for Bob, and he ended the meeting but asked JoAnn to stay. They were behind closed doors for a long time, and I'm guessing he read her the riot act and told her to start playing well with others."

"It worked," I added.

As I left Dad to return to the stage, I passed Mr. Hutcheson sitting in a seat next to the aisle. He touched my arm. "Why is it whenever I have to 'cut a baby,' you're involved?"

"Sorry?" I muttered.

"Keep your head down. JoAnn will look for someone to blame," he warned.

"Yes, sir."

The rest of the rehearsals went smoothly, and the play came together well. It ran for three sold-out nights, and there were standing ovations at each one. Everyone was proud of their work, and a cast party was planned for after the last show.

However, JoAnn was never the same. I think she blunted her sword on the rock of stubbornness and never regained her preeminence at the top of Allegany's faculty kingdom. Lindalee, on the other hand, made a positive impression on Big Bob that served her well for the rest of her tenure.

The queen is dead; long live the queen.

Chapter 16 - One Toke over the Line

— Cast Party —

The cast party was at the home of twins Kaley and Marv Miller. Everyone was ready to unwind—maybe a little too ready. The play was a success, and we had all survived except for JoAnn's ego. Jimmy Eaton had played the bass fiddle in the orchestra, so we planned on going to the party together. He'd volunteered to buy the booze, and before curtain time Saturday night, I leaned into the orchestra pit and asked, "Eaton, you got it?"

"Of course, and you're going to love it," Jimmy answered.

After the last curtain call, we met backstage and left for my car.

"Where's the beer?" I asked Jimmy as we walked to the Barracuda.

"It's not beer," Jimmy said.

"What the hell is it, then?"

"Bourbon." Jimmy grinned. "I stole a fifth of Canadian Club from my old man. He's got a case in the basement, and it will be a year before he misses it.

When we got to the party, we could see it was going to be a doozy. All the lights were on, and we could hear the music from the street. Neil Young's "Heart of Gold" was pouring out of the house as we approached, and my mind flashed back to Dennis Swain's party and the next morning's communion crash.

I looked at the bottle of bourbon Jimmy was carrying, and knew I had to get something different to drink. Walking through the kitchen door, I saw lots of happy faces and a cooler the size of an ottoman full of beer. I grabbed the bourbon out of Jimmy's hand and yelled, "Anyone want to swap bourbon for beer?"

I had two interested parties immediately, but before I could make a deal, Jimmy grabbed the bottle back from me and said, "Let me at least get a decent drink out of that before you pawn it all."

He found a large water glass and filled it with half the bottle of bourbon. As he wandered into the den, he yelled, "Make sure I get out of here alive! My dad said he'll ground me for a month if I don't come home tonight."

After exchanging the rest of the bottle for a six-pack of cold Old German, I elbowed my way into the living room. I had one beer open and was holding the other five by the plastic rings when I got a whiff of that rag-burning smell again. Only this time, the source of the smell was right in front of me. There on the living room floor were seven kids, all sitting cross-legged in a circle. They were passing around what looked like a black stapler; only it had smoke coming out of one end.

The dark made it difficult to distinguish at first, but as I got closer, I saw it was a black clay pipe. This would be a very different party than Dennis's. Smoking at Dennis's was done out of sight. Here, it was the floor show. I knew everyone in the circle including the guy repacking the pipe.

He was Jake Franklin, an old family friend four years older than me. Our families had often vacationed together at Deep Creek Lake. Jake was always the wild kid of the group.

"Jake, what are you doing here?" I asked.

He was right in the middle of relighting the pipe when he looked up at me through two watery, red rubies that might have once been his eyes. He paused for a moment, not releasing any of the smoke he'd taken in. Then, with a big pop of his lips, he let it all out at once.

"Oh, far-out. Is that you, Shelby?" he coughed. "And is that beer? Oh, you gotta give me one of those, buddy."

"Sure," I said, kneeling down next to him as I pulled a can free from the rings. "Here." I handed him the can as he passed the pipe to his right. "What have you been doing since I last saw you?"

"I'm doing it, man, smoking Mother Nature. Sit down," Jake wheezed.

He made room for me in the circle, and I noodled my way in. Jake and I had always gotten along fine during those summers at the lake. He knew how to drive the ski boat and was driving it when I first water skied.

Putting his arm around me, he leaned in and said, "You try this shit yet?"

"No, I don't even like Winstons, so I'm not sure I'm ready for weed," I replied.

Sucking about half the beer down in one gulp, Jake rocked me towards him and said, "Oh buddy, you've got to try it, man. This is mellow shit, and it's laced with hash oil. It's smooth."

Sliding out of his grip, I stood and said, "Thanks, but I need to say hi to friends first. Save a puff for me."

Shit! Did I just say puff? That can't be cool. What is that word freaks use for smoking dope?

"Toke, man, say toke. Puff is only for pastries and magic dragons," Jake laughed as he rocked backward, laughing uncontrollably. He was having a good time, and I knew I needed to get away from him fast, or he'd have me sucking on that stapler. I melted into the crowd near the curved stairs to the second floor. Stacey, the star of the show, was about halfway up the staircase.

Saying "Hi," she grabbed me and gave me a big wet kiss. Have you ever noticed how some girls' kisses are dry as a desert and others are sponge baths? Stacey's were the latter, and she held onto me until I was fully bathed.

"Hello, Dolly," I sighed.

"Thank you," she said, looking at me lovingly. "Thank you for filling the void during that awful day. I really thought it was all going to be shut down when that bitch JoAnn kicked Lindalee out."

"Me, too," I answered, wondering if I would be kissed again.

I took a sip of my beer and took another step up the stairs when she pulled me in for another washing. I indulged, but as soon as she was finished, she went back to talking to her friend a step down from her. Alone again, I continued up the stairs, but I planned on checking back with her.

Reaching the top of the stairs, I saw a hallway leading both to the left and right, with the left side having a cut-out window on its wall looking down on the living room. It provided a perfect view of the pot party below, so I leaned through the opening and sipped my beer.

Derek and the Dominos' song "Layla" was ending, as James Goodfellow—my piano playing orchestra pit partner—came into the living room carrying a 45 rpm record over his head.

"It's sing-a-long time," he announced as he put the record on the Miller's console stereo, a huge piece of furniture about the size of a coffin. As James turned up the volume, you could hear the needle scratching its way to the beginning of the song. Then, the twangy tones of Delaney and Bonny sang out from the coffin's speakers:

"I've got a never-ending love for you,

From now on that's all I want to do,

From the first time we met I knew,

I'd have a never-ending love for you."

But, that's not what the party-goers were singing. They had different lyrics that were a little more graphic:

"I've got a never-ending hard-on for you,

From now on, you're all I want to screw,

From the first time we balled I knew,

I'd have a never-ending hard-on for you."

Everyone was singing along at the top of their voices.

Whenever I've heard this song since, I can't help but sing the alternative lyrics, but at a very low volume—honest.

The singing broke up the pot circle, and I saw Jake making his way up the stairs. Before I knew it, he pushed me out of the way and leaned out of the cut-out window yelling, "Fire drill!" With that, he was up and sitting on the ledge with his legs dangling about five feet above the heads of the rest of the guests.

"Bombs away!" he cried and pushed off into open space.

I heard a loud crack and a thud and looked down expecting to see Jake dead on the floor.

Instead, he was sitting upright in the center of the couch like he'd been there all night. Somehow, he'd executed a perfect seated fall and landed next to a rather startled girl. This was the cue for the other tokers to move the furniture out of the drop zone and position the couch cushions on the floor, making a safer landing area. Two more jumpers appeared and launched themselves creatively down to the cushions to the applause of all below. Soon, there was a train of partiers snaking up the stairs to have a try. Seeing no one was seriously hurt, I joined the line, and when it was my turn, I slid over the edge while clutching my unopened beers to my chest. Landing feet first on the cushions, I thought back to my BASE jump off the light tower on Turkey Day.

As I was opening another can, Jake grabbed my arm and said, "We're lighting up in the dining room. You ain't got a hair on your ass if you don't join in."

Following him across the foyer, I saw a group of kids sitting or standing around the dining table. The stapler was there, and Jake pulled a small brown bottle from his jeans and said, "Don't forget the secret sauce."

He grabbed the pipe and carefully dribbled a drop of what looked like balsamic salad dressing on top of the oregano-looking clippings already there; then he put his lighter up to the bowl, and an orange glow filled the room. After he'd sucked in enough gas to fill the Hindenburg, he passed the pipe to me, and while still holding his breath, he nodded vigorously up and down.

Figuring I had no other choice, and interested in what dope smoking was like, I put the warm pipe up to my lips and inhaled. It was strong—really strong—and I had to work very hard not to cough it all out, but I held it in. There was no great rush of euphoria, but I definitely knew I'd ingested something different. The one thing I will never forget, and the primary reason I never became a pot smoker, is that the smoke was full of hot acidic resin that coated and burned my palate.

If this was smooth, I'd hate to try rough.

After two go-rounds, Jake slipped into a kind of coma, and I saw my opportunity to escape. When I stood, I got my first rush from my first taste of reefer, and I had to grab the back of the chair to steady myself.

Okay, so that's what everyone's talking about.

I saw I had three beers left, so I went in search of Dolly or should I say, Stacey. She was no longer on the stairs, so I checked the kitchen. Almost all the beer was gone from the cooler, and an outdoor-size garbage can had been placed beside it. It was filled with empty beer cans, bottles, other trash and what looked like cream of mushroom soup pooling on top of an empty potato chip bag. I chose not to look closer.

"Who wants to go on a munchy hunt?" someone yelled from the den. "If we leave right now, we'll get to the White Coffee Pot before they close."

"I want to go," I heard Miss Dolly Levi say, and I saw Stacey skip through the kitchen, waving her hand in the air.

Suddenly, I had the urge for late-night greasy food, and I followed her into the den. It turned out the guy seeking diners was party king and sousaphone player, Dennis Swain.

"I'm in," I said as I moved up behind Stacey and slid my arms around her waist. "Do they have anything good to eat there?" I whispered in her ear.

"Does it matter? They're the only place open this time of night," she quipped.

"Let's go!" Dennis yelled, and we all marched out the side door towards his Ford Econoline van. Sam was on the patio outside the door having a smoke, and seeing us, he joined in.

Today when you say the word "van," you may conjure an image of leather-clad captain's chairs, plush carpet, and benches that fold down into beds. That was not the case for Dennis's van. It was essentially a metal box with wheels, two thinly padded bucket seats up front, and windows for only the driver and front-seat passenger. It was built to haul stuff, and it did that well, easily holding the eleven drunken kids piling into it, but it was not going to be a comfortable ride. It had only two accessories: a heater and an AM radio and both were on full blast. The trip was dark and rough and awkward with Sam moving in on Stacy, so any hope I had in that department was gone. We shared one of the three beers I had left and bounced and swayed our way to the White Coffee Pot, singing along to the strange new song by America called "A Horse with No Name."

The wait staff was not happy to see us because our arrival meant they had to work all the way to closing time. As we devoured our grilled cheese sandwiches, Stacey asked Sam, "Are you still working at Gehauf's?"

Sam looked up with a mouthful of grilled cheese, smiled, and said, "Yes I am, but I don't wait tables like these hard-working girls. In fact, all I've been doing this past week is inventorying food stored in the outdoor refrigerator."

My head popped up, and I looked at Sam wondering if he would share the story of our cattle rustling, but what he said next took me completely by surprise.

"Yep, the boss thinks the meat company he buys from is shortchanging him. He ordered twenty bags of hamburger three weeks ago but can only account for eighteen of them. Now, either the butcher is stiffing him, or those two thirty-pound bags of chuck got up and walked right out the door."

Sam was looking at me as Stacey giggled at his cheesy smile, but I was laughing for an entirely different reason.

The dining room lights blinked twice, and a waitress announced, "We're closing, folks."

We grabbed what food we hadn't finished and went back to the van. By the time we got to the Miller's, it was after 2 a.m., and most of the lights were off. We found out later that Mr. and Mrs. Miller came home, and finding evidence of underage drinking, shut the party down. They also found their living room couch broken in two.

Dennis dropped Stacey off at her car and Sam and me at mine.

"Sam, I need to go back to the Miller's and find Jimmy," I said, knowing it would provoke a harsh response.

"That dude is weird. He treats everyone like shit, and nobody likes him. Why do you care?" Sam asked.

"Look it's my car, and I'm going back to find him. You can help or not—it's your call," I said.

I drove the few blocks to Miller's with Sam staring at me and shaking his head in disgust. There were still lights on in the basement, so while Sam waited in the car, I walked up to the house and squatted to look into the sliding half window slightly below ground level that was protected by a corrugated metal barrier. I could hear music, although it was very soft, and it looked like the room was lit with candles. I reached down and knocked, but there was no response. I moved to another window and knocked again, and after a few seconds, a face appeared. I signaled him to open the window.

"What do you want?" he grunted.

"I'm looking for my friend who came to the party with me. I've got to get him home," I said.

"What do you want me to do about it?" My window friend asked.

"Can you look around and see if he's in there?" I pleaded.

"What's in it for me?"

"I'll give you two beers."

"Okay, what's he look like?" He answered clearly interested.

I had to think about that for a minute then I said, "His name is Jimmy and he's kind of a cross between a hippie and a leprechaun—he's short, hairy and has a pixie nose."

"Gimme a minute," he said and disappeared from the window.

I could see him carefully stepping around sleeping bodies as he went from one to another looking at their faces. He came back with his arm around one of them who was leaning on him with great desperation.

"Is this him?" he asked.

I squinted into the dark. The face looked right, but there were two big problems—boobs.

"That's not him. That's not even a him," I said.

Letting his first choice slump to the floor, he went back to look again. When he returned, he had a helper, and together they were dragging a body like a sack of flour towards me.

"Is this him?" he said as he reached out and grabbed the hair of the flour sack and lifted the face so I could see it.

It looked like Jimmy, but it was a tough call because there were no glasses and his hair was matted with that stuff I saw in the kitchen garbage can. "Can you wake him up?"

They shook him, and he revived enough to stand on his own.

"Fuck you," Jimmy belched.

"That's him. Hoist him up please," I said.

I stepped down into the window's gully and reached in for Jimmy.

"If you can't lift a thirty-pound bag of hamburger, you sure as shit can't lift that 150-pound pussy," Sam said as he leaned down beside me and reached out to help lift Jimmy.

"Thanks Sam," was all I said, and we pulled Jimmy up and over the metal barrier and onto the front lawn.

"Hey, what about our beer?" I heard echo up from the window.

"Coming," I said and passed the last two cans down.

"What are we going to do with him?" Sam asked. "He stinks."

"You're right about that, but I'm responsible for getting him home. I think I have a rag to clean him off with in the back of the car," I said and walked towards the Barracuda.

Finding the rag I used to wipe my dipstick clean when checking my oil; I went back to Sam. As I did, I heard the unmistakable sound of someone turning on a garden hose and saw Sam standing over Jimmy, hosing him down. Stunned and wet, Jimmy rolled out of Sam's range and jumped up, only to tumble earthward again as if his head weighed five times normal and was dragging him down.

"Fuck you," he gurgled as he hit the grass.

"He looks like a scalded cat," laughed Sam.

"That's what half a bottle of bourbon will do to you," I said as I wiped Jimmy's face with the rag. "I'm glad I swapped my half for beer." I took Sam and Jimmy home, smiling the whole way knowing I'd survived my first pot party.

— Junior Prom —

As the school year came to a close I was focused on only three things: Another potential Drum Major tryout, JoAnn's revenge, and Junior Prom. I dodged a bullet on the tryouts when no one challenged me for the job, but JoAnn got her pound of flesh when report cards came out. She gave me a C in Drama.

What! I'd had all A's and B's before, and I'd done everything she'd asked me to do for Hello Dolly.

I decided not to give her the satisfaction of hearing me whine about it and it wasn't like I'd never had a C before.

The Junior Prom could not have been more fun. Janice looked great in her lavender granny dress, and I matched her style with a light blue seersucker sports coat and red pants.

Stop laughing! Remember, it was the early 70's.

The theme was "Our Desert Oasis," and we had our picture taken standing next to artificial palm trees with a watercolor desert scene painted on huge sheets of brown wrapping paper behind us.

The gymnasium was entwined with hundreds of yards of crepe paper and was lit softly by tiki torches. The live band was great, and we danced all night. My favorite song was Chicago's "Colour My World," and as I rocked back and forth with Janice, we hugged each other tightly under the acrylic basketball goal decorated as a camel's head.

High school magic at its best.

Shelby & Janice 1972 Junior Prom (Syckes Family Photos)

Chapter 17 - Dave's Not Here

— All Caught Up —

Here we are, back where I started this book. It's June 1972—the end of my Junior year—and I'm feeling pretty good. Cocky would be a better word, and now you know why. I'm the drum major and a quasi-cool kid. I have my driver's license, a fake I.D., a beautiful girlfriend and girl friends with benefits.

I know what you're thinking. *Are you ever going to band camp?*

Yes, I am. I promise. But, first I have to go back to drum major camp.

— Drum Major Camp Again —

"Hey, where are A.R. and Junior?" Marty asked, looking up from the syllabus he'd been handed at the camp's check-in desk.

Marty Gandell had been voted in as captain of the band right before the Junior Prom.

"I don't know," I said, as I scanned the syllabus for the coming week. The name Casavant was nowhere in sight.

"You've done nothing but talk about A.R. and Junior for the last hour, and now I find out they will not be here," Marty said in a voice loud enough to draw attention. He was good at that.

Marty was my age and had been the first chair of the saxophone section for a year. He was a bright, serious guy who was always ready to help. Built like a brick, he looked a bit like Burgess Meredith, a.k.a. The Penguin on *Batman*, and he had his acerbic wit as well.

We had things in common other than the band. His dad was an educator like mine but had quit teaching and gone to work for the Board of Education. We had become good friends in our freshman year when we shared a room during the band's week at Ocean City. Sand had gotten into Marty's bed, and all night long as he tossed and turned, he'd slap the mattress with his hand and yell, "Damn sand."

Looking up from the syllabus I spurted, "Wait. There is something wrong here. Not only aren't the Casavants involved but according to the syllabus, drum major training only lasts three days. The rest of the week is focused on dance team leadership."

"I don't dance," announced Marty. "And if I did, I sure as shit wouldn't do it on a team. Do I look like an Arrowette?"

The disturbing image of Marty in an Arrowette outfit, kicking his hairy leg high into the air, flashed before me. Shaking away that visual, I went looking for someone to talk to. I pushed my way back to the front of the line at the registration desk and asked to see someone in charge. A man in a blue sports coat and tan pants appeared and said, "Can I help you?"

He was about thirty and was letting his close-cropped hair grow out to fit in better with the hippie fashion that was overwhelming the older generations.

"Yes, sir, I'm confused by the syllabus. Is Mr. Casavant teaching at the camp this year?"

"No, the Casavant family is no longer affiliated with this program," he answered with the warmth of a turnip.

"Oh, okay, and how many days of camp are dedicated to drum major training?" I asked as calmly as I could.

"Three. The demand for dance team instruction has exploded, and our new staff is highly skilled in dance team performance and leadership," he shared.

"When was this change made?"

This question caught him off guard. He looked at me trying to decide whether he needed to take me seriously. "The end of April. That's when we found out the Casavants would not be taking part."

"Then we have a problem," I said trying to sound like Perry Mason. "My school sent my friend and me here because it was advertised as A.R. Casavant's Drum Major camp, not a dance team camp."

"It is a drum major camp, just not with the Casavants," he cut in with the clear intent of shutting down the conversation. He turned away from me, and I decided to use the subtle negotiation technique of yelling.

"Bait and switch!" I bellowed. "Bait and switch!" I yelled again, and I had his attention and that of much of the crowd.

"You are not providing what we paid for."

The crowd started murmuring, and Marty chimed in with, "Fix! The whole thing is fixed!"

Blue Sports Coat turned around and shot me a look that could have parted my hair. He raised his arms over his head and said, "Calm down, everyone. Calm down. Let's go into my office and discuss this." He grabbed my arm and led me into a hallway.

I grinned at Marty and signaled for him to follow. "Fix!" he yelled one more time and scooted in behind me. We found ourselves in a small office, with a standard teacher's desk and chair and two other chairs for guests. I saw the name Richard A. Henderson, Associate Director School of Music on a nameplate sitting on the desk.

"What's your name?" Mr. Henderson asked as he scanned what looked like a list of attending students.

"Shelby Syckes and this is Marty Gandell. We're from Allegany High School in Cumberland, and I attended this camp last year. I came back expecting things would be the same."

"Right, but things change, and the university may modify course curriculum at any time," Henderson said.

"Don't you have a responsibility to notify people who have already paid when the thing they paid for will no longer be offered?" Marty added. "I think we should call our principal and let him know how you are cheating us."

"Go ahead," Henderson said as he picked up his desktop rotary phone and turned it so Marty could use it.

"Call him, Marty. The number is (301) 722-2184," I said with confidence, having given him my home phone number.

"Call Mr. Hutcheson while I go out to the car and get the camp's announcement sheet we got from the university advertising this year's drum major camp. There isn't a word on there about dance teams, and it's got A.R. Casavant's name all over it. Do you think the rest of the kids out there in the lobby know about this?"

Marty picked up the phone and dialed, but stopped when Mr. Henderson pushed the button, disconnecting the line.

"Wait. Let me talk to my supervisor. He may be able to help you," he said as he got up and left the room.

"You better go get that announcement sheet," Marty whispered.

"I can't; I don't have it. I made the whole thing up," I confessed.

"Whoa," Marty snickered, "This is going to go very well or very badly."

The office door opened, and in came Henderson and another older man who had no intention of changing his hairstyle to conform to current fashion. "This is Dean Baxter of the Indiana University School of Music," Henderson announced as if the Pope had joined us. "He'd like to talk to you about your concerns."

"We don't have concerns," Marty stated. "We want what we paid for."

"Yeah," I added with much force and little effect.

Dean Baxter said nothing and sat at the desk. Henderson stood behind him like a little boy with a black eye who hides behind his mother before she throttles the neighbor's kid for hitting her precious baby.

Baxter looked at me for a long time, then at Marty, before saying, "How can we settle this?"

"We want our money back," said Marty deciding on our opening bid.

"You paid for drum major camp, and we are providing you drum major camp. Why should we refund your money?" Dean Baxter said in a low, even voice.

"We paid for six days of drum major camp, and you are only giving us three days," I shared, figuring it was my turn to reenter the conversation. "We don't want or need any instruction on dance team leadership. We are not on the dance team. We're in the band."

"I understand, but you have a dance team at your school, don't you?" Baxter interrogated.

"Yes," I said forcefully.

"And the band plays the music for the dance team, right?" Baxter continued.

"Yes," I said, much softer this time.

"And you lead the band, right?" I didn't bother answering that one.

"Our classes will assist you in that responsibility," Baxter assured me.

Well, that made way too much sense.

I'd been out Perry Masoned, so I looked at Marty hoping he had a good comeback strategy.

"Damn sand," he mumbled. I stifled a laugh, then saw his eyes brighten. He looked at the Dean and said, "Mr. Henderson stopped me from using the phone earlier. I want to call my father. He works for the Allegany County Board of Education, and I think he should be involved in this conversation, given we are minors, and I feel as if you are trying to pressure us."

Baxter shot Henderson a look that said, "How the hell did you let this get out of control," as if he said it aloud.

I put my fists up to my eyes and rubbed them as if I was holding back tears and said, "Let him call his daddy, I'm confused and getting uncomfortable."

There was a short pause, and then Dean Baxter announced flatly, "Thirty dollars, I'll give you thirty dollars for the missing three days of drum major training."

"Thirty dollars each," countered Marty.

"Okay, each. But, I want you off this campus at oh-dark-thirty of the fourth day," said Baxter as he stood up enough to knock Henderson back with his chair.

"Handle this, Dick. I've got work to do." With that, he brushed by us and exited the office.

"Wait here," Henderson said. It only took him ten minutes to return with $60 in cash. Marty and I just about peed our pants. We hadn't paid a cent for camp. It all came from the Camper Club, and I wish I could tell you we returned the money, but we didn't.

The drum major camp was a total snore. The instructors were not worthy to clean A.R.'s golf shoes, let alone teach his precision drill techniques. I floated through it, although Marty struggled. A drum major he wasn't, and he looked about as comfortable as a sumo wrestler dancing *Swan Lake*. But, he survived, and on the morning of the fourth day, we packed and were ready to go by 7 a.m. but took our time leaving the campus, hoping Dean Baxter would see us. Mom and Dad continued their *laissez-faire* attitude to parenting by letting me take the Barracuda to camp, so we loaded our suitcases into the back and drove south to Cumberland.

We'd only gone a few miles when Marty announced, "I'm hungry, and I saw a sign for a Roy Rogers up ahead."

That sounded good, so we followed the signs to Roy's. Parking near the door, we hopped out, and went in. It was quiet, with only a few other customers. Marty and I got our fast food favorites and sat down to enjoy an early lunch.

Before I could finish squeezing ketchup onto my fries, I smelled something odd. It was dank and musty like an old sneaker left to ferment in the bottom of a gym locker. I leaned down and sniffed my hamburger, but it smelled fine. That's when I saw Marty's face; he was staring blankly over my shoulder.

"Are these seats taken?" a gravelly voice said from behind me.

Marty still hadn't moved as I twisted around to discover the source of the musty smell. Standing a foot behind me were two guys dressed in what looked like worn-out Army fatigues, but they had no rank or unit insignias on them. One was short and stocky with a dark, bushy mustache. His tattooed embroidered tree-trunk arms bulged under his rolled-up fatigue jacket.

The other guy was tall and lanky, and he stood stooped from the weight of the overstuffed backpack he was carrying. He also had an unkempt mustache, but it was augmented with a shaggy beard with sprinkles of gray throughout. Both had long hair that shampoo hadn't touched in months and holding the hair in place were stained bandanas. If they weren't so menacing, you could have mistaken them for Cheech and Chong.

I wanted to say, "Dave? Dave's not here."

But—I couldn't. My throat was bone dry.

"Hey, man. Can we join you?" Chong said, as he dropped his backpack and sat next to Marty.

— Cheech & Chong —

We were seated at those omnipresent arrangements you see in fast food restaurants: a table and four chairs—all welded together into a cramped four-foot square. There is no escaping someone sitting next to you in one of these. Cheech dropped into the seat beside me. His smell hit me before his shoulder did. I would have gotten up, but I saw a three-foot-long machete sticking out of Chong's backpack.

"Whatcha eating? It looks good," Cheech said, as he scooped up my hamburger and took a bite.

"I'll be in the bathroom," Marty said as he stood. "I'm not feeling well. You can have the rest of my lunch."

"Great," Chong said as he slid Marty's roast beef sandwich toward his side of the table.

"We don't want any trouble," I finally squeezed out of my voice box.

"Trouble, you got trouble?" Cheech said as he put his thick arm around my shoulder.

"We know how to handle trouble," he continued while nodding to Chong, who was patting the handle of the machete. They both laughed and continued devouring our lunches.

As they finished, I said, "Would you like more? My treat."

Cheech belched then said, "Nah, man. It's cool. Where are you going?"

Okay, Shelby, think fast. How do you answer that? If you tell them where you live, they will follow you home and slit your throat. If you lie to them and they find out, they will slit your throat right here.

"Home," popped out of my mouth involuntarily.

"Where's home, man?" Chong asked.

"Down the road a ways," I answered as I got up from my chair. "I better check on my friend; he was throwing up all last night," I said as I turned towards the bathrooms.

I looked back and saw my new Vietnam veteran friends were still seated, as I pushed opened the bathroom door.

"Do you think they know we have the university's $60?" Marty asked me as he balanced on top of the toilet bowl so no one could see his legs from outside the stall.

Staring at him through the open stall door, I said, "No. Do you think they look like graduate students?"

"Good point," Marty sighed, as he brought down his feet and assumed the normal position on the toilet. "What are we going to do? We can't stay in here all day."

"I know, but I also don't want to anger them," I said.

"Anger them? Hell, we bought them lunch."

"Let's give them five more minutes; then you check to see if they've left, please," I said as compellingly as I could.

"No way. I'm staying right here," Marty cracked.

The bathroom door swung open, and a dumpy man of about thirty-five stood in the doorway staring at us suspiciously. He had on black pants, a white shirt, and a bow tie. On top of his crewcut hair sat a Roy Roger's paper hat. Seeing us both in the stall, he barked, "What's going on in here? If you boys are queer for each other, you take that shit out in the woods."

"No, sir," we both chimed.

"Then what the hell are you doing? You ain't smoking that marijuana, are you?" he asked.

"No, sir," we chimed again.

"Then get out of my bathroom. Now!" he yelled.

"Are those guys in the Army uniforms still out there?" Marty asked.

"What are you talking about? There isn't anyone out there but an old lady and her granddaughter. Now get out," the very frustrated restaurant manager snarled.

"Can we order food first?" Marty asked.

"Get it to go, and go fast," paper-hat howled.

We exited the bathroom and peeked around the corner into the dining area. It was clear of PTSD sufferers, so we reordered and started for the car. I was right behind Marty as he pushed through the exit. He stopped suddenly, causing me to spill half my Coke down his back.

"What the hell!" I started to say, but Marty cut off.

"They're in the car."

They must have seen us get out of the Barracuda because Chong was in the back seat on the driver's side, and Cheech was riding shotgun. Seeing us, he shouted, "You can give us a lift, can't you? We're going to Pittsburgh."

"I'm not going to Pittsburgh," I said with a wavering voice.

"Well, we'll go as far west as you can take us. Get in," he commanded.

I've asked myself a hundred times since then why I didn't turn around and go back into the restaurant and have the manager call the police. Maybe it was because we'd blackmailed Indiana University for $60. I don't know. Instead, I turned to Marty, and he said, "Well, I guess we can take them a little way down the road."

"Okay, but think of something," I whispered.

Cheech popped out and flopped the seat forward to let Marty get in the back as I moved around to the driver's side. I pulled out of the parking lot and realized I knew where Cumberland and Pittsburgh were, and that the natural middle point between them was a good hour's drive from here. I didn't want them in the car that long. Cheech asked me to turn on the radio as he fished in his fatigue jacket pocket for something. As the radio came to life, he produced what looked like a rolled up piece of tissue paper. Chong's arm brushed my right shoulder as he thrust it between the seats with an open lighter clamped in his hand.

"Here ya go, man," he said, as he spun the striker wheel.

Cheech turned towards the flame and lit the one end of the tissue paper while sucking on the other.

"So, that's a joint," I said to myself as I hunted for a station.

At least it smells better than they do.

The first station I found played country and western, and Cheech did not approve, so I kept spinning the knob until Credence Clearwater Revival's song, "Have You Ever Seen the Rain" wafted through the speaker.

"That's it, man, that's it. Leave it there," he said and rocked and sang along with the song.

"Remember when we first heard this?" Cheech said as he handed the joint back to Chong.

"Oh, wow, man, that was serious shit we were in back then," Chong rang in.

"Fuckin' A, man, I remember. We were in that cathouse in Bien Hoa, sucking on a bong while the girlies sucked on us. Those were the days. We could do just about anything we wanted."

As Cheech said this, Chong slammed his machete down on the console beside my seat. The sun glinted off the blade into my eyes, causing me to swerve the car.

He started to use the machete like a drummer beating out the rhythm of the song as the last chorus finished with, "I want to know, have you ever seen the rain, comin' down on a sunny day?"

Marty belched convincingly and lurched forward in his seat, using his hands to clamp shut his mouth. Pausing as if he was waiting for a wave to subside, he removed his hand and blurted, "Stop the car, I'm going to puke!"

Taking my cue, I slowed and pulled to the side of the road. Cheech opened his door and got out. Marty pushed forward and stumbled down the embankment into tall grass.

"What the fuck's the matter with him?" Cheech asked.

Before I could answer, Chong said, "I gotta piss anyway. Let me out."

I opened my door and Chong crawled from the backseat holding his machete in one hand and flicking his doobie into the road with his other. That's when Marty demonstrated his brilliance by yelling, "Hey guys, I found a ten dollar bill down here!"

Both Vets heads turned in Marty's direction and they started moving his way. I pushed the driver's seat forward, grabbed the backpack, and pulled it out of the car.

"Shit man, look! There's another one!" Chong said as I heard his machete slice through the tall grass. I got back in the car and revved the engine twice.

Marty yelled, "Hey is that a wallet over there?" and before I could rev the engine a third time, he was in the passenger seat and panting, "Go! Go now!"

I jammed the transmission into drive and took off. Marty's door slammed shut from the force of our launch, and I saw our fatigued friends waving their hands behind us saying things I was glad I could not hear. Marty was breathing hard, and we didn't talk for about five minutes. He then turned to me slowly and said, "You owe me ten bucks and a new wallet."

"Deal."

Chapter 18 - Madman across the Water

— On the Way to Band Camp —

"**M**ust we listen to that crap?" Jimmy wailed.

"What are you talking about? Elton John is our generation's Beethoven," I implored. "Two hundred years from now, people will listen to both Beethoven's *Fifth* and Elton John's 'Tiny Dancer'."

Jimmy groaned like a burst bagpipe. "Blue jean baby, L.A. lady, seamstress for the band," he sang in a whiny sing-song fashion. "Beethoven could fart better melodies than that."

I laughed. "Okay, maestro, you pick something. The tape box is on the back seat."

Jimmy leaned back and reached for the box, but as he swung back into his seat, he had the manila envelope that had come in the mail for me yesterday.

"What's this?" he asked.

"Photos from the prom. I think Janice and I look pretty hot." I said, smiling at the memory of that night.

Jimmy had the prom photo out and was holding it between two fingers like it was tainted with botulism. "I will never understand the mating rituals of the White Anglo-Saxon Protestant, and what in the hell is she wearing?" he hissed.

"Don't go there, Jimmy. I like that girl." I sputtered, not knowing how to respond to such an attack. "Pick out the music you want, and put the pictures down."

He pulled the *Madman Across the Water* tape out of the 8-track player and shoved in *Gershwin's Greatest Hits*.

"Good choice," I said, as "An American in Paris" began to play.

"It's better, but it's still not Beethoven," Jimmy seethed.

"Sorry, we're all out of Ludwig today," I said.

"Music is serious," Jimmy scorned. "If you are going to be a professional musician, you have to take it seriously. I plan to be a concert violist."

"Yeah, but you play the bass fiddle in the orchestra," I said.

"That was your dad's idea. My true calling is the viola."

"Well, you look more like a bass fiddle," I joked, but he did not laugh. I had struck a nerve.

Jimmy and I were on our way to band camp. Well, we were actually on our way to West Virginia University's annual Fine Arts Music Camp but, I called it band camp, and it cost $155. That's about $900 in today's money—and both of our expenses were covered by the Camper Club.

Did I mention to you how much I loved the Camper Club?

As the formal name implies band camp was not just for band members, and that's why Jimmy was going. He was in the orchestra, and he didn't want anything to do with band because orchestra members do not accept band members as true musicians. Well, at least Jimmy didn't. Unlike him, I had no delusions about my musical skills. I was not going to be a professional, but I was good enough to hold my own in a high school band.

That doesn't mean I wasn't a bit apprehensive. WVU's Fine Arts Camp was bringing together the top high school musicians from twenty states, so I was in a different league. Jimmy knew how he would be received because this was his second year, and last year, he had been the second chair of the viola section.

Jimmy took a shiny new brass pair of glasses out of his shirt pocket and cleaned them on his sleeve.

"Hey, are those new specs? Gosh, what happened to your old ones?" I asked sarcastically.

Jimmy & Shelby at Band Camp (Syckes Family Photos)

"Fuck you," Jimmy said. "Kaley Miller gave me my old pair on the Monday after the party. She found them in her basement's toilet. They were bent and missing a lens. I want you to know; my old man is making me pay him back a buck a week for these."

"Remember, I got you out of there alive as you asked. You said nothing about accessories." I said with pride. Jimmy smiled, so I figured he'd gotten over the fat joke.

West Virginia University had doubled in size in the 1960's expanding to a second campus. That was where band camp was. The new Evansdale campus, as it was called, was linked to the old one by a bold, attempted leap into the future of transportation, and it was taking shape right before our eyes.

As we drove, we saw a massive construction project building an elevated motorway, but it was too small for cars or conventional trains. It looked more like a Disneyland ride. We found out later it was the soon-to-open Personal Rapid Transit system that promised to connect the two campuses with autonomously driven, computer-controlled vehicles that would eliminate the traffic congestion that plagued Morgantown. George Jetson would have loved it.

The PRT was not up and running yet, so we slogged on in traffic until we arrived at The Towers where we were to register. The Towers was a complex of four new high-rise dorms connected with supporting cafeterias, stores and recreation areas. It was a little standalone city for college students, and all the campers would be staying there.

It didn't take Jimmy long to introduce me to old friends from last year's camp, and I found myself having dinner with two odd birds. Gunther was a wild-eyed, long-haired German who played the French horn and always was in search of a coherent thought. Kathy, or Kat—as she wanted to be called—was a viola player like Jimmy. She was very outspoken, especially when it came to the women's liberation movement, and wore a "Yes to E.R.A." button constantly. Because I was with Jimmy, they both accepted me as a band camp friend.

Jimmy and I were roommates, and our dorm room was on the sixth floor of Bennett Tower. Gunther was on our floor as well, but Kat's room was on the ninth. Elevators got you to those floors, and they were the most entertaining elevators I have ever ridden. They appeared normal, but when the doors closed and the elevator rose, a woman's voice would call out each floor number as the doors opened.

Creatively interfacing with the elevator lady became a band camp sport. The object of the game was to come up with a cute phrase to say either before or after the elevator announced a floor that would crack up your fellow travelers. As an example, let's say you were going to the third floor. Before you reached it, you ask, "What's the square root of nine?"

And the elevator would answer, "Three."

Or as the elevator stops on the first floor and announces, "One," someone replies, "…is the loneliest number."

I thought my contribution to this game was the funniest. One day, I was standing next to Gunther as we rode with Kat to her floor. Before the doors opened, I asked: "*Sprechen sie Deutsch?*"

And the elevator answered, "Nine."

Come on; you have to admit, that's creative! Well, at least Gunther thought it was.

Unlike Bob Hartman, Jimmy managed his wardrobe the same way I did—what came in the suitcase stayed in the suitcase—so no drawers were opened during camp. I had learned from my previous dorm stays and brought along an 8-track tape player. We enjoyed music every hour of every day we were in the room. One tape that was getting a lot of rotation was Emerson, Lake and Palmer's progressive rock album *Tarkus*. Whether it was the professional-level musicianship of the members or their classically inspired compositions, Jimmy liked them a lot. *Tarkus* was okay, even though "Tiny Dancer" wasn't.

— Camp Begins —

Day one of band camp started with Jimmy, Kat, Gunther, and I climbing the steep hill that rose between The Towers and the Creative Arts Center. What made it particularly annoying was the path we took followed the PRT construction project that would make all future student treks like this obsolete. We were too early.

WVU's Creative Arts Center was an attractive building that sat on the crest of a hill. Its round design rose in rings from a moat-like base. Everything band camp would happen here. Inside were classrooms, practice areas, and a 1500-seat auditorium drenched in dark red velvet with glittering chandeliers dripping from an arched ceiling that made you feel you were sitting inside a wealthy woman's jewelry box.

We arrived early and saw three tables staffed by camp counselors passing out name tags. I found mine, and although I was very pleased to see they spelled my name right, below it was a word I did not know: Euphonium. I wasn't even sure how to pronounce it. Did it start with a hard *E*, or was it silent?

I looked at Jimmy's name tag and saw viola. *Okay, so I guess I play the euphonium.*

Settling into our comfortable red velvet seats, the concert hall was abuzz with anticipation of the adventure ahead. Then, everyone fell silent as the lights dimmed and the empty stage glowed. A man strode from the left wing dressed in a tailored, houndstooth suit with a perfectly knotted yellow and blue bow tie. The overhead spotlights reflected off his head of wavy black hair and shinny wingtips. This man had a presence that demanded attention, and he got it— every eye in the house was on him. He was Professor Donald Portnoy, Director of WVU's Fine Arts Camp. He did not smile. Like A.R. Casavant, he had a commanding air about him, but where A.R. was all martial music and marching, Donald Portnoy was total confident, classical correctness. He owned the stage.

"Good morning," he said in a self-assured voice. "I'm Doctor Portnoy, your director, and I'd like to welcome you to one of the most respected Fine Arts Camps in the country. You are fortunate to be here."

I expected to hear Jimmy fire off one of his cynical asides, but he was silent. He was sitting up straight like a little boy at the breakfast table. Looking at Portnoy, his eyes were sparkling as if he was Moses before the burning bush.

Wow, he's serious about this.

Gunther was picking his nose. Kat slouched beside him, deep in thought. She was near the bottom of the viola section and planned on studying nursing in college, so to her Portnoy was just another male overlord who would have to be vanquished in the coming Women's War.

I was thinking about where I'd be placed in the baritone—or should I say euphonium—section. I'd soon find out, for the next thing out of Portnoy's mouth was, "Please take note of what room your section will meet in." He was pointing at a projected listing of instruments or voices for choir members and room numbers that had appeared on a screen behind him. At the same time, twenty people joined him on stage and formed a line to his right.

"When we are finished here, you will report to your designated room and have your skills assessed by your section counselor. These good people are your counselor staff and are here to help make your Fine Arts Camp experience as rewarding as it can be."

After introducing them, Doctor Portnoy looked out at the audience and said, "That will be all." He crossed the stage, exiting on the opposite side he had entered. I was not looking forward to the skill assessment.

— Is that a Conn? —

I found my room, and as I entered, I saw four other boys, all either warming up their instruments or retrieving them from their cases. We all took a seat in the neatly arranged semicircle of chairs that each had a music stand in front of it. As I sat, I knew I was in trouble when the guy next to me looked disapprovingly at my horn.

"Is that a Conn?" he asked in a condescending voice.

"Yes, it belongs to my high school. I don't own my own instrument."

Snorting, he said, "Conn," like he was spitting something foul from his mouth. "The name says it all."

He was holding a gleaming silver wonder of an instrument that looked like it was made by Reed and Barton for the Queen.

"Mine's a Besson, and it cost $1000 ," he boasted.

"Shut the front door. For that kind of money, it ought to blow you," I deadpanned as I got up with my featureless but faithful Conn and moved to the other end of the circle. We were joined by a guy who didn't look much older than we were, and as he sat in the chair at the center, he introduced himself.

"I'm Zak Jackson, and I'm your section counselor." He was tall and slim with more hair than head and wore wire-rimmed glasses that could have been manufactured a hundred years ago. "I'm a sophomore here at WVU, and I'm majoring in music education. My principal instrument is the trombone, but I also play the euphonium."

My ears perked up as I heard the E-word pronounced for the first time.

So, the first letter is silent; good to know.

Zak continued, "Let's start by introducing ourselves. Please state your name, high school, and say a few words about what you want to achieve at Fine Arts Camp.

Achieve? I'm guessing getting laid wouldn't be an appropriate answer, even though it's my number one goal in life.

Luckily, I didn't have to go first, since he started at the other end of the circle. I found out that I was not the only non-serious musician in the group. First to speak was Ted Franks, who was from somewhere in Tennessee that sounded like East Jesus, but that couldn't be right. His southern accent was so thick; I had to listen carefully to understand him. He got a laugh when he said he wanted to achieve a good suntan.

"Okay, I can work with this guy," I mumbled. Next, was the Sterling Silver Conn hater. He announced his name as if it were something we should be honored to hear.

"My name is Preston Chandler, and I'm from New Haven, Connecticut. Wooster Square, to be precise."

"Hey, is that where they make that Worcestershire steak sauce?" my new best friend Ted Franks cracked.

"Woo-dog! That stuff will make your tongue tingle." We all laughed. Well, all of us except Preston.

"No," he said sharply. "That's an entirely different word. I live in Wooster Square, not Worcestershire Square."

We all laughed again. Zak broke in and asked Preston to continue. He spent the next two minutes listing his musical accomplishments. Finishing, he leaned towards Zak, "I want to be a truly great musician, and I know this camp will help me achieve that."

Zak grinned and replied, "Well, it's important to set high goals. Okay, who's next?"

"I'm Brad Miller," said the kid to Preston's right. "And I'm from here in Morgantown, so I'm not staying in the dorms. I just want to make new musician friends and do the best I can."

"Okay, that's good, Brad. Next," said Zak.

"Dan Lehrer," the guy next to me said. "I'm from Springfield, Illinois. I'm the drum major of our band, so I haven't been playing my baritone as much as I'd like to. Is it okay if I call it a baritone, or do we have to say euphonium?"

I had another new friend, and I was eager to hear the answer.

"Call your horn whatever you want to call it. My trombone's name is Daisy," Zak said as more laughs followed.

I took the opportunity to ask the obvious question. "What's the difference between a baritone and a euphonium?"

"About six years," Zak answered. "That's how long it takes to get a Masters degree in Music, and every baritone player I've ever met with a Master's in Music calls the damn thing a euphonium." More laughter followed, and even Preston joined in this time, but the shine on his $1000 baritone dimmed a little.

"And you are?" Zak said looking at me.

"Shelby Syckes from Cumberland, Maryland. I go to Allegany High School, and like Dan, I'm a drum major," I said, trying not to sound as if I were boasting. "I want to have fun and play good music." I finished, and with that, the enjoyable part of the first meeting of the euphonium section ended. Next up was the individual assessments—ugh.

"Okay," said Zak as he reached for music on the desk. "Let's start with something simple." He handed each of us a page titled "The Circle of Fifths Scales." On it was twelve scales that went from easy to hard as the number of flats and sharps increased. Zak's "something simple" had me sweating. I never liked practicing scales, and I'd never memorized many of them, so I'd be sight-reading some, which meant more mistakes. Then, I saw I had a bigger problem. All the scales were written in bass clef, and I didn't read bass clef. I only read treble clef.

Baritones are the only instrument that has music published for it in both treble and bass clef. To understand why, you have to ask another question: What instrument did you first play? You see, the baritone is not someone's typical first choice as an instrument. Most start out on one of the more popular instruments like the trumpet, trombone, or clarinet. As they progress, some branch off to alternative instruments like French horns, oboes, and tubas.

Some of these moves require you to learn to read a different clef which is why the baritone—with music printed in dual clefs—becomes an attractive option. Professional musicians usually read both bass and treble clef.

I started out on the trumpet then shifted to French horn before ending up on baritone, so I'd only been exposed to treble clef. I already knew I was going to suck, but if they asked me to read bass clef music, I was totally screwed.

"Zak," I said meekly. "I read treble clef, not bass." I heard Preston gasp as if I'd said I prefer communism to capitalism, and I knew I had identified myself as a less skilled musician.

"Oh, sorry," said Zak. "Let me get you a treble clef part."

"I'll need one too," said Ted.

Man-oh-man, was I starting to like this guy.

Zak was back quickly with treble clef parts, and we got down to the business of determining our chair placements for the section. He had us all play the simplest scale together as a warm-up, then asked each of us to play it separately. We all did well. Then, he asked Preston to pick any scale on the page and play it in any fashion he wished. Well, the Wooster Wonder went right for the hardest one and buzzed up and down the damn thing like a bee that found a wall of roses. He was good. He knew it, and now we did, too.

Ted was next, and he played a scale with one sharp in a straightforward fashion. Then, it was my turn, and I went for the next easiest one with one flat, only because it was one of the few I had memorized. I took my time and focused on not only getting the notes right but projecting a full and mellow tone. I was quite pleased with myself and started to feel better about my chances. After Dan and Brad ran through their scales, Zak had us all play together again, only this time he picked one with five sharps.

"Let's play it a bit differently. Give each note four beats before moving on to the next," Zak instructed, and I knew I was going to have trouble with the five sharps. I was doing great until I played a wrong note, so my full and mellow tone clashed with the others, and I stopped playing. I didn't recover until we were near the end.

I felt like crap.

Zak kept us for another twenty minutes playing sections of a march both as a group and individually. I continued to struggle. Then, he said we were to go back to the auditorium to receive our class schedules for the rest of camp.

"Shelby, can you stay for a minute?" Zak said as the other guys packed up their horns.

"Sure," I answered and stayed seated as everyone left.

"You've got a great sound, and you have a feel for the rhythm, but you depend too much on your ear instead of the music," Zak said.

"I know I'm not in the same league with guys like Preston," I mumbled.

"Forget him," Zak said in a motivating voice.

"I know you can do better, and that's why you're here. Unfortunately, I'm going to seat you as the last chair in the section, but I want to hear your beautiful sound come through whenever you can."

"Thanks," I said. My ego was bruised. Now, I knew how Chucky Grainfield felt the day he forgot his spats.

— Treble Clef Ted —

Ted was waiting for me in the hall and said, "You drink beer, Bubba? We treble clef queers have to stick together."

Smiling broadly, I nodded as we went up to the auditorium.

"Let's find us some tonight. If I'm gonna have to play with that tight-assed Connecticut Yankee, I'm gonna need a case or two," Ted twanged.

This made my day. When we got to the auditorium, we found out we had the rest of the day off. We met up with Gunther on our way back to the dorm and I introduced Ted.

"Gunther, this is Ted. He's a baritone player like me, only a better one."

"Hallo," Gunther said in his thick Bavarian accent. "French horn for Gunther."

"Boy, where are you from? That don't sound like Tennessee talk to me," Ted said nudging Gunther.

"Da, da. English second language only. I am born in Munich, but father moved family to U.S. three years before."

"Okay. You wanna get some beer with Shelby and I tonight? Ted asked.

"Da, da," Gunther repeated.

"Then, I'll do all the talking. There's a mini-mart two blocks from the dorm. I was over there last night, and they've got a whole section of their refrigerator wall dedicated to beer. All we have to do is figure out how to convince them to sell it to us."

"I've got a fake I.D. card," I said with pride. "And I've used it in West Virginia."

"Perfect!" Ted shouted. We walked back to The Towers, had dinner, then headed for the mini-mart.

"There it is," Ted said as we emerged from the shadows of the shady dirt lane that passed through a thick grove of trees that separated The Towers from a busy highway.

Ted was pointing to the strip mall across the road that had maybe five stores in it. The sun had set on our first day of band camp, but it was still warm, as we decided whether we should walk the half a block up to the cross street or make a beeline for the mini-mart. Ted decided for us and dashed for the center island through the traffic.

"Giddyup, boys. You ain't gonna find no beers in the bushes!" he yelled over the sound of cars whizzing by. Gunther looked at me with distress. I shrugged as I looked for an opening to make our move.

"Go!" I yelled, and we darted into traffic and quickly joined Ted in the center.

Ted dashed into traffic again and Gunther and I followed. Reaching the parking lot of the mini-mart I said. "Ted, I guess I should have told you I have a car."

"You've got wheels? Shit, Shel. Why the secret?" Ted barked.

"According to the camp brochure, campers with cars should only use them in emergency situations," I shared.

"Hell, Shel, this is an emergency. Do you think they'll be watching the parking lot 24 hours a day?"

That was a good point, and I realized I was acting like a ten-year-old camper and not a young-adult who was about to buy beer. We drove to the mini-mart from then on.

Ted didn't look anything like Jimmy, Gunther or me. His light brown hair was cut high and tight like a Marine, and his clothes were five years behind the times. He wore T-shirts and jeans like all the other guys, but his T-shirts were white, and his jeans were straight legged, no bell-bottoms. He was a couple of inches taller than me and a year older, but he didn't have a fake I.D. or even a driver's license. His dad wouldn't let him get his license until he was eighteen, and then he would have to buy his own car. His father was a strict disciplinarian. He only shared this with me after many days and even more beers. His home life was not happy, and he could not wait to escape to college. It made me appreciate my family even more than I already did.

"Okay, here's the plan," Ted whispered as we stood in front of the Buster Brown Shoe store next to the mini-mart. "I'll go in first and buy the snacks and chat up the desk clerk. When you see me at the register, the two of you come in and get the beer."

It sounded okay, but I wasn't sure why we needed a plan. They were either going to sell me beer, or not.

I kept these thoughts to myself and watched as Ted tucked in his T-shirt and marched toward the door.

The mini-mart was almost an exact copy of Pop Snyder's market where Sam and I first bought beer. It was crammed with homemade wooden shelves filled with everything and anything the late-night shopper might need. The only thing missing was live bait.

The checkout counter was on the right, and the back wall was aglow with glass-front refrigerators. I turned left and went down the wall farthest from Ted. I found myself staring at a vast selection of beers. We had decided that our first purchase would be a simple one, so I looked for the quarts and grabbed the first two I found. Gunther had gone down a different aisle, and we met at the counter as Ted was finishing his chat-up of the clerk.

"*Wurst*," Gunther said, as he held up a tin of Vienna sausages.

"Yes, I agree. They are the worst," I said.

Ted was taking his change, and I was placing the two quarts on the counter as I noticed a photo of Bobby Robertson, the star first baseman of the Pittsburgh Pirates, who won the 1971 World Series. It was hanging on the wall holding a rack that held row after row of cigarettes.

I'd fished my fake I.D. out of my wallet, and as I handed it to the clerk, I said, "Go Bucks."

His eyes brightened, "You a Pirate fan?"

"Lifelong and I've met Bobby Robertson many times. He grew up not too far from me, and his high school played ball against mine. He's a great guy."

My new Pirate fan friend was overweight and sporting a two-day stubble. My guess was his career was peaking in his current position.

"Oh yeah, what's he like in person? I've only seen him at games. I got that picture after standing in line at the dugout for an hour," he said as he pointed to the photo. "And he didn't say a word to me."

"That's Bobby," I said. "He's a quiet guy, and his success has come as a big surprise to him. All the attention he's getting is a bit overwhelming, I think." I didn't think this at all, and I had never met Bobby Robertson, but it was a good distraction.

"If you like, the next time I see him I'll get him to sign a baseball for you. That is if you pay for the ball. He shows up at parties my parents go to all the time," I lied through my teeth.

Glancing at my I.D., he rang up the beer then said, "That would be swell. I'm here every weekday night, six to midnight. You go to the university?"

"Yes, I'm a freshman taking a summer class to get a jump on my first semester. I'll be here for the next four years, so I'm sure we can work something out," I said and handed him a dollar.

"What's your name?" the clerk asked.

"Shelby, it's right there on my license."

"Right," he said as he glanced at it again before handing it back to me. "I'm Jess."

I stuck out my right hand and shook his. "Nice to meet you, Jess. I'll see you next time."

— Party #1 —

Ted was already back across the street when Gunther and I caught up with him. We had crossed at the light on our return trip, so it took more time.

"Nice of you to finally get here," Ted squawked. "For a minute, I thought you two had run off with my beer."

"Your beer? I paid for it," I said.

"Yeah, yeah, I hear you. How much do I owe you?" Ted asked.

I realized I had an opportunity here. I was the only one of us who could buy beer, and that should be worth something, so I said, "How about you two cover the cost tonight since I did all the leg work?"

Ted looked at me as if I'd said something he would have. He dug into his pocket for a dollar.

"Here, I'll cover Gunny's cost tonight, but he covers mine tomorrow."

"*Danke*," Gunther said as he popped a Vienna sausage into his mouth.

Wow, it's good business to be the beer guy.

Ted led us up the path but after about ten steps, he made a sharp right turn and pushed his way into the heavily leafed woods the lined our way.

"Where are you going?" I asked.

"To our table. We have a reservation for three," Ted said as he disappeared into the forest.

Gunther followed him, and I did the same. It was dark, and I had to walk carefully to avoid the low limbs of trees that flew back at my head as Ted and Gunther released them in front of me. After about twenty yards, the trees opened up to a small clearing that showed much evidence of having been used as a campsite. There was a circle of stones forming a fire pit with three logs aligned around it to accommodate our rear ends.

"How did you find this place?" I asked Ted.

"I didn't. I heard one of the dorm counselors talking about it. Apparently, this is party city for all the college pot-heads, but it's summertime, and they aren't here, so it's all ours."

"Great," I said, and we settled in for our first of many beer parties in the woods.

Chapter 19 - Are You Ready?

— Classes —

"**G**et up, pretty boy," Jimmy chirped as he flicked my ear with his fingertip.

"Ouch! Back off, or I'll shove your fiddle up your ass," I yelped.

"It won't fit. I tried it." Jimmy laughed as he grabbed his toothpaste and walked out of the dorm room.

I looked at my watch and saw it was ten after seven, so I pushed myself out of bed and followed Jimmy into the hall bathroom. It was alive with campers, and I saw Jimmy in front of a mirror brushing his teeth.

"You missed the fun last night," I said.

"Oh, I'm sure I did. Did you and your new hick friend have a tea party?" Jimmy gurgled as he spat into the sink.

"Yes, we did, only they weren't serving tea. I got beer from the mini-mart down the road," I boasted.

"Bravo for you."

I followed Jimmy back to our room. "What did you do last night?" I asked.

"Dr. Portnoy held a forum in the auditorium where we could ask him anything we liked. The guy is a musical genius. He even played his violin for us." Jimmy swooned.

"Thrilling, I'm sure. Was Kat with you?" I asked.

"No, she was off with her girlfriends, plotting the revolution," Jimmy said as he checked his music to make sure he had put it all away from practicing last night. I dressed quickly, and we went down to the cafeteria for breakfast.

Kat was waiting for us there and she smiled saying, "I've already eaten. Hurry up, or we'll be late."

Kat had a nice smile, but that's where her beauty ended. She was about the same height as Jimmy and had his figure as well. A WVU sweatshirt over a plaid wraparound skirt was all she ever wore, and they did not go together, but I got the impression she didn't care. She followed Jimmy and me as we got our food.

"I heard you had a beer bash last night," Kat stated.

"Yes, I used my fake I.D. to buy beer at the mini-mart," I said.

"Can you get my girlfriends and me a six-pack tonight?"

"I think so."

"How much?" Kat quizzed.

"Well, how about you give me two dollars, and I'll settle with you later," I said hoping I hadn't crossed a line.

"Sounds great," Kat said as she fished two dollars from her pocketbook the size of an overnight case.

Hey, this is becoming profitable, I thought as we left the cafeteria for class.

Professor Clark spoke from the bottom of a tiered lecture hall that held fewer than fifty students, "When you use your instruments to make sounds, you are applying music theory. Reading music is also applying music theory, and should you ever use notes to capture a tune on paper; music theory will be your guide. It is the foundation of what we do as musicians."

He was standing in front of a chalkboard of the green variety, and there was as much chalk dust on him as on the eraser he was using to clean it. Professor Ronald Clark was an elderly man who gave up caring about his appearance long ago. He still wore a suit and tie to work every day, but the suit was sad, and the tie looked as if he loosened it and hung it on a doorknob until he needed it the next morning, but it was his head that had my attention. While the rest of his countenance fit his social security-eligible age group, above his brow was a sun-colored hair hat. I'm sure he called it a hairpiece or toupee, but it was not made of hair. He could have bought it from a Fuller brush man. If overheated, I'm sure it would melt.

As he continued his clearing of the chalkboard, his faux-hair danced from side to side on his head as if it were on a pendulum hovering above his scalp, not quite able to keep up. Now and then, his hand would shoot up and stop it from departing his head entirely. From my vantage point near the top of the tiered seating, it looked like a little blond squirrel chasing an over-sized acorn. I couldn't take my eyes off it.

"What is that on his head?" I whispered to Ted who was taking the same classes as me.

"Beats me, boy. It looks like the potholder I wove for my mother in first grade. Yellow's her favorite color."

Snorting, I buried my face in my arm and pushed back in my seat.

"Do you think he has to feed it?" I asked, quickly covering my mouth to avoid spitting on the girl in front of me.

"Nah, but he might have to dry clean it now and then," Ted added.

My arm could not contain my laughter, so I bent forward and pressed my face to my knees; thus began our music theory class at band camp.

I began every morning listening to Professor Clark extol the wonders of notes and staves and a teaching assistant whose idea of a music appreciation class was to write the composer's name on the chalkboard, put an LP of his music on the stereo, then take a smoke break. Other than the hair-hat from hell, I remember none of it. Practice filled the afternoon either in the form of sectionals or an entire ensemble, and when we gathered for our first rehearsal, I knew I was in for a wild and windy ride.

— Portnoy's Kind of Practice —

Curved buildings are cool, but when you're in them, it's hard to find your way around (pun intended). The WVU Creative Arts Center was such a building. As Ted, Gunther and I entered the front door, we heard wind instruments coming from the right side, so we walked in that direction. At the end of the curved hall, double doors opened to the backstage. It was like entering a train tunnel. Dark was all around me, and my eyes fixed on what looked like the end of the tunnel, but it was the stage floor reflecting fifty spotlights shining from above.

As I became accustomed to the dark, I saw campers scurrying around preparing for practice. Cocooning the back wall of the stage was a temporary bandshell made from fifteen-foot-high by ten-foot-wide metal paneled sections that were wheeled into place to project the sound forward into the auditorium.

I put my baritone case on the floor near the wall and got out my instrument. Inserting the mouthpiece, I blew warm air through the twelve feet of tubing that constituted my Conn. Fluttering the valves with my fingers, I found the third one was sticking a bit, so I searched in my case for the valve oil I thought I'd brought. No luck.

Okay, so here's another way for me to show my unprofessional musicianship—no valve oil.

Looking around, I saw Dan Lehrer, one of the baritone team, walking on stage with his horn under his arm.

"Dan!" I yelled as I dropped my horn back into its case.

Looking up and remembering me he said, "Hey there, drum dude. Your chair's two down to the right, but you're going to need a horn if you want to play along."

"Right, it's in the wings. Hey, do you have valve oil I can borrow?" I asked.

"Borrow?" Dan laughed. "Dude, valve oil is like chewing gum. Once you use it, I don't want it back." Laughing, he got up from his chair and pointed back into the dark wings and walked in that direction. Once there, he bent down to his case and came up with a small glass bottle with an eye dropper top and handed it to me.

"I make my own from denatured alcohol and kerosene. I find it works much better than that crap they sell at music stores. The only downside is it smells like a camp stove. Drop it back in my case when you're finished, but dude, get your own valve oil. It's kinda basic."

"Thanks," I said and went to work lubricating my pistons. "Jesus," I muttered under my breath. He makes his own valve oil? The shit only cost 30 cents. How much better can his backroom chemistry concoction be?"

Dan was right about the smell, but it worked, and I had my valves sliding with ease in a few minutes. I played a few notes; then I turned back towards the bright lights. All of the other baritone players were on stage. My assigned chair was obvious; it was the one at the end of the baritone line farthest from the front of the stage. Ted's seat was second to last, and I noticed for the first time that his horn was very similar to mine.

I looked at the bell and saw what I expected: the word Conn, but Ted's horn was in worse shape than mine. It looked as if he'd thrown rocks at it during a hail storm. Every inch of it was covered with dents. On the music stand in front of him was an open folder with the music we needed to master before the concert on the last night of camp. There was also a mimeographed sheet listing the band sections and their members ranked in order of competency. Under the word euphonium, I saw my name right below Teds—dead last.

"I told you we treble clef fags had to stick together," Ted said as I eased my way into my seat avoiding the bass drum that sat a foot to my right. It was the back of the band for baritones, and since I was next to the bass drum that meant I was the bottom of the back end. I felt like a turd in one of those leather bags that hangs behind hansom cab horses in Central Park. Again, I thought of Chucky Grainfield and how he must feel when we make fun of his dinosaur death rattles.

I've got to be nicer to that guy.

I was surprised that Ted was second to last in the chair placements. I thought he did better than both Brad and Dan, but I guess it was his treble-clef-curse that damned him to be sitting next to me. There was only one treble clef folder. Oh well, at least we didn't have to be anywhere near Preston. I had a look at the music and saw "The Washington Post" behind another Sousa march, "El Capitan." I'd played both of them before, so I was feeling a wave of confidence. Then, I saw twenty odd pages of rather old, yellowing papers, all by the same composer: Modest Mussorgsky.

Mussorgsky? I thought. I've heard that name before, but I couldn't place it until I looked at the name of the piece, Pictures at an Exhibition. "Bingo," I said out loud. "I know this stuff."

I've got an 8-track tape in the car of it by Emerson, Lake, and Palmer of *Tarkus* fame.

Pictures at an Exhibition was composed to honor the death of Mussorgsky's artist friend Victor Hartmann. It tries to capture in sound the emotions Mussorgsky felt after his friend's death as well as celebrates his art. To do this, he recreated the experience of strolling through an art gallery, pausing to look at a painting, then moving on. There are ten pieces representing the art and a recurring piece ("Promenade") that reflects the stroll.

Mussorgsky didn't write music for beginners, and the aging yellow pages I was leafing through looked difficult. As an example, the first number ("Promenade") is written in the alternating time meters of five-four and six-four. These are unusual alone but smashing them together one after another is downright odd and creates an uneven, eleven-count phrasing. I was putting the music back into the folder when I felt someone's presence behind me.

"I think it is important that I establish guidelines on how I want our section to function," Preston announced as he leaned down between Ted and Dan and looked from side to side. "Learning the music is job one. Job two is—"

"Do you hear something, Shel?" Ted said loudly, interrupting Preston.

"Nope," I answered.

"I hear an annoying buzzing or clicking sound. I can't quite make it out, but it is definitely not human," Ted joked.

"Listen now," Preston whined. "Zak says I'm section leader and that you guys have to listen to me."

Ted stood and was staring Preston right in the eyes. "How old are you, boy?"

"Fifteen, but I'll be sixteen in September," Preston stated, knowing he'd just capitulated.

"Come back when you get your big-boy pants, son but until then, sit down and shut the fuck up.

Before Preston could answer, Ted leaned forward with his dented baritone and tapped his bell against Preston's Besson. There was a distinctive clash of metal impacting metal, and Preston's face went white as he hugged his horn and stepped back, rubbing and inspecting where the two horns had clashed.

"Don't do that!" he screamed like a little girl. "Don't ever do that!"

"Agreed, I won't do that, and you won't do this. *Comprende deja vu?*" Ted said snidely.

I was glad to see that Dan and Brad were smirking as Preston withdrew into the wings, rubbing and shining his bell as he went. That was the last time he said anything about section leadership. When Preston returned, he had what looked like a silver polishing cloth and was going over every inch of his horn.

"I'll bet you that homo sleeps with that thing between his knees," Ted grunted.

I noticed Preston also had a bottle of valve oil with him, and he dropped a few drops of it in the bottom hole of each of his valves before he took his seat. *Tap, tap, tap* sounded from the front of the band, and I saw Dave, the head counselor, standing on the director's podium with a baton. "Sharon, give us a C concert," he said, looking down to his right at the brunette sitting closest to him.

The first chair of the clarinet section stood and played the note. Dave used his baton to cue the tubas to join in, and we began the tuning ritual that would grace the beginning of every rehearsal. I was anxiously awaiting the arrival of Dr. Portnoy, and I was sure that after Dave finished the tuning, Portnoy would take the stage, and we would dive right into the music. I was right but in a very wrong way.

Dave stepped off the podium and joined the line of the other section counselors that had formed. They were almost at attention, and all of them were looking to their right in anticipation of something. Then, as if a neon applause sign had turned on, they all started clapping and nodding as Dr. Portnoy entered. Dave motioned to us with his hands for us to stand, and we staggered up.

Portnoy walked with purpose—he knew why he was there and what he wanted to do. His appearance was again impeccable. His dark cuffed slacks were creased sharply, and his white oxford shirt fit perfectly. He had on another bow tie; this one was crimson. Reaching the podium, he nodded to Dave, who scurried offstage returning with a high, cushioned chair that he placed next to the doctor. Portnoy studied the band from left to right, then front to back. He was not smiling. Then, he sat on the chair, and as he did, the counselors disappeared into the auditorium. He opened the leather music folder on his stand and took out one composition.

"We'll begin with 'The Washington Post,'" he stated at a volume too soft to be heard by most of the band, and we all strained forward to hear.

This was followed by a furious flurry of shuffling paper sounds as we searched for the right song. I blew warm air through my horn and toggled the spit valve. I knew we were about to roll through a rousing rendition of "The Washington Post," and I wanted to be ready, but that was not to be. No one played a note for the next hour.

"I wish to take this at a leisurely pace, around 115 beats per minute," the doctor began, as he held his copy of the march in his hand and studied it like a paint swatch he was using to choose a new color for his living room walls.

"Dynamics are key. Please note, I don't believe in double forte and will not accept its application in this auditorium. I want the music's beauty to come through like a warm breeze, not a hurricane. There was a long pause, then a final command in the form of a question, "Is that understood?"

Like Pavlov's dogs, we all instinctively answered, "Yes, sir."

So began band rehearsal. Dr. Portnoy did this with every piece of music in the folder. His instructions for the marches were easy, mostly focused on dynamics and pacing, but when he got to *Pictures at an Exhibition*, he delved deeper. He often spent minutes focusing on one phrase played by one instrument, making sure we understood what sound he was seeking, but we never played a note. Everyone in the band was furiously scribbling notes in the margins of the music or on the music folder trying to capture what the doctor was prescribing.

Then, suddenly, it was over. Portnoy tucked the last piece of music back into his folder, stood, and walked off the stage. He said nothing. No thank you or good job or eat shit and die.

The Lord had spoken, so let His will be done.

Dave returned to the podium and announced, "We'll take a thirty-minute break. Then, we will reconvene as sectionals. You'll meet with your counselors in the same rooms where your skills were assessed yesterday."

"That is all."

Chapter 20 - Let the Good Times Roll

— That Perfume —

I felt a bit stunned and looking around; I got the impression most of the other kids were, too. Preston was up and walking into the wings, still rubbing his horn with his rag. I noticed he left his valve oil sitting on his stand. Dan and Brad followed him, and I nudged Ted's horn and said, "Would you please hand me my valve oil?"

Ted gave me a questioning look. I pointed to Preston's stand. "Your valve oil? Oh, sure, boy." he laughed. "You'd think that little prick would have better manners and return things he borrows."

He grabbed the bottle of Holton valve oil and tossed it to me.

"Thanks." I grinned and slipped it into my back pocket. At the sectional, we finally got to play music, but it was hard to relate how our parts fit in with the rest of the band. It only lasted an hour. Ted and I made a beeline for the dorms as soon as it was over. Before we split up, we agreed to have another party after dinner. The elevator door had closed, so I waited for another. A crowd of kids formed behind me, so when the next door opened, I found myself pushed to the back of the car.

"Six, please!" I yelled as I got a whiff of a most intoxicating perfume. It was subtle yet magnetic, and I was drawn to it immediately. The source was the delicate neckline of a petite blonde in front of me, and I inhaled pulling in as much of the sweet nectar as I could. Her hair was pulled back in a tasteful ponytail that sat on her creamy skin.

Wow, could this be those pheromones that affect the behavior of mammals I heard about in biology class?

Well, this mammal was affected, and I leaned forward to say something to her as the elevator lady announced, "Three" and the doors slid open. She moved forward and disappeared down the hallway.

"Bummer," I whispered, but at least I knew she lived on the third floor. I would track her down later, for sure.

— Michael & Bill —

When I got to my room, I found Jimmy there talking to two older-looking guys.

"Shelby, come on in," the cleaner cut of the two said as I entered the room and put my baritone case down. "I'm Michael, and this is Bill. We're the counselors responsible for the sixth floor, and we're meeting all the campers to see if they're settling in well and have any questions."

Michael was tall and very preppy in appearance. Bill, on the other hand, could have been part of the *Mod Squad*. He had on a Che Guevara T-shirt that was overlaid by a loose-fitting army fatigue jacket. He was shorter than Michael but a bit more seasoned. His hair was longer, too, and he looked as if he only shaved every other week.

"Are you music majors?" I asked.

"Yes, we are," chirped Michael. "I play bassoon, and Bill plays trombone."

"Were you in the Army?" Jimmy asked Bill.

"Yeah, four years," he answered.

"Vietnam?" I quizzed.

"Nope, I only did two years active duty at Fort Bliss in an Army band, then two years National Guard duty. I finished my enlistment in the spring. If they had told me I had to go to Nam, I'd be in Canada right now."

"There will be a movie in the cafeteria tonight at seven. We're showing Disney's *The Love Bug,* so make sure you guys get there early to find a good seat," Michael said as he and Bill left our room.

"*The Love Bug,*" Jimmy grunted. "Disney would shit if he knew about the crap put out in his name now."

"He can't," I quipped. "He's as frozen as a TV dinner. Hey, how about you join Ted and me tonight for a couple of beers in the woods? I've got to get Kat a six-pack, so I can get one for you, too."

"Who will be there?" Jimmy asked wanting to make sure no undesirable might be in attendance.

"Just Kat, Ted, Gunther, and me" I replied. "Unless Princess Grace shows up again." Jimmy snorted, and I knew he wanted to come but would not admit it, so I let the subject drop and left for dinner.

Later in line at the mini-mart, I worried how Jess would react to all the beer I was buying tonight. I was glad to see he was alone again at the cash register, and I was also flying solo since Ted and Gunther had to stay behind for their meet and greet with the counselors. Jess's eyes brightened as I put my beer down on the counter.

"The Bucks killed the Dodgers last night," I said, repeating what I had read in the sports section of the newspaper at the dorm an hour earlier. I'd made sure I had Pirate facts to spew should I need to chat up Jess.

"Clemente shut them down with his fielding. He could catch a comet if he was tall enough," Jess joked as he rang up my purchases, then he stopped and looked at me.

Shit, here it comes. I was sure he would ask to see my I.D. again and this time, realize it was fake.

"I almost forgot." Jess smiled and ducked down under the counter. When he popped back up, he had a new baseball, still in its cardboard box, and he put it in the paper bag along with the two six-packs.

"How long do you think it will take you to get Bobby's autograph?" he asked, sounding like a kid wanting to know how long it will take Santa to fly from the North Pole.

"Not long, I'm sure. I'm going home this weekend, and I'll leave the ball with my dad. Like I said, he sees Bobby all the time at parties."

"Cool," Jess exhaled.

— The Counselor Cometh —

I was the first one at the fire pit, and it gave me time to relive that moment in the elevator and that delightful perfume. The truth was, I hadn't stopped thinking about that girl all evening, but I had no clue who she was.

"What's the best way to find her?" I said out loud.

"Find who?" A girl's voice answered me from the gloom of the woods.

I saw an outline of more than one person making their way along the last part of the trail to the party site.

"Who goes there?" I cried out like a sentry from his post.

"'Tis I, fair Maid Marian. Is that you, my Robin Hood?"

"No, milady, 'tis Friar Tuck," I said as I saw Kat, followed by two other people. One was a mousy little girl I didn't know. The other was Jimmy.

"You mean Fat Fuck, don't you?" Jimmy bellowed.

"Glad you could join us. You always steer a conversation right into the gutter, don't you, Jimmy?" I said tautly.

"It's a gift," he beamed.

"Who are you trying to find?" Kat asked again.

"Nobody important," I lied. "I saw an attractive girl today, and I want to find out who she is. Here's your beer." I opened the paper bag, removed the top six-pack, and handed it up to Kat. "I owe you 50 cents."

"Forget it," she said.

"What's this girl look like? Maybe I've seen her," Kat asked.

"That's the wild part. I don't know. I only saw her from the back," I answered.

"That must be some back," Jimmy cracked. "Does she have another set of boobs back there?"

"Enough, Jimmy," Kat scolded. "But, she must have a beautiful back if it caught your attention so fiercely."

"It was her perfume," I said.

"Kismet," the mousy girl said more boldly than I expected she could. "It's kismet, fate or destiny or maybe doom. You can't do a thing about it—what will be, will be."

"Thank you, Doris Day," Jimmy interjected.

Looking at him like a naughty child, Mousy continued, "Indians believe we all evolved from the original tribes of the Earth, and if you bump into someone from your old tribe your spirits connect. You can't fight it. It's kismet."

You could hear us all thinking deep thoughts until Jimmy ruined the moment.

"*Kismet* was a third-rate musical that stole the Tony Awards in 1954 only because there wasn't any competition."

"How in the name of Rogers and Hammerstein do you know that?" Kat laughed, looking at Jimmy in amazement.

"My mother has the soundtrack to every fucking musical, and I've had to listen to them every fucking day since I was born," Jimmy said as if he were describing how his mother skins and fries puppy dogs.

We heard a rustle in the bushes. First Ted, then Gunther stepped into the clearing, but it was the third guy who scared me stiff. It was Bill, the dorm counselor. I looked around for the best way to run and used my foot to push the two bags of beer away from me.

"It's Miller time," Ted called out as he came over and put his hands on my shoulders.

Gunther was giving me a thumbs-up sign and said, "*Ein bier bitte.*"

"Where is it?" asked Ted as he looked around for the beer. He dug into one of the paper bags and came out with a can of Schlitz. He then tossed it to Bill saying, "This is Bill. He's our sixth-floor counselor."

Bill opened the beer, and as the foam sprayed out of the thin opening created by the aluminum pull-top, he said, "It's cool. Don't worry; it's cool. Your secret's safe with me as long as I get free beer."

Everyone laughed, but I did it nervously, knowing I had the most to lose if this whole situation went south. I had enough beer for everyone except Jimmy and Bill, and it looked like Ted was taking care of Bill, so I opened a Schlitz and held it out in Jimmy's direction, saying, "Here you go. We can share tonight."

Jimmy looked at me suspiciously but took the beer. Ted reached into the paper bag for a beer and came out with the baseball. "What the hell ya doin' with this, boy? We gonna play some catch tonight?"

"Be careful with that. I'm supposed to get that signed by Bobby Robertson of the Pittsburgh Pirates for the cashier at the mini-mart. He thinks I'm best friends with the guy, and I'm pretty sure that's why he lets me buy beer," I said.

"Do you know Bobby Robertson?" Kat asked.

"About as well as I know Bobby Kennedy," I joked.

"Why do you need to know him?" the mousy girl asked. "All you need is his name on that ball. Gimme it." She sucked her beer dry and threw the can over her shoulder.

Ted tossed her the box with the ball in it, as Kat dug into her suitcase of a pocketbook and came up with a pen. Before I could protest, Mousy girl had scribbled something on the ball and put it back in the box.

Passing it to me, she said, "Don't worry. My dad works for the concession franchise at Pittsburgh's Three Rivers Stadium, and I've been staring at Bobby Robertson's autographed picture on the wall of my dad's office for years. He writes like a squirrel."

I looked at the ball, and there was definitely two words on there, but only three of the letters were legible; the first *B* in Bobby, the *R* that starts Robertson and the *T* near the end that had a religious look to it. The rest of the letters were just scribbles of ink.

Pointing at Mousy, I said, "Give that girl, I mean Bobby, a beer."

Both of them stayed for the rest of the party, as did Bill. We all had a good time discussing the mysteries of unrequited love, Broadway musicals, and baseball. Bill even volunteered to go back to the mini-mart and get us another six-pack when we ran out. We didn't stumble back to the dorm until after midnight.

— Valve Oil —

Morning classes were a total bore, and as I walked with Ted and Gunther to our afternoon band rehearsal, I asked Ted, "Why in the world did you bring a counselor to our party last night?"

"He asked to come," Ted answered.

"Weren't you worried he'd turn us in for underage drinking? They'd throw us out for sure," I said.

"Nah, it's not like that. Gunther and I were to meet with Bill and Michael after dinner, but only Bill showed up. Michael was in charge of movie night, and they couldn't get the projector to work. Anyway, it turns out Bill hates this counselor gig. It makes him feel like a drill sergeant. We talked, and he told us all about Fort Bliss and Army band life. He and his friends spent most of their off-duty time drinking, like us."

"But, how'd he find out about our party?" I quizzed.

"I asked him if he was going to the movie, and he said he'd rather go to a bar, and one thing led to another. But, like he said, it's cool. Hell, boy, he bought us beer, so he's in deeper shit than we are if caught," Ted assured me.

"You're right. I hadn't thought of that," I said as we wheeled around the Creative Arts Center.

I got to my seat before any of the other baritone players and tried playing through the first few bars of "Promenade," the recurring song from *Pictures at an Exhibition*. Knowing how the tune went from my Emerson, Lake and Palmer 8-track, I ignored the confusing, alternating time-signatures and just read the notes using my ear to guide me.

"That don't sound half bad, boy," Ted said as he dropped into his seat beside me.

"How do you keep the measure count straight with all that back and forth between five-four and six-four time?"

"I don't. I only read the notes and hold them the appropriate amount of time, I said.

Brad and Dan joined us, but there was no sign of Preston, and we were only minutes away from rehearsal.

Ted leaned over to Brad and asked, "Where's the asshole?"

"Don't know," Brad said as he stood and looked back into the wings.

The tuning process had begun when Preston appeared behind us and blasted, "I can't find my valve oil!"

"It's tuning time, son. You've gotta shit or git." Ted laughed as we all played C concert.

Preston's face turned red, and he dashed back into the wings. Portnoy had already taken the podium when Preston reappeared and attempted to sit without notice. He failed when his horn bumped his stand and all his music fell on the floor. I saw a bottle of valve oil drop out of his shirt pocket and skid under the seat in front of him. There was an audible gasp from the other band members as they all turned to see who was self-destructing.

Tap, tap, tap blared loudly as the good doctor used his baton to draw all attention back to him.

"Zak," he said, and almost instantaneously our section counselor's face appeared at the edge of the stage.

"Your first chair is late. That's one demerit."

Ted jabbed me in the rib cage with his elbow as he bent forward, hiding his laughter behind the stand. I tried not to move, but I felt my cheeks push out as I smothered a howl.

"No, that's not fair. I was looking for my valve oil, and—" Preston pleaded while trying to gather his things.

Tap, tap, tap sounded louder.

"That's another demerit for quibbling. Sit down, sir. We have work to do," Portnoy ordered.

Preston melted into his chair like a stick of butter in a microwave. Even Dan and Brad were giggling.

We spent most of the practice going over the two marches, but near the end of the two hours, Doctor Portnoy said, "Bring up 'Promenade.' Before we begin, let me tell you about how you should approach this piece. Mussorgsky deliberately wrote this phrase to be uneven to mimic the gait of someone leisurely walking through an art gallery. When playing, it is easier not to count each measure but just to play the notes for their appropriate amount of time. The note's value does not change whether you are in a five-four or six-four measure."

Ted elbowed me. Turning, he looked astonished as he said, "Well, ain't you the little Portnoy."

I beamed.

When band practice ended, Preston was the first one off the stage. I was about to ask Ted if he wanted to do anything that night when I heard a loud crash from the wings and a furious voice yell, "What the hell are you doing in my trumpet case?"

We all moved towards the sound and saw Preston sprawled on the floor under a fire extinguisher. Tossed there like a discarded beer can, he cradled his horn in his arms like an infant. He had sacrificed his body to save it from touching the ground. Standing over him was a trumpet player much larger than Preston using his horn as a pointer, thrusting it in Preston's direction.

"I borrowed a little of your valve oil. That's all," Preston whimpered as his face flushed and tears appeared.

"Stay the fuck out of my trumpet case, faggot, or I'll break all the fingers on your right hand. Oh, and give me a buck for the valve oil you stole," the trumpet player bellowed.

Preston said nothing else and quickly took a dollar from his wallet and handed it to his master.

"I feel bad," I said to Ted. "I didn't expect this."

"Are you kidding, son?" Ted chuckled. "This is the most fun I've had since I got here."

— In Search of Kismet —

I had a two-hour break before dinner, and I decided to track down my mystery girl. I figured the best place to start was the third floor. After dropping my baritone off in my room, I took the stairwell down three floors. Exiting, I walked slowly down the hall trying to look as innocuous as I could until I felt someone tap me on my back and say, "Can I help you find something?"

Turning around, I found myself face-to-face, or should I say chest-to-face, with a little globe of a girl. She couldn't have been over four feet tall and was about the same in diameter. She was looking up at me sternly, and I almost said, "Let me guess? You want me to follow the yellow brick road."

But before I could, she announced, "This is a girls-only floor. You must exit immediately, or I'll call campus security."

"No problem. I must have gotten out of the elevator on the wrong floor. Sorry," I said.

She reached out with her little Tyrannosaurus Rex arm and pulled me towards the elevator. I saw that a few girls on the floor were watching as she led me away. She pushed the "down" button, and we waited together for the car.

"Do you play an instrument?" I asked.

"No, I'm a counselor for the chorus. I'm a sophomore here at WVU," she answered.

"Are you a soprano?" I continued to quiz.

"No, contralto. It's the same as baritone for men—I've got a very low voice for a girl," she said glumly.

"Get out of town! I play baritone in the band," I stuck out my hand to shake hers.

"I'm Shelby, and we baritoners have to stick together. Sorry for the mix-up."

She looked at my hand suspiciously then gave it a limp shake. "I'm Jill. It's time to go."

The elevator opened, and her little mouth smiled for the first time. I think I'd made a friend. A few girls got off the elevator; then I went in. My nose shot up, and my olfactory lobes screamed, "The perfume! We smell the perfume!"

Kismet was one of those girls. The doors started to close. I stuck my arm forward hoping the safety stop mechanism would activate. It did, and I looked down the hall and much to my delight, I saw that beautiful little blonde ponytail bouncing happily along. I also saw the gorgeous body attached to it.

Oh, my God, I have got to meet that girl.

I felt knuckles in my stomach and looked down to see my new little friend jabbing her fist into my gut.

"Back on the elevator, or I call the cops," she ordered, and I let the doors close.

— Hamburger Vending Machines —

We took a break from partying in the woods for a third night and instead hung out in the lobby of The Towers. It was my idea hoping my mystery girl might pass by while we were there, but no such luck. I went to bed early, but Jimmy woke me up when he came in at about midnight and announced, "Did you know they have a hamburger vending machine in the basement of this place?"

"No, they don't. There's no such thing." I groaned and rolled over to avoid the overhead light.

"Yes, there is. Come on down, and I'll show you," Jimmy insisted.

Well, I was awake, so I figured I'd see the marvel of technology that so impressed Jimmy. I pulled on my jeans and T-shirt and slipped on my loafers.

"This way," Jimmy giggled.

"Are you high?" I asked.

"Just a little, maybe a little too much."

We rode the elevator to the first floor, then had to walk down the hall to another set of elevators that only went down to the basement. When the doors opened, in front of us was a large room filled with fast food-like tables with those fixed chairs. All along the left side of the room were vending machines. Most of them were the standard types, but in the center was a six-foot-long, floor-to-ceiling, refrigerated box with small glass doors checkering its front. It reminded me of an automat in New York City. Through the little doors, you could see boxes labeled "hamburger," "cheeseburger," or "hot dog."

"Okay," I said to Jimmy. "They have hamburger vending machines. But, what do you do with a cold hamburger?"

"Heat it up in the Radar Range," he said as he pointed to a heavy-looking aluminum box about two feet square that had a handle on the front and a rotating timer.

"A Radar Range? Do you mean a microwave?" I asked.

"Yeah, let's try it out," Jimmy said.

I was intrigued. Microwave ovens were new to me. I'd only read about them in *Popular Science.*

"The burgers are 35 cents each, and the Cokes are a quarter," Jimmy said, holding his hand out in my direction.

It was clear now why I had been coaxed down to the basement to see the future of the culinary arts. Jimmy wanted me to pay for his food. I knew he didn't have much disposable income, but I didn't expect him to be mooching off me. I found out later he'd invested most of his money on an ounce of marijuana earlier that day and now had to rely on the kindness of strangers for the rest of camp. I was his principal stranger.

In normal circumstances, I would have said no, but I was making money. Even though I'd bought over $5 in beer and snacks, every penny of it was paid for by other people, and I had a lot more money than when I started, so I bought Jimmy a burger and one for me, too.

They were different but not bad. They'd been pre-cooked, God knows how long ago and sealed into cellophane bags. We found out the hard way you needed to tear a small hole in the cellophane before microwaving it, or the bag would pop and spray your hamburger all over the oven. You also had to like your hamburger well done and your bun soggy, but they were the perfect post-pot-party treat, and Jimmy inhaled his.

— Demerits —

"Today we will enjoy composers of the Baroque musical style," our music appreciation class teaching assistant said as he began to write on the chalkboard. As he scrawled each name across the green surface, he over-enunciated the syllables of each word. "Johann Sebastian Bach, Antonio Lucio Vivaldi and George Frideric Handel."

Ted whispered in my ear, "Are three silly names required to write this crap? And with names like that, you'd think they'd have lots of money." I looked at him and tried to figure out if he was serious.

"What makes you think they didn't have any money?"

"Hell, Shel. The T.A. just told us..." He paused, got a huge smile on his face, and then said, "wait for it." After another pause, he said, "They're ba-roke."

Ted hissed with delight as the girl to his right rolled her eyes and moved her chair away from him.

As I had hoped, as soon as the T.A. had the record playing, he was out the door for his long-awaited smoke break. Hearing the first notes of "Air on a G-String," I wrapped my knuckles on Ted's head and said, "Time to go," and stood and walked to the door. I waited in the hall, and Ted soon appeared.

"Where are we going, boy?" he asked.

"Believe it or not, I need to give something to Preston. He's in his conducting class next door," I said.

"What are you talking about?" Ted asked.

"I have to give him his valve oil back. I feel like shit for stealing it and then watching him get in trouble," I answered.

"Get out of Dodge." Ted laughed.

I looked through the door window of the classroom next to ours, and I saw Preston in the front row. I opened the door a crack and heard the instructor talking about the importance of a visibly strong downbeat. I made a *psst* sound at Preston. It got his attention, and luckily not the teacher's, who had turned to write something on the blackboard. Preston looked at me scornfully and was about to turn away when I held up his half-empty valve oil bottle. His jaw clenched, and his eyes squinted. He got out of his chair and walked to the door.

"Did you steal that?" he snarled.

"No, I found it on the floor of the stage. I figured it was yours. Is it?" I said matter-of-factly as Preston grabbed the tiny bottle from my hand and shoved it into his pocket.

He was about to say something unkind when we all heard, "Gentlemen, shouldn't you be in class?"

Preston looked as if he was trying to stop shit leaking from his ass, and I turned to see Ted smiling and nodding at Doctor Portnoy who was slowing as he passed us. His eyes were thin slits, and his mouth was taut with disgust.

"We were discussing when we could have a mini-sectional this evening to practice our music," Ted improvised.

Portnoy didn't stop, but his unsmiling lips said, "You are not to be out of your class for any reason not authorized by the faculty. Is that understood?"

"Yes, sir!" we barked, and he disappeared around the curving wall.

"Leave me the hell alone. I've already got two demerits, and Zak says if I get another, I can't be first chair." Preston agonized as he reopened his classroom door and vanished inside.

"Grateful little twat, isn't he?" Ted smirked.

"Let's scram. I've done my good deed for the day," I said and turned back towards the front of the building.

"Where are we going?" Ted asked.

"I don't know, but I can't stand Preston or Baroque music. He sounds like a baby, and that music sounds like fingering exercises to me. Let's go for a ride."

"Now you're talkin' sense," said Ted as he skipped to catch up with me.

We spent the rest of the morning driving around town annoying any pretty undergraduate girls we saw. We got back to the Creative Arts Center just in time for sectionals. We were the last to arrive. Everyone was there, either fluttering their valves or practicing scales.

Zak asked for quite then said, "Let's work on 'The Old Castle' and the transition into the third 'Promenade.'"

Ted leaned forward and took out the two corresponding pieces from *Pictures at an Exhibition*. Before we could start, there was a knock on the door. Zak stood, but the door opened before he could reach it, and in stepped the unsmiling Doctor Portnoy.

"Zak, I need a minute of your time," he said, and the two of them left the room, closing the door behind them.

It wasn't long before Zak came back in. He was shaking his head, looking at the floor and sort of fell into his chair like a bag of dirty clothes.

"Shelby, Ted, and Preston," he said sadly. "Did you see Doctor Portnoy in the hall this morning when you should have been in your classes?"

Before Ted or I could say anything, Preston answered for us. "Yes, we saw him. Shelby found my valve oil and was returning it."

"The valve oil again," Zak said with exasperation. I've had enough of you and your valve oil, and so has Doctor Portnoy. "You each are awarded a demerit, and I'm sorry to say that makes three for you, Preston. As I warned you the other day, with three demerits, you cannot be the first chair of the section."

Preston looked like someone had sliced open his entrails, and he wasn't sure whether he should try to put things back in or succumb to the inevitable.

Zak turned away from Preston. "Brad, you are first chair of the euphonium section."

Preston let out an animalistic sound, like the cow realizing the slaughterhouse chute isn't just another ramp to a food trough.

"Shelby and Ted, don't skip any more classes, or the consequences will be more significant," Zak warned.

"But, I didn't skip any class!" Preston wailed.

"Enough, I said," Zak interjected. "You have already admitted that Doctor Portnoy caught you in the hall."

I looked at Ted as Preston's mouth dropped open. Air came out but no sound. Before Preston could vibrate his vocal cords, Zak ended the conversation with a loud, "Enough!"

Ted was doing his best to look distraught, but his grin was still visible. I stared down at my feet. Preston's face was red and his eyes were moist as Zak got the sectional underway, but when Brad played the euphonium solo in the third "Promenade," Preston's head sank. When it was over, he looked like he'd spent six hours on the Cross at Cavalry.

Chapter 21 – Drowning in a Sea of Love

— Strings vs. Horns —

"If I understand your position correctly, the orchestra is the preeminent ensemble of the Fine Arts Camp. Is that right?" I asked Jimmy, who was sprawled on one of the modern, brightly colored couches in the first-floor lounge of The Towers. Kat was next to him in a paisley armchair, and she was the one to answer.

"They're both important, only different. Orchestras came first and initially played what we call classical music today but, they rely on wind instruments like trumpets and clarinets. In other words, orchestras need band geeks. My friend Martha plays in both the band and the orchestra, and so does Gunther."

Upon hearing his name, Gunther looked up from his Batman comic book and said, "Why not bands have string musicians? Discrimination it is." We all stared at him for a few seconds before he went back to his reading.

"You've got a good point, *Kat*," I said, emphasizing her name so no one would think I agreed with Gunther. "But I'm not sure Jimmy sees it that way. Tell us, Jimmy, do you think the camp orchestra is the top ensemble, above the chorus and the band?" I insisted, but there was no answer.

I knew there wouldn't be because I'd found out that Doctor Portnoy, the highest-ranking member of the university's faculty involved with the camp was only directing the band this year. His assistant was directing the orchestra, and Jimmy was not happy. It quashed his plan to get some quality face time with Doctor Portnoy.

"It's the last ensemble to perform at the concert next week, and they always save the best for last," Jimmy grunted without unfolding his arms or turning to look at me.

I was sitting on the square, wooden coffee table that looked like an oversized child's block, feeling quite pleased with myself. Jimmy had been rubbing the inferiority of band instruments in my face since I'd met him, and suddenly he was confronted with a fact that did not fit into his worldview. How could string instruments be superior if the superior professional musician was not directing them?

"He must feel sorry for you low-lifes," Jimmy huffed. I felt I'd made my point, so I changed the subject.

"Kat, I'm having another party in the woods with Ted tonight. Do you want to join us, and if so, do you want me to get you another six-pack?"

"Sure, I'll ask Martha if she wants to come again," she answered.

Martha? Mousy Martha. "So that's her name. What's her story?" I asked.

"She lives in Pittsburgh but, you already know that from the baseball signing. I met her last year, and we've kept in touch, given I only live about forty-five miles south of her in Uniontown. She's going to be a nurse, like me."

"What about you, Jimmy? Need some beer for tonight?" I asked.

"Beer? Did someone say beer?" a voice from behind me said.

Turning, I saw Rich Jeffrey, another ALCO kid who was attending band camp. "Shh! Ixnay on the eer-bay, asshole. Do you want us to get thrown out of here?" I hissed.

"Right. Sorry," Rich said in a hush as he crouched beside me.

"Can you get me beer, please? I've got the cash."

That caught my ear, and I decided that there was always room for another customer in the Shelby retail beer distribution business. "Two bucks for a six-pack and you can only get one."

"Two bucks!" Rich roared as he stood back up and looked at me angrily.

"Quiet! Yes, two bucks. Take it or leave it, and I want the cash now. You get the beer tonight in the woods," I said.

Rich dug into his pocket, found two dollars, and handed them to me.

"Follow Jimmy to the woods tonight at eight. He's going to the party because I'm buying him beer to soothe his bruised ego." Jimmy glanced over at me and nodded with a dry smile, and I went to the cafeteria for dinner.

"You'll be buying a lot of beer tonight," Kat said as I followed her through the line.

"You're right. I hope my baseball-loving boob doesn't mind," I answered. "Hey Kat, what is it with Jimmy? Why is he such a downer all the time?"

Kat stopped pushing her tray and looked at me, "He's got his own private cloud that follows him around like Pig Pen, and he loves sharing the storm. Don't let him ruin your day or your life. He's got a bad habit of smoking his friends down to the filter."

— The Woods & The Drunk Dial —

Getting the beer was a breeze, but I enlisted Ted to help me carry it to the woods. He stayed to guard it while I drove back to the campus parking lot. When I returned, I found a party well underway, with three new faces attending. All previous participants were there, including Bill, the counselor, but Rich Jeffrey brought along two friends, so I immediately thought we'd need more beer.

I was wrong because Jimmy provided an alternative. He had his weed, and to my astonishment, shared it with those so inclined. Bill started a fire, and Ted turned on a transistor radio he brought, so what started a few days earlier as three guys drinking beer in the bushes had now matured into a full-grown campfire shindig.

About two hours into it, Jimmy migrated to my side of the fire. Emboldened by his inebriation, he was forcefully engaged in convincing me that it didn't matter that Dr. Portnoy wasn't directing the orchestra; string instruments were still the royalty of music.

As he droned on, I noticed Kat and Mousy Martha were making out.

"Jimmy," I said, not taking my eyes off them. "What the hell are they doing?"

"What do you think they're doing? They're kissing. You got a problem with kissing?" Jimmy scolded.

"No, I like it, but they're both girls," I said with honest amazement.

"Yeah, so what's wrong with that?" he replied, slurring his w's, making them sound like z's. I thought about that for a moment and didn't have a good answer, so I kept quiet.

"There is nothing wrong with two girls kissing," he continued. "Love is not gender restricted. I suppose you'd freak out if you saw two men kissing."

The answer was yes, but the question so unnerved me that I got up from my log and left the party for the dorm. Watching girls make out made me long to be kissing Janice or maybe the perfume girl or any girl for that matter. I decided to call Janice using one of the pay phones in the lobby of The Towers, and after depositing three quarters, I heard a bell sound, and Janice's phone rang. Her father answered, and I did my best to sound sober and asked if I could talk to Janice.

"It's after eleven, Shelby, and she's in bed," her father said in a much more understanding voice than I would have used. I started to say I was sorry and would call back tomorrow when Janice's voice came on the line.

"I've got it, Daddy."

"Okay, but keep it short," he stated in a much more forceful tone than before.

"I will," she answered and waited till she heard the click of his receiver hanging up.

"Hi, sweetie." I gushed, and we spent the next three minutes cooing and billowing about how much we missed each other and how we longed to be together.

It was both arousing and frustrating, and when it ended, I sat in the phone booth for a few minutes questioning what I was doing. I'd just told a wonderful girl how much I loved her after two days of lusting after another mysterious girl, not to mention the other make out sessions I'd had with Elena or my nude exploring with Linda. My "scales of justice" was unbalanced.

— WASP Chains —

I opened my dorm room to find the lights were off, but I could see Jimmy's outline on his bed. I turned on the desk lamp, and he said meanly, "I suppose you called your girlfriend to tell her all about the queers in the woods?"

"Yes, I called Janice, but no, I didn't talk about Kat. Look, it surprised me, that's all. I've never seen two girls make out before. What brought it on?"

"Are you that blind? Did you not have a single clue that Kat is a lesbian?" Jimmy castigated.

Lesbian! Now there's a word you don't hear in Cumberland every day.

I'd read about them in *Playboy* but always figured it had to do with threesomes in the mansion's grotto. The thought of two girls in a romantic relationship solely because they are attracted to each other was hard to fathom.

"Not everyone chases after the opposite sex. There are girls who like girls, girls who like both girls and boys, and boys who like boys," Jimmy scolded.

"Got it," I said trying to shut down the conversation. We'd passed my comfort level, but Jimmy wasn't finished.

"You know, for a while, I thought you might be more open to ideas like this."

What? Why you little. A wave of anger boiled in my chest. "What the hell are you implying?" I demanded of Jimmy, who was still lying on his bed fully clothed.

He turned his head away from me to look out the window, "Nothing. It disappoints me you're so completely locked into your WASP chains and don't even know it. You're not only blind but dumb."

Not realizing I was doing it, I moved closer to him and struck him hard on the chest. There was a thudding sound, and I knew it had to hurt, but Jimmy just rolled over to face the wall.

"Typical response," he grunted, and I stood over him feeling very small. I turned off the light and went to bed.

— Pamela —

I woke up to find Jimmy gone. There were no classes because it was Saturday, so I took my time dressing and replaying last night in my head.

"What was wrong with Jimmy?" I said to the mirror as I brushed my teeth. "Is he for real or goading me?" I honestly didn't know, but I was furious at him. I don't believe in resorting to violence, but he pushed me over the edge last night. Jimmy just got the wrong idea somehow, so this was all on him, not me, I reassured myself.

I saw Kat and Jimmy were eating in the cafeteria, so I didn't go in. It would be mushy cheeseburgers for breakfast . Riding the elevator back to the main floor, I stepped off and faced a wall of floor-to-ceiling windows that looked out on a lawn surrounded by flower beds, beyond which were tennis and basketball courts. It was a beautiful summer morning, and the sun was high enough to bathe the lush greenery in warm shimmering light. That's when I saw her.

She was wearing a blue, cotton, one-piece, exercise outfit. Her lustrous, blonde ponytail was bouncing as she first twirled, then threw her baton in the air, and then after catching it, twirled it again. I moved to the window and leaned against it with my palms pressed flat and my forehead resting on the cool glass. "That's her," I said. "My Kismet Queen." I swear I could smell her perfume through the wall.

"Pamela. Her name is Pamela," a familiar voice said from behind me.

I was so focused on the lovely sight that the voice didn't register at first.

"Is that who you were looking for?" the voice added.

Coming back to reality, I turned to see Jill, the Munchkin counselor, who had stopped me on the third floor.

"Yes, that's her. What did you say her name was?"

"Pamela, I don't remember her last name, but she's a clarinet player in the band."

"The band!" I blurted out laughing. "Ha, she's been sitting a few rows ahead of me two hours every day for the last week, and I never noticed!"

"Do you want to meet her?" Jill asked.

"You can do that?" I inquired trying not to drool.

"Oh yes, I cannot only do that, but I will if you want. We baritoners have to stick together, right?" Jill smiled.

"You bet!" I answered and followed her as she walked down to the lawn where Pamela was practicing.

She was twirling and dancing in a pattern as we walked towards her. Pick-up lines were racing through my head as I blew into my hands to check my breath. It was a bit cheeseburgery but passable. I'd keep my distance at first.

"Love your perfume," I rehearsed.

No, that's stupid. How about,

"Wow, that's a great onesie you're wearing."

Onesie? She's not an infant, you idiot.

I was studying her like a roadmap, and I loved her topography. Her legs were long and slim but had a mature curve to them that blended perfectly with her bouncy bottom. Her waist was tiny, and she blossomed from there up very nicely, well, from what I could see given the concealing form of her outfit, but it was her face that stole my heart. I saw it when she turned to catch the baton that was plummeting from her fifteen-foot toss.

"Pamela," Jill called. "Pamela, can you stop for a minute? I'd like you to meet a friend of mine."

Finishing an elaborate swirl of her arm, Pamela spun around to us and halted. I'm not sure she saw me at first, but when she turned my way, her eyes opened wide, but her lips stayed tightly together.

"This is Shelby. He's in the band too, and I caught him sneaking around your floor the other day. I think he was looking for you."

Geez Louise, Jill, I didn't expect you to tell the truth.

Pamela's eyes narrowed, and her jaw tightened as I put on my best golly-gee smile. "I wasn't sneaking."

This made her snicker, and before her hand could cover her lush, full lips, her dazzling white teeth peeked through a big, happy smile.

"I'm not a stalker, honest. Just a bashful band boy looking to meet a good-looking band girl. You sure do know what you're doing with that baton. My sisters tried to teach me how to twirl, but I could never get it right."

"My work is done," Jill announced, spun around on her size-four shoes and went back to the building.

"Boys are born without the twirling gene," Pam joked.

Hey, she's talking to me.

"I guess you're right about that, but you sure got a few extra ones," I said.

She laughed again, and I saw her eyes twinkle. I forgot what I planned to say next as her face transfixed me. She had soft, petite features, and blue laughing eyes surrounded by lush, long lashes. Her cheekbones were high but not overly prominent, and her nose was a turned-up Irish cute. I was a goner.

"What were you doing on my floor?" she asked in a sharper tone than before.

"I was looking for you," I said clearly. I figured confidence was the key if I was to have any chance at all. I pressed on and told her about our elevator encounters and how her perfume had compelled me to search for her. I made it sound like a fairy tale, with me playing Prince Charming with a glass slipper looking for Cinderella. I'm not sure she bought it, but she didn't run.

"Are you a majorette?" I asked.

"I'm not anything that ends in an 'ette.' I prefer to be called a twirler, please." And for the first time, I heard a distinctive West Virginia twang in her voice that I hadn't noticed before.

"Sorry, it's twirler from now on. Where are you from?"

"Charleston," she answered, and twirled her baton again. "I'm trying out for solo twirler this fall, so I need to practice as much as I can."

I took that as a hint, and I told her I'd leave her to her practice but was glad I'd found out who wore that perfume. She stopped twirling, and with a mischievous look in her eye, leaned forward. A wave of her wonderful fragrance wafted over me. My knees went weak, and I felt a great desire to grab her and kiss her, so I knew I needed to exit fast before I ruined what was turning out to be a wonderful introduction.

"Maybe I'll see you at band this afternoon," I said as I began to back away from her.

"Maybe," she replied as she went back into her routine as if I'd never been there.

— Kat Scolding —

A surprise greeted me when I returned to my room; Kat was sitting on my bed.

"You're not supposed to be on this floor. I wouldn't want you to get a demerit," I said.

"I know," Kat answered quietly. "Don't worry about it. Boys don't see me, and I need to talk to you."

I felt like my mother caught me with my hand in the cookie jar.

"Jimmy told me you hit him. Is that true?" Kat asked.

"Yes, and I'm sorry I did, but he made me very uncomfortable," I mumbled.

"He's good at that. I told you he's a mean one, but he can't help it. He hasn't figured out who he is yet, and until he does, he will hurt whoever gets in his way, but that doesn't mean you may strike him." Kat scolded.

"Right. It won't happen again," I promise.

"Good. You know he likes you." She paused, letting her words sink in.

My stomach tightened, and I changed the subject, "He's not acting like a friend."

Kat looked down and said, "He's not great at friendship, and he's terrible at sharing." Looking up she continued, "You may have to decide about him someday."

"What do you mean?" I questioned.

"I'm afraid you need to think of yourself as Travis in the 'Old Yeller' movie. If your friendship with Jimmy starts frothing at the mouth, you might have to shoot it. The friendship that is—not Jimmy," Kat explained.

"Okay," I answered.

"Oh, and I'm sorry I scared you last night," she said as she opened the door to leave. "I know who I am, and I'm not ashamed of it. Will you still buy me beer?"

"Absolutely," I said and thanked her, but I was more confused than before.

— Mousy Martha Helps Again —

I got to band practice early and watched carefully for Pamela to arrive. I was still standing when Ted plopped down beside me and said, "You can see better if you get on your chair. Are you looking for something in particular?"

"Yes. I met my mystery girl today. She's a clarinet player."

"Hot diggity damn!" Ted howled. "Point her out so I can see this vexing goddess."

"No way! If she thinks I hang out with Tennessee trash like you, I'm finished," I said louder than I should have.

"Oh, sweet peas and corn," Ted wheezed. "I think someone's in love."

I was about to tell him to shut up when I saw Pamela enter from the audience stairway on the right. It was as if a spotlight was following her as she crossed the stage and took her seat in the second row of the clarinets. She was gorgeous, or maybe she just looked gorgeous to me. It didn't matter, but I sensed I was losing control. What was I thinking? Even the most optimistic scenario would all end with band camp.

Jesus, she lived 250 miles away from me, and I had Janice waiting patiently for me at home.

However, sanity was not on my side. Lust blinded me, so I planned to push on. "It's go time," I said to Ted.

"Well, don't be long. Portnoy will be making his grand entrance in less than five minutes, and if you get another demerit, you'll be sitting in the bass drum."

I moved to the side of the stage and started working my way to the front. I saw Pamela sitting ten feet away with her signature ponytail in full view. Still not sure what I would say, I was about to call her name when I felt a tug on my right sleeve and heard "Baritones aren't allowed up here."

Looking down, I saw the sharp features of Mousy Martha smiling up at me from the clarinet section's second chair.

"Hell, Martha, I didn't know you were a real musician."

"Yeah, I'm one licorice stick lover" she giggled.

"What are you doing? You better scram before Doctor No-Joy sees you."

"Kismet," I whispered to her. "I found Kismet."

"No way." She grinned.

"Way," I answered as I knelt beside her and pointed through her to the second row of clarinets. "She's the blonde with the ponytail behind you."

Martha leaned back and turned her head to the right and then snapped back to me. "You mean Pamela Glass?"

"Glass, what a nice last name," I murmured.

"I don't know much about her, but she's a sweet girl. How did you meet?" Martha asked.

Dave the tuner brushed by me and stepped up to the director's podium. I had about one minute to get my horn and get into my seat before Doctor Demerit saw me.

"Let's talk later," I said, standing. As I did, I looked straight at Pamela, and I don't know if it was dumb luck or animal magnetism, but she looked at me at the same time. I smiled and nodded, and she did too. I blushed brightly and turned to escape to my seat.

After practice, I made my way back to the front of the stage. I'm sure I looked odd, especially since I was holding my baritone under my arm, so I went over to Martha, who was pulling a stained cloth through the center of her disassembled clarinet, removing the saliva she'd just spent two hours depositing there.

One thing you have to get used to when you play in a band is spit. It's everywhere. No matter how hard you try to avoid it, when you blow air through a horn, moisture is going to go too, and it's going to pool in there somewhere and eventually spill out. Band rooms are covered in spit. You've been warned.

Nodding up and down like I was responding to Martha, I said, "I'm pretending to have a conversation with you to justify why I'm standing up here with my baritone. I want to talk to Pamela, and I'd appreciate it if you'd say something nice about me."

"Sure," Martha said.

Pamela saw me as she moved from her seat. I smiled again and said, "Hi there, Twirler Girl."

She gave me that look you give pestering little kids, but said, "That's a big horn you have there."

Reflexively looking down, I'm sure I turned red as a stoplight.

"Pam, I understand you know my buddy Shelby here," Martha injected.

"Well, I'm told he's been following me for a while. Can I trust him?" Pamela asked.

"He's harmless but valuable. He's become the camp's beer dealer and has been sponsoring a fun party about every night in the woods. You should come to the next one. Is there one tonight, Shel?" Martha asked.

"I don't know yet, but maybe," I blurted.

"What are you doing tonight?" Martha asked Pamela.

"I guess I'll go to the movie they're showing in the cafeteria. I think it's Disney's *Old Yeller*," she said.

"Get out of here," popped out of my mouth before I could stop it.

Old Yeller? Is a cosmic clown controlling all this from above?

"Sorry, I know how that one ends, and I cry every time I see it," I shared.

"Me, too," said Pamela. "Maybe I'll see you there."

"Maybe," I said, knowing that's where I'd be tonight and right beside her should she need consoling.

— Old Yeller —

I was late getting to the movie because Ted demanded that I buy him and Gunther beer first. There was an accident near the mini-mart, and we sat in traffic for twenty minutes. By the time I got to the movie, it had started, and I stayed in the back trying to identify Pamela among all the shadowy heads. I couldn't, so I sat and hoped for an intermission. There wasn't one.

When the movie ended, I waited near the door as the teary-eyed audience filed out, and it wasn't long before I saw Pamela with a tissue in her hand. Putting on my best forlorn face, I slid in beside her and said softly, "It's so sad."

She stopped and said, "Yes," put her arm under mine and leaned on me as we walked down the hall.

"How about a late-night Coke? I know where there's a top-quality vending machine nearby," I said.

Pamela nodded, and we walked to the elevator.

— Visitors —

Jimmy and I did not speak that night, nor did we talk the next morning as we prepared for our first camp performance. Each of the ensembles was to play two musical numbers at the Mont Chateau State Park outside of Morgantown. We were going by bus to the concert. No one knew where the audience would come from. All I knew was it was an excellent opportunity for me to spend quality time with Pamela.

Our after-movie Coke had gone well, and I remained the total gentleman knowing I was still in my probation period as a suitor. We'd discussed the movie, but the best part was that Pamela agreed to ride with me to the concert and spend the rest of the day exploring the park.

As we wound our way through the streets of Morgantown, the bus radio blared, "Hello, Americans, this is Paul Harvey. Stand by for news,"

"Turn that shit off!" yelled a kid in the back of the bus. "Harvey's nothing but a Dick Nixon stooge."

It was high noon, and the right-leaning, Nixon loving, profusely patriotic Paul Harvey was about to share his unique version of current events. The bus driver obliged and turned off the radio.

We arrived and milled around wondering where we were going to perform until a counselor showed up and organized us for a group photograph. I still have the photo, and it shows a gaggle of casually dressed teens either bored or boisterous focused on anything other than making beautiful music. One kid up front looks like he's at attention while another one in the back row is thrusting the universal peace sign over the heads of his friends. What stands out the most to me now is that we are all so young.

Band Camp Photo (Syckes Family Photos)

Pamela and I spent our free time before the concert walking along the river and enjoying the warm summer day. We talked about our schools, and she told me how she was anticipating the twirler tryouts she was facing. I shared my drum major tryout experience, and I made it sound like I was much more in control than I was. We got along great, and I had high hopes for a Pamela party in the woods.

The concert was a non-event in that most of the audience were campers not performing, although there were a few others sprinkled here and there. One surprise attendee found me after the band finished. I was putting my horn away when I heard, "Hello, son. You guys sounded great."

"Dad, what are you doing here?" I said with genuine surprise.

"I'm here to hear my boy play in a superior concert band; I'm proud of you," he beamed.

He was the last person I expected to see. Dad heard me play every day in school, and I figured he had his fill there, but seeing him made me feel good.

Dad wanted to talk to the other two ALCO students. We found Rich Jeffrey quickly, but I wasn't looking forward to finding Jimmy. Dad did not give up easily, and he finally spied him talking to others near the refreshment table. As we got closer, I realized one adult Jimmy was talking with was the grin-less Doctor Portnoy.

Slowing a bit, I said, "Dad, we better not interrupt."

"Why, I've known Don for years," Dad stated. "I hate to break this to you, but you're not the first Allegany band member I've sent to this camp."

This did not calm my nerves. My father was leading me into a conversation with the guy who awarded me a demerit for skipping class, and my roommate, who was acting like a jealous lover.

This was not going to go well, and it didn't—but for an even more embarrassing reason.

I stood beside Dad as he waited for a break in the conversation, and I saw Jimmy shooting me the evil eye from the other side of the gaggle. Doctor Portnoy, recognizing Dad, spoke first, "Lu Syckes. It's good to see you again. Thank you for joining us." he said, without showing any teeth.

Dad rolled right into his jovial hail-fellow-well-met banter that included saying how good it was to see him and how much he enjoyed the concert.

"Thank you, Lu," Portnoy said dryly.

Dad continued, "You know, I only send my best music students to your camp."

I knew something was very wrong, for when Portnoy heard that last part, for the first and only time, a broad smile appeared on his face. His eyes danced as he stepped forward and reached out to put his arm around my shoulders.

Looking first at me, then at Dad, he said, "Then, what's he doing here?"

I felt all of the connective tissue in my body release, and I would have collapsed into a puddle of pulsating flesh if it wasn't for the doctor's arm. Jimmy made a *yip*-like sound and bent forward.

Everyone endured a long, awkward pause before Dad, as the nice guy he was, turned the attack into a joke and laughed out loud saying, "Because he's my boy, and I get to pick who comes."

The others around us nervously joined in laughing, and Dad caught me as Portnoy removed his arm. The conversation shifted to others, and we moved away. I stayed silent for a minute, and so did Dad.

Then, he said, "Who was that cute girl I saw you with before the concert?"

"Nobody," I stammered.

"I don't think that's true. Why don't you find her, and we'll get an ice cream cone? I know where the Tastee Freez is in this town," Dad said with a big smile.

I was glad he didn't dwell on Portnoy's jab, and I could always eat an ice cream cone, so I did as I was told. Pamela agreed to come along, but only after I invited her two friends. Dad never mentioned what Portnoy said about me again, and after the ice cream, he dropped us all off at The Towers.

Alone on the elevator with Pam, I asked if she'd join my friends and me in the woods tonight for a beer party.

"Maybe," she answered.

It wasn't as positive a maybe as I would have liked, but it wasn't a no. As the elevator continued to my floor, my mind returned to Portnoy's stinging attack. It bugged me.

I ate dinner with Gunther, and it was no more than thirty seconds after we started that he said, "Portnoy put you down bad today."

"Been talking to Jimmy, have you?" I asked.

"Yes, he told me, but not meanly," Gunther soothed.

"Yeah, right. He loves Doctor Portnoy more than he does his viola," I said as Jimmy sat beside me.

I said nothing and stirred my soup.

"As much as I enjoyed it, what Portnoy did to you today was wrong," Jimmy said, looking directly at me with a supportive smile. "You've never claimed to be a great musician, and there is no real entry requirement into this damn camp other than paying the fee."

Did Jimmy mean that? "Thanks, I think," I mumbled. *What's your game, Eaton?*

"Anyway, I know Ted took over planning the party tonight, and since we skipped yesterday, we all should be in the mood for a good beer buzz in the woods," Jimmy said to everyone.

Wow, he's laying it on thick.

We finished our meal and adjourned to the lounge area of The Towers. Pacing there was the second of my two surprise visitors of the day: Sam Nutter.

He had a cigarette hanging out of the side of his mouth, and when he saw me, his eyes lit up. "There you are, dickless. I've been looking for you for the last half an hour."

"Sam, what are you doing here?" I said with honest shock.

"I start freshman orientation tomorrow, and I thought I'd track you down," he answered with the cigarette still in his mouth. A half-inch ash fell from its tip as Jimmy saw us talking.

"There's no smoking in here," Jimmy announced as he quickly walked to the elevator and pushed the "up" button. The old Jimmy was back.

"Well, I see the vomitorium is still following you around," Sam cracked as he shook his head and pointed at Jimmy.

"Remember, you wouldn't even be here if we hadn't pulled your ass out of that cellar!" he yelled at the elevator.

"Fuck you!" Jimmy yelled as the doors closed.

"Come on, Syckes, let's go get a beer," he said as he dropped his cigarette to the floor and rubbed it into the carpet.

"Sam, I can't. We're having a beer party in the woods tonight, and I've already bought into it, so I've got to go. How about you join us? It should start in about thirty minutes."

"I'll try, but I've got to go to a freshman mixer first at the student union," Sam said, slowly mock-punching me on the arm. "By the woods, do you mean that fire pit about a block away from here?"

"Yes. How did you know?" I asked.

"I know where everything is on this damn campus. This is the first summer I haven't been to this camp in three years," Sam boasted on his way out the door. I'd forgotten that he had earned a full music scholarship to WVU based on his outstanding trumpet performance at camp. I guess Portnoy loved him.

If only he knew the real Sam.

Chapter 22 - Anticipation

— Back to the Woods —

There were sixteen kids at the party, making it the largest one yet. What we once thought was a wide open area was becoming an overcrowded campsite. Ted did not disappoint, showing up with three cases of beer, five bags of snacks, and a package of hot dogs ready for grilling. He'd taken over the party planning duties and gotten Bill to buy the beer. Seeing no Sam, Jimmy was back as my best friend and chatted me up, talking tough about Portnoy and over praising my musical talents. He sat next to me pounding down beers and doing his best to pretend nothing between us was wrong. I knew it wouldn't last, and when Sam showed up, Jimmy's happy mask came off.

Sam came crashing through the trees, announcing his arrival by saying, "Anyone here want a real drink?"

He held a pint bottle of Southern Comfort over his head, looked around, and when he was sure he had everyone's attention, he took a healthy swig. Jimmy made a grunting noise and moved away from me. I'd given up any hope that Pamela was coming, so I stood and took the bottle out of Sam's hand.

"To band camp," I toasted, raising the pint above my head before taking a sip. It tasted like cough syrup. Finishing, I looked over to Jimmy to offer him a drink, but he was gone. The hot dogs were hanging on sticks over the fire and were about done, so I gave the pint back to Sam and said, "It's dinner time."

Sam and I got right down to catching up. It was great partying with him again and hearing all about his latest conquests, which would soon include a fellow freshman girl he'd met tonight and already had a date with tomorrow. Sam worked fast.

— Jimmy Scares Me —

It was a little challenging staying upright as I walked down the hall from the elevator to my room. The party was going strong, but when Sam left, I'd had enough and figured I'd better go home while I still could. I was considerate and did not turn on the light in the room, thinking Jimmy was asleep. Before I could get my clothes off and get in bed, the mean voice of my roommate rang out from the darkness.

"I don't know what you see in that loser Nutter. He's going nowhere fast, and he's using you to get there."

With my inhibitions freed by the Southern Comfort, I was in no mood for Jimmy's badgering.

"Who in the hell do you think you are Eaton?" I stated with clarity and impact.

"I'm your friend, and I want us—" Jimmy started to say before I cut him off.

"I decide who my friends are, not you, and I'm not so sure you're one of them anymore. You go your way, and I'll go mine. Got it?" I shouted louder than I should have while flipping on the light. What I saw stunned me, and my already unsteady stance gave way. Jimmy was naked on the bed, looking at me.

"That's it. I'm out of here!" I screamed and spun around and left the room. I spent the night on Ted's floor.

I'm told that memoirs are supposed to be more about feelings than facts. Well, here are some feelings for you.

The confrontation with Jimmy scared the hell out of me. Today, I'm a staunch advocate for gay rights, including same-sex marriage, but that was not the case then. I was immature and focused on girls and trying to "fit in" with the cool kids. Jimmy was threatening all of that with his open attraction to me. If others thought I welcomed it, I'd be labeled gay and be destroyed. The name calling would return, and I'd lose my cool kid status and maybe my ability to get girls. The maddening part was I knew I wasn't gay, and so did Jimmy, but there was something else I was afraid of. I was terrified that I was somehow attracting him. What was it about me that made him think I was interested? I needed to figure that out.

Well, I never did, but what I did figure out—in the intervening decades—is it doesn't matter.

Why others are attracted to you or why you are attracted to others is not controllable—it just happens. I was attracted to Pamela and I didn't know why. Jimmy was attracted to me, and he probably didn't know why either.

Mousey Martha was the only one who knew why; *"It's Kismet."*

Looking back on this with the prospective of time, I wish I would have told Jimmy how I felt. Tell him his attraction to me was making me uncomfortable, and he needs to look elsewhere, but I didn't—I couldn't. To talk openly to a male friend then about how his attraction to me made me feel would have required me to acknowledge that there could be an attraction between two men—and to do that was social suicide. All I did was focus on protecting myself by keeping a lid on the subject.

It took me a long time to understand it but worrying about what other people think about you is a waste of time. I wish I had known that then, but I didn't. I decided I had time to work this out before we were back at ALCO. I'd have to keep Jimmy at arm's length and hope that what goes on at band camp, stays at band camp.

— The Party Plan —

In the morning, I ignored Jimmy as I dressed for class, and he cooperated by not speaking. There were only four days left of camp, and I wanted to avoid Jimmy as much as I could, so I told Ted we needed to stop having parties until the last night of camp. He did not need to know about Jimmy, so I convinced him we were pushing our luck with getting caught and should focus on only one more big party. Ted agreed, and we strategized how we'd pull that off. We discussed changing locations, but we couldn't think of a safer, more convenient place, so we focused on the party itself.

Except for Sam's small contribution of Southern Comfort, we'd relied on beer as our adult beverage of choice. I was happy with it, but I thought the last night of camp deserved something a bit more special. I also wanted to have a drink that might be more appealing to Pamela. I was running out of opportunities with her, so I needed a good lure to draw her in. We settled on champagne, but we knew it would be expensive, so we planned to have only a few bottles—just for us. That's when Ted had an epiphany, "Hey, Shel, why don't we charge kids to come to the party instead of having them pay us to buy them beer?"

I understood his logic immediately and ran with it saying, "You're right. That way, we don't have to buy what they want. We control both the quantity and quality of the drinks. It will make our job a lot easier. We can charge them two bucks each, and they'll think they are getting six beers, but instead, we'll provide a variety of drinks. There'll be beer but also cheap wine and weak mixed drinks—food, too. They'll love it, and again, we control it, not them. And if they don't like it, well, tough. Hell, I bet we'll collect enough cash to pay for our champagne."

"Boy, that's brilliant," Ted gushed. "Absolutely brilliant!"

We found paper and made a detailed list of what we needed to buy and other logistical needs.

— Kat Attack —

"You two were at it again last night, weren't you?" Kat accused as I walked past her in the hall of the Creative Arts Center. She was standing near a water fountain with her viola case clutched between her knees.

"Guilty as charged," I answered but kept walking. "Jimmy's the one pushing my buttons, and he's got to stop. I'm sick of it, and I'm not interested in whatever he's selling."

She grabbed her case and followed me. "I know that, and he knows it too, now."

"Are you sure?" I asked as I stopped and looked at her.

"Yes, he understands."

"And he won't go apeshit whenever I party with other friends like Sam?" I asked.

"I think so, but he's still Jimmy, you know. That will never change."

"I guess you're right, a zebra can't change its stripes, and given Jimmy is a horse's ass, I shouldn't expect it. Hey, new subject. Are you and your feminist mafia coming to the party after the concert? Ted and I have big plans. Instead of folks paying for individual six-packs, we're going to charge a flat fee of $2 a head for all you can drink. There will be plenty of snacks, too."

Kat gave me a thumbs up, and I continued down the hall, happy that she may have solved the Jimmy problem. I was wrong. When I got back to the dorm, our door was open, and the floor counselor, Michael, was there. Jimmy was in bed with a thermometer in his mouth and a wet washcloth on his head.

— The Clinic —

"Jimmy's feeling poorly," Michael said as I entered the room.

"I think he needs to go to the clinic, and he says you have a car. Can you drive him and make sure he gets seen?"

Hell, no, popped into my head, but I said nothing for as long as I could.

I wanted to assess what I was dealing with. I smiled at Michael and passed him to get to the bed. Jimmy looked fine except he was doing his best to sound sick. There were faint moans and sighs as he rocked back and forth.

"What's the problem, buddy?" I said tenderly, kneeling beside him. "Got a tummy ache?"

There was no answer, just more rocking, and moaning.

Okay, I give up

"I'll take him, Michael," I said aloud. "Where's the clinic?"

It was after 4:00 when we got to the WVU campus hospital, and the walk-in clinic was about to close, but I convinced them to see Jimmy after dropping Doctor Portnoy's name. The patient was quieter, and I felt his forehead. Just as I thought; it was cool—this is all a big, attention-getting, pity party.

After a few minutes, Jimmy's name was called, and I looked at him and said, "You're on your own, big boy," and got up to look for a magazine.

Jimmy huffed and hobbled to the desk, and they quickly whisked him into another room. I busied myself reading *Rolling Stone* hoping I wouldn't have to spend the rest of the day here. Before I could finish an article, I looked up to find Jimmy standing in front of me with a prescription in his hand.

"They think I have either food poisoning or stomach cancer," he said.

"They diagnosed you with stomach cancer in fifteen minutes at a walk-in clinic?" I asked incredulously.

"Give me a break. I vote for food poisoning. I know at least three potential poisoners, and I'm at the top of the list."

"Fuck you." Jimmy laughed with his old strength. The mask was off.

"I suppose you need me to take you to a drug store?" I asked.

"Fuck, no. I'm not spending another dime. They already want $5 for this visit." Jimmy huffed.

Knowing he had inherited no money since the hamburger vending machine night, I asked, "Do you need five bucks?"

For the first time, Jimmy looked like he was honestly contrite. "Yes please, but I'll pay you back, and listen, about last night."

"What about it?" I interrupted, letting my anger sound in my voice.

"I get it. I won't bother you again. Kat said you talked, and how I reacted made me feel like shit. That's why I skipped practice today, but I didn't plan on the counselors getting all bent out of shape. They found me in the room, and I faked the illness to avoid getting a demerit. That's how we ended up here. Sorry."

I nodded, but I was laughing on the inside. Who would go through all of this to avoid a demerit? Jimmy, that's who. "You're a piece of work, Eaton. A real piece of work," I said.

"Thank you. I try." Jimmy smiled.

— The Dance —

Ted and I decided to name the big party the Last Party. *Not very creative but clear.*

I penciled the name at the top of our "To Do" list. "We've got to get help setting this thing up. You and I will be busy buying the booze with Bill and can't be bothered with moving what we need to the woods."

"Get that little beer-hungry shit from your high school to do it. Tell him you'll give him back his two dollars if he makes sure a decent size table and ten chairs show up at our party place a half an hour after the concert's over. We already know where they are, so all he has to do is manhandle them to the woods from the storage closet," Ted instructed.

"You mean Jeffrey?" I asked, already knowing the answer. I paused and realized I had a better solution, and that was Jimmy. "Nope, forget him. I've got someone who owes me big time." I said, "Have you lined up Bill to buy the booze?"

"Bill is meeting me in my room right after practice this afternoon," Ted stated.

It was only Wednesday, and we already had twenty-five kids who had paid their two dollars for the party.

Had we overachieved? This thing was getting big, and everyone was paying with dollar bills. I was having trouble stuffing them all in my pockets, so I offloaded some in the Barracuda.

Ted asked me if I was going to the dance that night, even though he knew I was. I think he enjoyed rubbing my infatuation with Pamela in my nose. I didn't care. Of course, I was going to the dance. Although I'd spent quality time with Pamela at the waterfront concert, she hadn't shown up at the last party, and there had been no real opportunities for me to talk with her since.

I drove to the dance at the WVU Student Union instead of taking the bus like everyone else, so I could take Pamela home if she let me. As I passed through the entrance, I saw Ted, Dan, and Preston standing to one side of a double door on the mezzanine leading into a large hall. Zak, our euphonium section counselor, was with them.

Zak waved and said, "Shelby, I have news I was telling the others. You need to hear it, too."

I bounded up the stairs as Zak continued, "Brad had to leave camp today due to a family emergency and will not be here for the concert. I checked with Doctor Portnoy, and he approved Preston reassuming the position of first chair. That is if he wants it." Zak looked at Preston, knowing it was a silly question.

Preston's eyes were as big as tea plates. You could feel his body wanting to jump for joy, but all he could do was open his mouth and plead, "Please, yes please."

Ted smacked him on the back, "Damn, boy, you're back on top of the donkey now. Try and hold on next time he bucks. Zak left us, and we all moved into the room that would serve as our dance hall for the night.

"We need to celebrate, Shel," Ted said.

"I know the big party is tomorrow, but let's have a small Euphonium-only bash tonight in honor of Preston retaking his rightful place as King Shit of the Baritones."

I was glad Preston was back on top. I still felt guilty for my part in getting him demoted.

Who knows, it might be fun to party with him.

I looked at Preston, and he was nodding. Dan was, too, so I told them if they each gave me a buck I'd be happy to supply the beer. We decided to meet in the woods at ten.

The dance hall was a large, unadorned box with photographs of old WVU sports teams lining the walls. At a table in the corner sat a DJ who was playing the *Hollies'* "Long Cool Woman in a Black Dress." Another table had a punch bowl and what looked like a sheet cake with a stack of paper plates sitting beside it.

Along every other wall were campers clustered in groups looking like ants swarming food crumbs at the kickplates of a kitchen floor. They knew they were at a dance, but they didn't know what to do. I looked for Pamela while trying to be as nonchalant as I could. I passed by the punch bowl and helped myself to one of the paper cups filled with a brown liquid. I quickly returned it, finding weakly sweetened iced tea with about as much flavor as a postage stamp.

As is the case at most teen dances, it was the girls who first took the floor, and I felt my face smile as I saw Pamela lead a few of her clarinet friends onto the floor.

I was just about to interrupt her when the DJ's speakers squealed as a mic turned on, and Dave, the head counselor, made an announcement. "I hope you're enjoying WVU's Fine Arts Camp's appreciation dance. Before we return to the music, Dwayne Steadman, your orchestra's concertmaster, would like to make a presentation to Doctor Portnoy."

Oh, my God. What are we thanking that prune-faced fascist for?

Dave passed the mic to Dwayne, who could have been Mickey Rooney's stunt double in the Andy Hardy movies. He was holding a plaque and wearing a sports coat that was two sizes too small.

"Who in the name of all things holy picked that dude to represent us?" Ted asked as he moved in beside me on the edge of the dance floor.

"Not me," I stated. "And why are we thanking the great Doctor Porkpie?"

"Shit if I know, boy," Ted said as the speakers squeaked again.

"Thank you, Counselor Dave," Dwayne said as he realized he had everyone's attention. "Would Doctor Portnoy please come forward?"

With that, the stiff-faced doctor appeared from behind the DJ and moved to Dwayne's side. There was applause, and as it died down, I continued to clap slowly, sustaining my disdain for five seconds. I felt Portnoy's Medusa-like eyes on me, and my legs felt like stone. Ted pulled me to safety in the crowd.

"Don't push your luck, boy. Remember, we want to survive until tomorrow. There are a lot of kids counting on us for the best party of their lives," Ted hissed from the side of his mouth as we both endured a short but sappy thank-you speech from Dwayne to Portnoy.

When it was over, the ego-inflated doctor asked the DJ to start the music again. Then, Portnoy exited the room faster than a marble rolls down a rain spout. I went looking for Pamela and found her eating cake near the punch bowl. She looked great. She had on a light yellow, tight-fitting, scoop-neck T-shirt tucked into blue hot-pants.

"How's the cake?" I said to her when I knew she'd seen me.

"Dry," she answered, twisting her face in disappointment.

"Well, the weak tea will wash it down, but don't expect to be any happier. I'm not sure there was a tea bag in the room when they made it, and there sure wasn't any sugar." This got a laugh, so I went in for the kill.

"Do twirlers dance? Without batons, that is."

I could see she was listening to the music, deciding whether or not it met her danceable standards. The DJ was spinning *T Rex's* "Bang a Gong," and its slow-paced rocking beat must have agreed with her. Instead of answering me, she took my hand and led me to the middle of the dance floor. I've heard you find out more about a person in two minutes of dancing than two hours of conversation, so I wanted my two minutes to score well.

As we reached the center of the floor, I pulled her towards me and twirled her to my left. She instinctively followed my lead and finished the spin as I pulled her closer and looped my arm around her waist. *Perfect*, I thought until she smiled devilishly and pushed me away to dance apart as the rhythm of the song demanded.

I applied my best American Bandstand-inspired dance steps while praying to the DJ; *Please make the next one a slow song. Please.*

Pamela could dance, and I enjoyed watching her swing and sway stylishly. The song ended with T Rex's lead vocal singing, "For a meanwhile I'm still thinking," and my prayer was answered, for a moment later, the stylus slid into the next record's groove, and Don McLean's clear voice sang out, "Starry, starry night, paint your palette blue and gray..." We effortlessly locked together and rocked back and forth to the loving sound of "Vincent."

Absolutely perfect! I drank in the nape of Pamela's neck and the wonderful fragrance that was only hers. I was in heaven. We danced to four more songs, and during the last slow one, I whispered in her ear, "Let's go for a walk," and pulled her gently towards the door.

We were on the second floor of the Student Union, and like all modern designs of the day, exterior walls were bathed in glass from floor to ceiling. Below us, illuminated by hidden ground lighting, was a small park with a paved pathway and benches. I led Pamela in that direction.

I will kiss this girl if it kills me, and the park is the perfect place to do it.

As we exited the building, we found ourselves on a deserted, broad terrace lit by towering lampposts at its four corners. A stairway led down to the park, and as we reached the first step, I decided not to wait. I pulled Pamela close and kissed her. It was good, I thought, one of my best kisses.

When we broke away from each other, I expected to feel her melt in my arms. Instead, she looked at me quizzically, like she was assessing the kiss as she had the music before we danced. I must have passed the test for she dove in for another round, but this time she opened her mouth, and we explored each other with passion. My knees felt fragile, and I grabbed the stair railing to steady myself.

"That was nice," I said.

"Yes, it was," Pamela answered, and we both leaned in for another round, but the loudspeaker broke our private moment with an announcement that the bus to return to The Towers would leave the Student Union in ten minutes.

"I have my car with me. Would you like me to give you a ride back?" I said. This caught her off guard. I guess she didn't expect a camper to have a car, and I think she was impressed but also hesitant.

"No thanks, I'll catch up with my friends on the bus. Did I hear you were having a party tomorrow night?"

Stung by the ride home rejection, I almost missed the importance of her question.

Did she hint she wants to come to my party?

She was turning to go when I snapped back to reality and said, "Yes, the Last Party. Please come. I'm going to have a bottle of champagne for us."

She stopped, turned back, leaned in, and kissed me sweetly on the cheek. "Okay, I'll see you tomorrow."

She looked spectacular as she pranced down the wall of windows, and I savored her on my lips.

— Shotgun —

It was ten 'til ten when I got to the mini-mart, and I was the only one in the place other than Jess behind the counter. "Heads up!" I yelled to him as I tossed him the small box I'd been storing in the console of the Barracuda for the past week. He caught it with style and got a big grin on his face, recognizing the Rawlings MLB Official baseball he'd given me eight days ago.

"Cool," Jess said as he took the Mousy Martha autographed wonder out of the cardboard box. "Thanks a million."

I slid three six-packs onto the counter and said, "No problem. Anything for a Pirate fan friend." Jess rang up the beer, then reached beside the register and pulled a beef jerky from a display box and dropped it in the bag.

"Here's a little something extra, from me to you," he said, and I reached out and shook his hand before grabbing the paper bag and moving for the door. We were counting on Bill buying all the drinks for tomorrow night, so this would be my last stop at the mini-mart, and I would miss it. It was the first place I'd ever bought beer without fear.

When I got to the woods, I was surprised not only to find my fellow baritoners there but also Kat, Martha, Jimmy, and another guy I'd never seen before. I thought of it as my private party area, and it never occurred to me that others might use it without me. Ted stood and said, "They were here when we got here."

"It's okay," I said. "We'll make them honorary euphonium players for tonight. Kat, I didn't see you at the dance."

"I don't twist, frug, mashed potato or swim. None of it," Kat said flatly as I saw what she had been doing.

Between her lips was a diminutive reefer she was sucking on with great intensity between each word. It had to be burning her fingers as it glowed bright red in the dark. Inhaling all that was left of it, she dropped its tiny remains on the ground and rubbed it into the dirt.

"Light up another one, Jimmy," she ordered, and I saw him dig into his shirt pocket.

"Okay, boys, we're here to celebrate Preston's anointment as euphonium head," Ted trumpeted. "Where's the beer, Shel? Let's get this party started."

"Euphonium head?" asked the unidentified new guy sitting close to Jimmy. "What's that?"

"Ignore him," said Martha.

"He's in the choir and doesn't know the difference between a bari-sax and a baritone."

"I do, too," replied the new guy as he accepted the zigzag-wrapped weed from Jimmy. Taking a substantial but more refined hit on the newly lit cannabis, he bumped against Jimmy in a way that made me think he wanted to be introduced.

"This is Ben, everyone," Jimmy said dryly as he took the dope back.

There were hellos all around. Ted fished a beer from the bag I'd set on the ground and said, "Stand up, Preston."

He did as he was told, and Ted handed him a beer, but as Preston reached for it, Ted jerked it back, saying, "You gotta drink it like a man, boy."

"What do you mean?" Preston asked in surprise.

"I'll show you." Ted reached into his front pocket and retrieved a church key.

He turned the beer upside down and leveraged a hole near the edge of the can's bottom with the sharp end of the opener. He then put his thumb over the hole and lifted the can to his mouth. He closed his lips over the opening he'd made and used his other hand to find the pop-top on the top of the can.

When his finger pulled it open, a rush of air entered the can, releasing the vacuum that was restraining the beer from flowing freely out of the bottom hole. In less than five seconds, all twelve ounces of beer drained down Ted's throat. Finishing with a big smile, he crushed the empty can and threw it at Preston's feet.

"Shotgun is what I'm mean, big boy. You got to drink it shotgun style," Ted ordered.

"Shotgun! Shotgun! Shotgun!" we chanted as Preston looked at Ted.

"Help me, please," he said with sincerity.

Ted grabbed another beer and expertly applied the church key again. He handed it back to Preston who lifted it over his head and locked his lips around the hole. Fumbling a bit, he took a while to find the pop-top, but when he did, we all knew when he released it. His face blushed bright red, and his chin jutted forward as he tried to swallow all the cold carbonated liquid flowing into his mouth faster than he could gulp it down. Three seconds into it, he jerked the can away from his mouth, allowing the last few ounces of beer to spill down the front of his shirt.

He coughed as Ted yelled, "Good job, boy! Not great, but good. Let's try it again."

He pulled another beer from the six-pack's plastic rings and pushed it out to Preston. Stunned but still standing, Preston was enjoying all the attention, and he took the beer from Ted and asked him for the opener. After two tries, he got a hole in the bottom of the second beer and executed the shotgun without dripping a drop on his front.

We all applauded, and Ted put his arm around Preston and said, "I'm impressed, boy. I'm honestly impressed."

Preston pushed him away and tried to crush the empty can in his hand. He bent it, but finding it harder than he expected, he threw it on the ground and dug into the bag for another beer.

"You've created a monster," I chided Ted.

"Let's wait and see what that beer does to our wunderkind," Ted whispered.

It didn't take long, and although Preston didn't shotgun his third beer, by the time he finished it, he was feeling the effects of ingesting that much in so little time. Kat asked if there were any euphonium solos in the upcoming concert, and Preston shared way more information than needed, but that wasn't what toasted my oats. No, it was how he finished his tutorial.

"The most difficult one is near the end of the seventh piece of *Pictures at an Exhibition*. It's in 'Bydlo,' and I mirror the lead saxophone player, but I've mastered it. It will sound spectacular, especially now that it is going to be played on a proper instrument." Preston said with his old arrogance. "Brad plays one of those crappy Jap-made horns from Yamaha. It's better than a Conn, but it's no Besson."

You little shit, I thought as I felt my blood begin to boil. "Pride goeth before the fall," I said under my breath, then followed out loud with, "Do they eat beef jerky in Boston?"

"Yes, I love those hillbilly hamburgers," Preston burped.

"Okay, I've got one here with your name on it if you shotgun another beer for us," I challenged.

"Shotgun! Shotgun! Shotgun!" The chant started again, and without a second thought, Preston obliged.

The party chugged on, and I enjoyed finding out more about Dan, my fellow drum major. I told him about my A.R. Casavant experience, and he told me he used one of those huge tasseled drum major maces to direct his band.

"I hate flapping my arms," Dan said. "With the mace, I direct everything the same way. Marches, waltzes, ragtime, it doesn't matter. I get the band started and move that mace up and down to the beat. Easy-peasy."

As he finished, I heard a watery gushing sound followed by a low moan.

"I think Preston's had it," Dan said, pointing to what looked like a pile of clothes heaped next to the log. Preston had vomited, passed out, and fallen forward from his seat, just missing the fire pit rocks. He was still on his knees, face down in the dirt with his butt sticking up in the air.

"Pen, a pen! My kingdom for a pen!" I yelled as I rose from my log.

Kat looked up from enjoying Martha and said, "Aye, my lord, your wish is my command." She dug into her Mary Poppins-size bag and came up with the same pen Mousy had used to sign the baseball at our second party (which felt like months ago). I saw Jimmy and his new friend, Ben, lying side by side near her, and I knew he would not be bothering me tonight.

"Thank you, milady," I said as I bowed, and taking the pen, I turned to face Preston's upended physique.

"Steady the calf," I commanded Ted. "Sometimes they don't take well to branding."

He looked at me with a question in his eye but knelt down beside Preston and held him so he wouldn't fall over from his face-down perch. I joined him and avoiding the vomit deposited around Preston's face, I pulled on his collar, exposing the back of his neck. There, I drew four capital letters, taking my time to fill in each with as much dark blue ink as possible. When I was finished, I stood back to assess my work and asked Ted, "Do you approve?"

"Yessiree Bob! You done captured my thoughts precisely." On Preston's neck written boldly in inch-high block letters was CONN.

"Wow, you guys show no sympathy, do you?" Martha said as she pulled Kat back down to her level.

"If you're looking for sympathy, it's in the dictionary—somewhere between shit and syphilis," Ted replied.

When the party broke up, we left Preston in the woods, figuring the summer night was warm enough for him to sleep it off outside.

Chapter 23 - Everybody Plays the Fool

— Reluctant —

As Ted and I walked to the Creative Arts Center the next morning, we had nothing on our minds other than the Last Night party. All our classes were over, and the only thing that stood between us and the celebrating was three hours of rehearsal and the concert tonight.

"I talked to Jimmy, and he'll make sure the tables and chairs are there on time. What's the story with Bill?" I asked.

Ted hesitated, and I got a knot in my stomach. "He's reluctant to help us. The counselor staff knows of our parties, and he's worried he could get expelled if caught."

"Where in the hell are we going to come up with all the booze we need for tonight?"

"Calm down, boy, I didn't say he wouldn't do it. I said he was reluctant, but after I reminded him we already had his balls in a vice for buying underage kids beer and smoking dope with them to boot, he agreed to help."

"You're blackmailing him?" I worried.

"Let's just call it a persuasive argument. He knows if we blab to Portnoy, we all get in trouble, but his trouble is spelled J.A.I.L."

I didn't like it, but it was what it was, and the party was my last chance with Pamela. I did not want to screw it up. No Bill meant no booze, which meant I'd have nothing to share with Pamela. Therefore, blackmail was okay by me.

Preston was alive and seated in his newly re-anointed first chair position. He looked green around the gills although it was hard to see his gills because he was wearing a turtleneck shirt that blocked any view of the back of his neck. He said nothing to us as we took our seats. Maybe he didn't remember the previous night, or maybe he was realizing that humility is the path to wisdom—even if you own a $1000 baritone.

The rehearsal was a full run-through of the concert, and it went well. Too well, many thought, maybe jinxing the performance that evening. I didn't care. The whole time I was playing, I was thinking through the list of things we needed to do before the party.

The plan was for Ted and I to drive to the A&P first and buy the food and mixers, then swing back to the dorm and pick up Bill. We'd identified a liquor store in downtown Morgantown that sold everything we needed including beer, champagne, and grain alcohol.

Yes, grain alcohol. Ted's idea for a mixed drink was to dump a fifth of it into a gallon of grape juice. He called it Purple Jesus because, after two drinks, you see God. We'd stolen a bucket from the PRT construction site that would serve as our punch bowl and paper cups from the cafeteria would be our glassware.

Once rehearsal ended, Ted and I ran back to the dorm and jumped into the Barracuda. At the A&P, we spent as little money as possible going for the most bang for the buck. We got three, store-brand super-sized barrels of pretzels and ten bags of whatever potato chips were on sale. We threw it all in the back seat of the car and then went to pick up Bill.

I pulled up in front of The Towers, and Ted jumped out. It was over thirty minutes before he reappeared with Bill dragging behind him.

When we got to the liquor store, Bill turned and said, "Pull into the parking lot across the street. I want you guys to stay in the car. I don't want to be seen with minors anywhere near this place."

"No problem, I'll park way in the back of the lot." I said calmly. "You come get us, and we'll help you carry everything."

"What do you mean help carry? How much shit do you guys want me to buy?" Bill answered with what sounded like anger creeping into his voice.

"Didn't you tell him?" I asked Ted.

"I've got a list right here for you, Bill," Ted shared. "Don't worry about a thing. You get those nice boys at the store to put it all in a couple of shopping carts, and you can bring them over to the car one at a time. No problem, boy."

"Don't call me boy, you Tennessee turd. I wouldn't be here at all if you didn't threaten to tell the doctor. My whole life depends on me graduating from college, and if you screw it up, I'll hunt you down and kill you." Bill exploded with full-blown rage that had me looking for an exit.

"Bill, get a grip, we're all friends here. All we want is to have a fun party to end what has been a great couple of weeks at band camp." said Ted.

Bill was reading the list, and I knew it was much more than he expected. We had over forty attendees, so we were asking him to buy six cases of beer, six bottles of Boone's Farm, four bottles of cheap champagne, and a fifth of grain alcohol.

Just enough for a typical little high school celebration—ha!

I think he was calming down when he asked me where the money was, and I pulled the two-inch thick roll of one dollar bills I'd put a rubber band around and kept in the glove box.

"Jesus Christ, you want me to pay for it with this? It looks like something a pusher would carry," Bill bellowed.

"That's about all the crap I'm gonna take from you, Army boy. Man up!" Ted screamed as he kicked the back of Bill's seat with both feet.

"Either get the fuck into that store and buy our shit or get the fuck out of this car so we can go tell Doctor Portnoy all about your adventures smoking dope with the campers. You habla escargot, Pancho?"

I was petrified and had already opened my door when Bill grunted and opened his and lumbered towards the store.

"Damn! It worked!" Ted said as he wiped a few beads of sweat from his forehead.

Bill was back faster than we would have ever thought possible, pushing an oversized shopping cart that was loaded to the top. We quickly put everything in the trunk except the champagne. I wanted to take special care of it, so I set it on the floor in the footwell under Bill's legs. He said nothing as we dropped him off at The Towers, then parked in the lot. It was quarter after four in the afternoon, and we had to be dressed and ready for the concert at 7 sharp.

— The Jig is Up —

Two hours later, I was finishing tying my tie when there was a knock on my dorm room door. Jimmy had dressed earlier and was meeting his new friend before the concert to smoke a little pre-performance pot. I opened the door to find head counselor Dave, Michael, Bill, and Ted staring at me. I swear the temperature dropped 40 degrees, and I bit my cheek knowing the next few minutes would be hell.

"Shelby, we need to talk to you immediately," Dave, the most senior counselor, said.

I stood aside, saying nothing as they entered the room. Ted was last in. He would not look me in the eye, so I knew we were totally screwed.

"Bill has confessed to buying you and Ted alcoholic beverages for your party tonight," Dave said in a monotone voice, pausing for a few seconds to let it sink in.

"When we share this information with Doctor Portnoy, it will mean the end of camp for you and Ted. Your parents will be contacted and told to pick you up immediately, and a letter of admonishment will be sent to each of your high school principals so that they can take appropriate action."

There was another long pause.

"That's the easy part. It will be up to Doctor Portnoy to decide if the state police will need to be involved, given we are dealing with a violation of the liquor laws. If that happens, you all could be arrested and charged and may find yourselves incarcerated tonight, but that's not all. I'm afraid Bill's punishment will be significantly more severe. I'm sure he will be expelled from the university, and his dreams of a music profession will be over."

Another pause. "And, it will be all your fault."

I tasted blood in my mouth as I bit the inside of my cheek.

Well, I've finally been screwed by the big Portnoy pooch, and he was going to get to throw my no-talent ass out of his Fine Arts funhouse. Jesus, how would Dad and Mom react? If the police where involved, I'd lose my license, and I'd be grounded for at least a year, but what about Bob Hutcheson? Would he end my career as a drum major? God, could he expel me from Allegany?

My mind was spinning, and I was sure only the worst of the worst would happen until I heard what Dave said next.

"However, there may be another way we can handle this without involving your parents, Doctor Portnoy, or the police. You two have to agree to do as I tell you, when I tell you, and exactly as I tell you."

I saw Ted's head snap up, and like me, he was eager to hear what the alternative to eternal damnation was. I glanced at Bill, and he gave me a wink.

There's hope.

"You'll give Michael and me a list of everyone who is coming to the party. You will inform them all that the party is canceled. You will allow us to confiscate all the alcoholic beverages, and you will tell no one about this incident." Dave commanded. "Will you do that?"

A Planck is the shortest unit of time measurement devised by man. It is used in physics to describe the length of time required for light to travel a distance of 0.00000000000000000000000000000000629921 inches (14).

Ted and I answered yes to Dave's question in less than one Planck.

With our capitulation in hand, we all went down to the Barracuda. As we walked, I began to breathe again, but I also calculated the impact of our exposure. There would be no party. All the booze would be gone. All the kids would blame me and want their money back, and most distressing, I would not get to sip champagne with Pamela in the woods.

"Shit," I hissed to Ted as we crossed the parking lot.

I was thumbing through my car keys and saw the two Plymouth keys for the Barracuda. There was one with a pentagon-shaped head for the doors and ignition, and one had a round head that would only unlock the trunk.

"Don't wet your pants, boy. We already dodged the big bullet. Now, all we have to do is weasel our way past the next pile of shit," Ted whispered. "Here goes." Speaking louder Ted asked, "Say, Dave, what you boys plan to do with all our booze?"

"It's no longer yours. The University is confiscating it," Dave replied, strolling forward with confidence.

"Well, how do Shel and I know you boys aren't gonna drink it all up yourselves or maybe sell it?" Ted challenged.

Stopping abruptly, Dave turned around glaring at Ted. "Because I wouldn't do that."

"But, how do we know for sure?" Ted said, barely avoiding running into Dave.

"It's just that it's a lot of booze, and we paid a lot for it, and usually when you turn over something of value, you get something in return. What's it called, you know the thing that will make sure it is taken care of properly?"

"I'd like a receipt, please," I said, realizing that was the word Ted was searching for.

"A receipt?" Dave and Michael asked simultaneously.

"Yes," Ted chimed in. "It's only fair."

"Yeah," I added, now realizing how this might work. "You are taking $80 worth of stuff Bill bought with my money. Now, you're responsible for it. I need something to prove that you have it so that when I'm old enough to drink, I can get it back."

"You're kidding," Dave said.

"We don't have time for this. Remember, we can all go tell Doctor Portnoy, and you can explain it to him and the state police."

I looked at Ted quizzically, and he whispered into his hand, "Portnoy, that's the key. He's as afraid of Portnoy as we are, and if he tells him now, it will blow up the concert."

Turning to Dave, Ted continued, "Go ahead and tell Portnoy. We still want a receipt."

"You little—" Dave started to say before I interrupted him.

I was holding up the keys to the Barracuda as I announced, "I've got an idea. How about we compromise? You want to keep the liquor away from the campers, right? We want a receipt. You don't have time for that. How about you confiscate the booze in place?"

"What do you mean?" Michael asked.

I showed him the round-headed key. "My car has a lockable trunk that can only be accessed with this key. All of the booze is in the trunk, so I'll give you the key until the end of camp. That stops us from having the booze, stops the party, ends the need for a receipt, keeps Portnoy out of this, and saves us a lot of time and effort lugging all that stuff to the dorm."

Dave and Michael looked at each other for a moment. Then, Dave asked, "Is that the only key to the trunk?"

"No," I answered honestly. "There is another one on my mother's key ring 70 miles from here in Cumberland."

Ted looked at his watch, "It's 6:35, and we all have to be in the concert hall at 7:00."

"Is all the booze in the trunk?" Dave asked.

Shit! Shit! Shit! Do I tell them about the champagne in the front seat? For a second, I had a slim hope of saving that for Pamela and me, but if I don't tell them, Bill might. Shit! Shit! Shit!

"Yeah, it's all in the trunk. I put it in there myself. There's nothing in the car except snacks and party crap," Bill said matter-of-factly.

Yes! Bill's back on our side. I wondered why he supported that preppy shit Dave and his evil twin Michael. Hell, they were nothing but wimpy woodwind players, not manly brass players like Bill, Ted, and me.

There was a pause, Dave stroked his chin as he walked around to the driver's side of the Barracuda.

Please, God, don't let him see the champagne in the footwell, I prayed.

He was at the front of the car when Ted announced, "It's 6:40."

"Okay, open the trunk so I can see all the booze," Dave said as he stopped and returned to the back of the car.

I jumped forward with the key and popped it open.

"Is it all there, Bill?" Dave asked.

Bill inspected the contents and counted aloud the six cases of beer and six bottles of wine, and finally, the fifth of grain alcohol. He looked up at Dave and said, "Yup, every bit of it's here."

Dave reached into the trunk and felt the wall that separated it from the passenger compartment. "Can you open this from inside?"

"No, sir," I said and told them an abbreviated version of my parallel parking incident with Dad.

"Okay, give me the key," Dave sighed, holding his hand out in my direction.

I slipped it off the ring and handed it to him as he slammed the trunk closed.

"I'll hold this until you leave campus tomorrow, but if I find out any of this booze leaves your car tonight, I will immediately notify Doctor Portnoy and the state police myself, and I plan to recount every bottle tomorrow before I give you the key back, to make sure. Do you understand?" Dave bellowed.

Another light speed record was broken with my instantaneous, "Yes, sir."

— The Concert —

Dave shared the list of party goers we gave to him with the other camp counselors. Each camper whose name was on it got the same warning, "There will be no party, and if you decide otherwise, you'll be expelled."

There was lots of whining and demands for money back, but all Ted and I said was, "Talk to Dave." We figured they'd never do that because they were too scared.

I was blowing air through my horn in the wings of the stage, getting ready to take my seat for the performance, when Pamela came up behind me and slid her arms around my waist. "I heard the party's off."

"Yes and no," I answered, as I dropped my horn to my side and turned around.

"It's off for everyone else, but not for you and me."

"But, I heard all the drinks were confiscated?" she asked.

"I can't talk about it now," I told her. "I'll find you after we play, and you can decide what we do."

Her face was quizzical, but I think she realized I was in a precarious situation, so she smiled and went back to the clarinet section.

As Ted and I prepared for the performance, he asked me, "We're gonna drink that bubbly tonight, aren't we?"

"You bet. Let's meet in the woods at ten," I said.

I won't bore you with a description of the concert. It went well, and each of the ensembles performed far above normal high-school-level musicians. The audience, consisting entirely of campers not performing and family members, loved every minute of it. The orchestra played last, and I enjoyed hearing all the magnificent string instruments play John Philip Sousa's "The Stars and Stripes Forever" as their encore piece.

How about that, an orchestra playing a march composed for a band. Ain't that a twist of natural law?

Pamela and I sat together during the orchestra's performance, and I told her the whole story. I asked if she would like to have a private party.

"How private?" she asked.

"Well, I was hoping you could invite some of your girlfriends to join Ted and me for a champagne and potato chip campfire," I answered nuzzling her neck.

For once, there wasn't a long pause and a suspicious look. I'd crossed the threshold of trustworthiness.

"Sounds fun," she said and squeezed my hand. "You are an adventure."

No one had ever said that to me before, and I liked it.

— Last Night —

To avoid being seen by any counselors, as soon as the music stopped, I bolted from the Creative Arts Center with my baritone and ran to the car. Swapping my instrument for three bags of potato chips and the four bottles of champagne, I ran for the dorm. I stashed the champagne and chips behind a bush near the entrance and went up to my room. There, I retrieved the stolen PRT bucket and paper cups. Next, I took them all to the basement snack bar and filled the bucket with ice from the ice machine. I exited the building by way of the garden where I first met Pamela to avoid going through the lobby with my dirty bucket of ice.

After gathering my loot from behind the bush, I trotted towards the woods. There, I did a bit of house cleaning by clearing the area of empty beer cans and cigarette butts and gathered firewood. Then, I slid two bottles of champagne into the ice, hoping to bring their temperature down below the 80 degrees it was that night. As I was finishing, I heard someone moving through the forest on the path from the road and expected to look up and see Ted, but instead, I stared at Bill.

"I figured I'd find you here," he said, as he put both hands on his hips. I said nothing and glanced around to see if other counselors were converging to arrest me in the name of the West Virginia State Police. I saw nothing.

"Hi, Bill," I forced from my throat. "Thank you," I said sincerely. "I appreciate you not telling Dave about these." I held a bottle of very warm, cheap, carbonated wine out in his direction, nodding, and hoping he was open to my bribe. He smirked and grabbed the bottle from my hand.

"Let's just say I like you slightly more than that asshole Dave."

I relaxed enough to laugh along with him, but then I remembered it was because of him I almost got arrested. "Why did you confess?"

"I had to. They had me cold. That dick, Michael, was downtown today and saw us at the liquor store. He and Dave cornered me and threatened to take me down if I didn't help them confiscate your booze. I know I said I liked you more than Dave, but I like my ass a whole lot more than the both of you."

Ted popped out of the path's opening and said, "Last night for a party. Let's get to it, boys."

I handed him the fourth and final bottle of champagne. "Right, get a fire started. I've got to go get our dates."

"Dates?" Ted exclaimed.

"I hope so. I asked Pamela to invite some girls, but I gotta go now if I'm going to meet them on time," I explained.

"Go, boy, go. We'll get this fire started and have things swinging by the time you get back." With that, Ted turned on his radio that was now a party regular, and I heard *Looking Glass's* "Brandy" fill the air as I ran back through the woods to The Towers.

Pamela and two of her friends were waiting for me in the lobby, and I escorted them to our party site knowing it would be the last time I'd take the path through the woods. What a perfect place it had been, and how lucky it was that we found it. Without a location like this, we would have never had such fun. Like the mini-mart, I would miss it.

As I hoped, Pamela invited girls who matched her cuteness. We emerged from the path and saw Bill crouching down, blowing air onto his nascent fire. Ted was taking his champagne bottle down from his lips when he saw us.

"Feed me corn and watch me grow. Welcome, ladies, to the Last Night party. Can I offer you a glass of champagne?"

There were giggles all around. Pamela and I found our way to a comfortable log and popped open our somewhat cooler bottle of wine. Ted and Bill wasted no time ingratiating themselves with Pamela's friends. The champagne was sweet, and the potato chips made for a perfect *hors-d'oeuvre*, but it was Pamela's company that made the night special.

She drank without concern, and after her second glass (or should I say Dixie Cup), she snuggled up, and we kissed. It is these moments of that night I savor the most today. It wasn't what I planned. I wanted a big party with scores of drunken adolescents frolicking in the woods, but what I got was a quiet romantic evening beside a campfire, sipping champagne with a beautiful girl.

We started kissing, and things accelerated quickly. Making out while sitting on a log in the woods is not ideal. I knew we were going to end up on the ground. I didn't want that, and Pamela didn't either, so we decided we needed to find a more accommodating spot. My first thought was the Barracuda with its fold-down back seat, but then I remembered the trunk area was locked, so there wouldn't be enough room for us.

"How about we move to the dorms?" I shared. "There are lots of comfortable flat surfaces behind lockable doors up there." Pamela nodded in agreement. We filled our Dixie Cups with champagne, bid *adieu* to our friends, and left the wild and wonderful woods party site for the last time.

— Seeking Horizontal —

The Towers were alive with campers and their parents. Some were sitting and talking in the lounge while others were touring the building while still others were manhandling suitcases in a bid to leave early. It was a zoo. Finishing our drinks, Pamela and I boarded an empty elevator car. Unfortunately, as the doors closed, Gunther's familiar grin appeared and he entered the car. "*Guten abend*, you are up going?" he said with a knowing look. I introduced him to Pamela as I pushed the third-floor button.

"Ah, you must be Kismet," Gunther continued as he nodded vigorously. "So sad that we have no party to go to. I paid for one, but no party was given."

His voice was pleasant, but his message was clear, and he looked at me. I decided it would be worth two dollars to avoid any further discussion, so I reimbursed him. He pocketed the money as the elevator announced the floor.

"Three," the recorded voice said, and Pamela replied, "Is a crowd," as we pushed past Gunther and left him grinning at us.

"Kismet?" she quizzed as she pointed in the direction of her room.

"It's all good," I reassured her and was about to spin her around for another kiss when a very unwelcome voice sounded from behind us.

"Hold it right there, kiddies. Do I need to explain to you again the camp rules about boys on the girls' floors?"

It was Jill. We hadn't noticed her sitting to the right of the elevator. Her tiny legs dangled a few inches from the floor. There was no escape, so we returned to the elevator and waited for a car.

As the door opened, Jill said "Don't bother going to any other floors. There are counselors stationed on all of them."

"Thanks, Jill, you're an ass, but I still love you for introducing me to Pamela. Don't enjoy your work too much, or you'll end up a prison guard," I cautioned.

She smiled at me, and I waved goodbye as we entered the car. Finding ourselves back on the first floor, I said, "How about a hamburger?"

"Can we split one? They're too mushy for me," Pamela replied.

"It's the nature of the beast," I said, remembering the *Popular Science* article I read about microwave ovens.

"The microwaves excite the water molecules. That's what heats things up. Unfortunately, the bread absorbs the moisture, resulting in a soggy bun," I intoned. I knew immediately I had shared too much.

"Are you going to major in science in college?" Pamela asked.

I shook my head and told her about *Popular Science*.

"What are you going to major in, music?" she quizzed.

"Nope, I don't think so. From what I've heard, it's way too much work. I honestly don't know yet what I'll study, other than your beautiful body," I snidely finished and leaned in for another kiss as we rode the elevator to the basement.

Coming up for air as the doors opened, I asked, "What about you?"

"Not sure either, but I'm thinking about psychology," she answered.

"Oh my God, are you studying me like a lab rat?" I asked.

"Hardly. Laboratory rat standards are very high. I'm not sure you'd make the cut," she answered, and with that, I pushed her forward and playfully spanked her behind. It was round, firm, and fabulous.

I saw the room was nearly vacant. The mass of humanity filling the ground floor was not interested in microwaved food. There was an older woman near the Coke machine, but that was it. Eyeing a coat closet on the opposite side of the room, I put my arm around Pamela and kissed her neck.

"How about we skip the soggy burger and continue our conversation from the woods?"

I spun her around and kissed her while continuing to move her towards the closet. It wasn't really a closet. There were no clothes or doors. It was more a finished recessed space in the wall, a sort of alcove that sat back from the rest of the room. It reminded me of the cloakroom in my first-grade classroom where Mrs. Mullendore had scolded me for "paying too much attention" to that pretty little girl. *How fitting.*

Upon reaching it, I backed Pamela up against the side wall and reignited the fire we'd started at the party. She was all for it, and it wasn't long before she pulled me down to the floor, and we lay side by side. My hands were all over her, and she reciprocated.

This is it—my big night had arrived. On this evening—during my seventeenth trip around the sun—while at the West Virginia University's band camp, I was finally going to lose my virginity to a beautiful young twirler in a basement closet. I had gone from pecks on the cheek to pressed lips on a couch; from backseat temptresses to passionless nude exploration to passion without hope of penetration. I hadn't known what second base was, but now I had hit a home run and was rounding third base with the manager waving me on.

I had my hand up Pamela's blouse, and she was fumbling with my belt when we heard an overly loud "Ahem."

Looking up, we saw the older woman with a Coke in her hand staring at us with a very disapproving look.

"Don't you children have better things to do?" Our buzz-killing grandmotherly overlord said.

It was over. Hopeless.

I rolled off Pamela as she hurriedly sat up and straightened her blouse.

"Yes, ma'am," Pamela squeaked. We stood and quickly moved to the elevator. I rode with her to the third floor, and as the doors opened, I hugged her tightly and said goodnight. She gave me a little squeeze and left the elevator. My band camp summer fling was over.

— It's Just Business —

"My mom and dad came to the concert and want me to go home with them tonight," Jimmy said as he slid his bulging suitcase off his bed and carried it to the door. "Did they really confiscate all the booze?"

"Yes, but I'll tell you a secret if you promise not to say a word," I shared.

"Fuck you." Jimmy shot back in his loving way. "I don't give a shit. I'm glad the party was canceled because it meant I didn't have to schlep all that furniture down to the woods."

I had to laugh. Jimmy was one of the most interesting people I'd ever met, and although he scared the hell out of me, I couldn't help but like him.

"Do I still owe you five dollars?" he asked while setting his viola next to his suitcase.

"Nah, forget about it. I'll see you at the Tastee Freez," I said.

"Thanks, but what happened to the booze? I won't tell."

"It's all in the car," I told him. "They made me lock it up and took the key, but listen, you can't say a word to anyone, or I'll get mobbed. Everyone thinks the university has it."

"What are you going to do with it all?" Jimmy asked.

"Share it with friends like you who don't go telling stories about band camp. Understand?" I said while sticking my hand out in hopes he would shake it.

"My lips are sealed," he answered. Jimmy shook my hand, then picked up his things and left.

I slept fitfully that night, with Pamela haunting my dreams.

We were so close to going all the way. Why didn't I push forward? Why did we leave the woods? Why don't I go down to the third floor right now and have my way with her?

Nighttime is for crazy thoughts like this, and I was smart enough not to act on them. Instead, I forced myself to make plans of staying in contact with her, but I knew it would be tough.

Morning came, and I packed my things. It was easy. I just forced my suitcase closed. I took it to the car, then hurried back to the dorm to try to see Pamela one more time. I found her in her room with her father.

"Hello, Mr. Glass. My name is Shelby, and Pamela and I have become friends while at camp."

He nodded but said nothing.

Pamela spoke to break the ice forming quickly between us. "Daddy, Shelby plays the baritone in the band. It's a little tuba-like instrument that sounds like a trombone."

He still was quiet and bent down to pick up her suitcase.

"Maybe I'll be able to visit you someday. Can I have your address and phone number?" I asked Pamela.

That got a response from her dad. "Where do you live, son?"

"Cumberland, Maryland, sir. I'm a senior in high school there," I answered.

This calmed him back into silence. He smirked. He knew 250 miles would keep me from sniffing around his porch too often. Pamela gave me a slip of paper with her address and phone number. I held onto her hand as she passed it and wanted to pull her close and kiss her, but she pulled away.

"I'll call you," I said.

"Okay," she answered, and they left the room.

I didn't follow. Shoving the paper into my pocket, I stayed in her room taking several deep breaths, inhaling, for the last time, any fragment of her fragrance.

The Towers' lobby was empty of campers when Ted and I returned from eating a farewell lunch at the Tastee Freez near campus. Dave had told me to meet him there at one o'clock to get my key back, and I would not be late.

"There's that stiff-laced bastard," Ted said, pointing to Dave as he approached us. He was in his full-blown preppy regalia: an oxford shirt with button-down collar and sharply pressed corduroy pants.

"Gentlemen, shall we adjourn to the car?" Dave lorded.

"Do you need to do that? I'm here, and all the booze is there, and all the campers went home without having a party. How about you give me the key, and we'll get out of your hair?"

Dave reached into his pocket for my key. He smiled and said, "How was the warm champagne last night?"

I took a step back, wondering what was coming next. Would it be a trip to see Portnoy? I heard Ted hiss, and I was worried he'd do something stupid, so I said, "Not bad, and thank you for your discretion."

I put out my hand as Dave twirled the key in his fingers. Then, he pushed it into my palm, sharp side down.

"Go straight home now, and do not apply to camp next year. Doctor Portnoy has your name on a list. You will not be welcome back."

"Well damn, Shel, aren't you special," Ted boasted. "Hell, you're *Portnoy's Complaint*."

Both Dave and I looked at Ted in amazement. That was a reasonably literate pun. *Portnoy's Complaint* was the Philip Roth novel about a lust-ridden, mother-addicted, Jewish boy who spent most of his time masturbating.

"*You can read*?!" Both Dave and I asked as if controlled by a single brain.

"Only the Bible and *Playboy*," Ted answered as he pushed me towards the door.

"Let's get the hell out of this dump. I don't like the way this corduroy-covered cowboy is looking at me."

I turned my back on Dave, and we walked to the car.

I popped the trunk and told him, "Take whatever you like. It wouldn't be here if it weren't for you."

"Damn straight. How about I take that fifth of grain alcohol? It's the only thing I can hide in my suitcase. My parents will be here soon, and there is no way they'd let me come home with four cases of beer."

"Your call, my friend. Thank you," I said.

"Sure, Shel. You are one hell of a businessman."

"Well, I am going home with more money than when I got here, along with six cases of beer and a half a case of wine. Not bad for two weeks' work." I said, grinning with satisfaction.

"You should major in business administration, boy. You'll make a fine manager someday," Ted counseled.

I looked at Ted and nodded, then looked at the trunk full of booze and smiled. "Maybe I will, Ted. Maybe I will."

We did a man hug that was more demonstration of strength than affection. Ted walked away holding his fifth of grain alcohol in the air and whistling "Dixie."

I rolled down the windows in the Barracuda and fired it up. I pulled my 8-track tape box near and selected the appropriate music for the ride home, then turned the car down the road in front of The Towers. Shoving the white plastic box into the player, I held the gear shift in low and floored the accelerator. The back wheels chirped as I shifted into drive and passed the front doors.

I waved farewell to the woods, leaned back, and enjoyed Led Zeppelin's "Rock and Roll" as it streamed from my speakers.

Next stop, senior year.

Epilogue

I have not lived in Cumberland since 1978 when I graduated from college and joined the Air Force. I have visited often and observed with sadness the changes that have occurred. By fault of its location, Cumberland got caught in a downward spiral of aging factories, outsourcing, and a decreasing population. Despite the best intentions of its remaining citizens, the city I knew and loved is gone. The people I've included in this memoir have changed as well, and I thought I'd share with you what I know about them now.

The Cumberland Girls - The local girls of my story, be they girlfriends, friends with benefits or tryout competitors, all went on to college and successful professions. One is an attorney, one is an educator, and a third is an online entrepreneur. I'm friends with some of them on Facebook, and I've seen photos of the others, and I'm happy to say they're all still beautiful—well, at least they are to me. Janice and I broke up soon after I returned from band camp. Our relationship was done in by the same force that stopped Patty and me dating—my stupidity.

Walter and Tim - Walter and I were roommates at the University of Maryland where we both majored in business administration. We have remained friends over the decades. He became a successful manager of resorts and hotels and enjoys his life as a bachelor to the fullest. Thankfully, he gave up smoking.

Tim and I have also remained close. We have put the Janice incident behind us, and we get together regularly to reminisce about our nocturnal Cumberland adventures. He spent a decade in the Army and another decade as an agent for a three-letter government agency and continues to serve his country now as a civil servant. I'm very proud to call him my friend, but I doubt any of his employers know I got him arrested under a pine tree.

Sam Nutter - Sam continued his pirate ways and left WVU near the end of his freshman year. He joined the Navy and spent a few years sailing the high seas and charming women of the world. We stayed distant friends during the seventies but lost track after that—until I decided to crash his 30th class reunion. Held in Cumberland, the second Sam and I saw each other, we fell back into our old ways and talked as if we'd only been apart a few days. Both of us were alone, so we chased after a few of the class's remaining pretty girls and then hit the road in my car—with Sam driving—and went straight to the Purple Heart. I learned a lot from Sam.

Big Bob - Robert M. Hutchenson served as a principal for one school or another near Cumberland until he retired in 1994. He also served as a County Commissioner and vocal advocate for education until his death in 2017. I last saw him at a "Turkey Day Snow Game" reunion, and we chatted about my drum major tryout troubles. I reminded him of what he said that day in his office with Ray Kline. He laughed and said, "You were worth it."

JoAnn and Al Homburg - JoAnn never regained her preeminent position at Allegany, and Al never got his big singing break. Early one morning in the winter of 1973 they packed up and left Cumberland telling all they had accepted teaching jobs at Shenandoah College. I learned later from a prominent member of the Downtown Cumberland Businessmen's Association that when the Homburgs departed the city they left a wake of unpaid bills at numerous stores. The positions at Shenandoah College did not last long nor did the marriage, and soon afterwards, JoAnn returned to Cumberland alone and took a teaching position at Bishop Walsh High School. She did not start a drill team there.

Uncle Lu and his Tastee Freez - Dad retired from teaching at Allegany in 1974 and turned his full attention to the Tastee Freez and golf. In 1982, a local businessman offered to lease the LaVale property and turn it into an Arby's restaurant paying Dad a flat monthly rent plus 7% of the business' gross sales. It was an offer Dad could not refuse, and it allowed Mom and he to sell their home in Cumberland and move to Sun City West, Arizona. They lived happy, active lives there until Dad's death at 91 in 2010. Mom moved to North Carolina to live near me and continued to enjoy a nightly scotch and water until her death at 90 in 2017. I miss them both terribly.

Jimmy Eaton - Jimmy and I did not stay in contact with each other after high school, and it wasn't until 2008, when he unexpectedly showed up at our 35th reunion, that I saw him again. He looked very different than I remembered. It appeared that life had done a good job of wearing off the rough edges of his personality. He did not use the *F*-word once. What was left was a little middle-aged man you could have mistaken for a librarian.

He took his music seriously and received a degree from the Peabody Conservatory in Baltimore, Maryland, and a Master's degree in Music from the New England Conservatory. During his career, he performed with several professional orchestras, including the Government Orchestra of Caracas, Venezuela. By 2008, he was teaching music in Connecticut. We had a good talk and became friends on Facebook but seldom interacted. Jimmy died from complications of ALS in 2016. His death was one of my motivations to write this book.

Pamela Glass - Soon after returning from band camp, I lost Pamela's address and phone number—and any hope I had of contacting her. After Jimmy died, I toyed with the idea of writing this book and began doing some research. Of course, Pamela's was the first name I searched for on Facebook. To my dismay, there were more than 100 results for Pamela Glass, and I did not relish wading through them. I couldn't even be sure she'd be listed under that name. So, I gave up.

A few weeks later, while I was searching for yearbook pictures on Classmates.com, I realized maybe I could find Pamela by looking at yearbooks from Charleston, West Virginia, high schools. That worked. From there, I found her on Facebook (she has a hyphenated last name now), and I sent her a text message. I'd check every day or so for a month to see if she replied, but there was no response, so I figured she was not interested in reconnecting with that handsy boy from band camp. I promised myself I would not try to contact her if I didn't hear back, and I kept my promise.

Nine months later, I finished the first draft of this book and damned if I didn't hear from Pamela. We became Facebook friends and exchanged a few notes. It was very surreal to reconnect with someone I had such an intense attraction to all those years ago, but in actuality, knew nothing about. She's a successful educator and happily married, loves dogs, and enjoys ballroom dancing, but she no longer twirls her baton. I did not ask her about her perfume.

Allegany - My high school began its last year of operation at the Sedgwick Street campus in August of 2017. A new campus is under construction about two miles away on a plot of land large enough to house any and all facilities necessary for a 21st-century high school. The fate of the old building has not yet been decided, but most believe it will be torn down for lack of funds to renovate it for other uses. When that happens, I will grieve.

Me - In July of 1982, I transferred from Eglin Air Force Base in Florida to Andrews Air Force Base in Maryland. By then, I was a captain in the Air Force and married with two young children. My parents were still in Cumberland, so we took time off to spend with them. While there, I saw an ad in the local paper announcing that the 1982 West Virginia Fine Arts Music Camp would present their annual concert that weekend in Morgantown. Awash in memories of my band camp summer ten years earlier, I convinced my wife and parents to attend the concert.

This began a ritual of revisiting the WVU Campus every ten years. I go back to walk the halls of The Towers and the Creative Arts Center and try to recapture the magic of that earlier time. Many things have changed, but there are enough things that have not changed to make it very special. The PRT is now fully functional and filled with students and campers whisking their way from The Towers to the Creative Arts Center. The wooded area where we did all our partying is gone, replaced with a huge retail sales facility, but when I made my first return trip in 1982, the mini-mart was still there, and I made a point of stopping in to buy a six-pack of beer.

As I was checking out, I noticed on a shelf behind the cashier a plastic globe-like display case with an autographed baseball in it. It was sitting prominently next to a yellowing photograph of Bobby Robertson. It made me smile.

Acknowledgments

I did not intend to write a book, but I did. It started as a list of things: cars I've owned and places I've lived, but that wasn't enough. I had a blog for awhile, but blogs died, so I tried Facebook, but Facebook is more socializing than writing, so I told my story to Microsoft Word.

I found I enjoyed writing, but when I finished, I faced a void of knowledge about what to do next and a fear that what I had written was embarrassing. It was my family and friends who got me through it.

I'd like to thank my wife for tolerating me during all phases of this process and for never telling me what she honestly thought of my writing. I would also like to thank Eddie Deezen for his generous foreword. In addition, Vicki Hancock, Kelly Taylor, Amanda Hitt, Paul Ryan, and Donna Welch all deserve credit for their expert editing support. However, it was my sons Stan and Steve who did the most to slice-away the unneeded or poorly presented prose, and for this, I am genuinely grateful.

Shelby L. Syckes

Turkey Day 2017

References

1. Vinyard, J. V. (2005, 1 1). FLYING THE HUMP. Retrieved 2017, from China-Burma-India Hump Pilots Association: http://www.cbihpa.org/history.html

2. Daprice. (2007). Albert Richard Casavant . Retrieved 2017, from http://etsboa.org/wp-content/uploads/casavant-a-r.pdf

3. Timeline of World War II (1942). (2017). Retrieved 2017, from Wikipedia: https://en.wikipedia.org/wiki/Timeline_of_World_War_II_(1942)

4. Doolittle Raid. (2017). Retrieved 2017, from Wikipedia: https://en.wikipedia.org/wiki/Doolittle_Raid

5. Hsu, T. a. (2015, 7 24). For novice restaurateurs, risk of failure is high. Retrieved 2017, from Los Angeles Times: http://www.latimes.com/business/la-fi-chef-business-20150726-story.html

6. List of Recessions in the United States. (2017, 9 7). Retrieved 2017, from Wikipedia: https://en.wikipedia.org/wiki/List_of_recessions_in_the_United_States

7. Live Births and Birth Rates, by Year. (2017). Retrieved 2017, from Infoplease: https://www.infoplease.com/us/births/live-births-and-birth-rates-year

8. Goldsworth, J. (2014, 3 29). Lew who? He's a man we should remember. Retrieved 2017, from Times-News: http://www.times-news.com/news/local_news/lew-who-he-s-a-man-we-should-remember/article_7bd6e3bf-22d1-5ced-8393-9147fa8b92ec.html

9. Cigarette Smoking in the United States 1950-1978. (1978). Retrieved 2017, from Office of Smoking and Health: https://profiles.nlm.nih.gov/ps/access/nnbcph.pdf

10. Chinese Traditional Drumming (????). (2011, 9 11). Retrieved 2017, from Chinese Language Blog: https://blogs.transparent.com/chinese/chinese-traditional-drumming-%E4%BC%A0%E7%BB%9F%E9%BC%93%E4%B9%90/

11. Kay, B. (2015, 10 16). It's official: drummers are smarter than you (and everybody else).Retrieved from consequenceofsound.net: https://consequenceofsound.net/2015/10/its-official-drummers-are-smarter-than-you-and-everybody-else/

12. Beck, T. (2012, July 19). When the beat goes off. Retrieved from https://news.harvard.edu/gazette/story/2012/07/when-the-beat-goes-off/

13. D. B. Cooper. (2017). Retrieved 2017, from Wikipedia: https://es.wikipedia.org/wiki/D._B._Cooper

14. Planck Time. (2017). Retrieved 2017, from Wikipedia: https://en.wikipedia.org/wiki/Planck_time

Made in the USA
Middletown, DE
29 June 2019